TANK
A History of the Armoured Fighting Vehicle
by Kenneth Macksey and John H Batchelor

From an original idea by John Batchelor, designed by Chris Harrison

BALLANTINE BOOKS · NEW YORK

ISBN 0-345-25481-3-495

This edition published by arrangement with B. P. C. Publishing, Ltd.

Manufactured in the United States of America

First Edition: February, 1971
Third Printing: April, 1976

FOREWORD
By R. M. Ogorkiewicz

Armoured vehicles are a subject which arouse widespread interest. One of the reasons for this is their intriguing history which may be traced back, through centuries of ideas for battle cars, to ancient siege engines. However, their development had to await the evolution of the motor car and it began in earnest only during the First World War from 1914 to 1918, when tanks made their first dramatic appearance. Since then armoured vehicles have made considerable progress but this has been chequered and their highly successful employment in the two world wars and more recent conflicts has been interspersed with periods during which they were misused and out of favour.

No less intriguing are the technical features of armoured vehicles, many of which are peculiar to them and represent ingenious solutions to the difficult problems posed to their designers. These include powerful and yet lightweight tank weapons, tracked running gear designed for high-speed travel over broken ground as well as for negotiating muddy terrain, and armour devised to achieve the highest possible degree of protection against hostile fire.

Other interesting questions about armoured vehicles concern their military importance and the different ways in which they have been employed. When tanks first broke the deadlock of trench warfare during the First World War they were regarded as specialized assault vehicles and for many years their value was thought to reside chiefly in the passive attributes of armour protection. However, even in their early form, tanks also represented the solution to the problem of combining firepower with mobility in ground warfare and they have come to be employed more and more as mobile weapon platforms while various other, more specialized, armoured vehicles have been developed to support them.

The different historical, technical, and military aspects of the subject are vividly brought out in this book which covers the development of armoured vehicles from their ancient forerunners to the latest battle tank designs. Its preparation has had the advantage of a noteworthy combination of complementary experiences brought to it by its authors: Kenneth Macksey brought to it the experience of many years' service in the Royal Tank Regiment and of writing on different aspects of tank history, while John Batchelor brought to it the experience of an accomplished illustrator of military subjects. As a result their book offers an attractive as well as comprehensive and up-to-date treatment of an interesting and important subject, which armoured vehicles undoubtedly are.

Bibliography and Acknowledgements

Anonymous	RAC Tank Museum Guides	Bovington Camp, Dorset
	Tank Data	Aberdeen Proving Ground USA 1967
	An Account of Our Stewardship	Vauxhall Motors Ltd
	The Story of the 79th Armoured Division	Privately 1946
	50 Years on Tracks	Holt Caterpillar Traction Co
Birnie, A.	The Art of War	Nelson 1942
Fuller, J. F. C.	Memoirs of an Unconventional Soldier	Nicholson and Watson 1936
	Machine Warfare	Hutchinson 1942
de Gaulle, C.	The Army of the Future	Levrault 1934
Guderian, H.	Achtung Panzer	—
	Panzer Leader	Michael Joseph 1952
Hargreaves, R.	The Siege of Port Arthur	Weidenfeld and Nicolson
Heymann, F. G.	John Žižka and the Hussite Revolution	Princeton University
Liddell Hart, B. H.	The Rommel Papers	Collins 1953
	The Tanks (2 Vols)	Cassell 1959
	The Other Side of the Hill	Cassell 1951
Macksey, K. J.	The Shadow of Vimy Ridge	Kimber 1965
	Armoured Crusader	Hutchinson 1967
Magnuski, J.	Wozy Bojowe	M.O.N. Poland 1964
Martel, G. le Q.	An Outspoken Soldier	Sifton Praed 1949
Mellenthin, F. W. von	Panzer Battles	Cassell 1955
Newman	One Hundred Years of Good Company	Ruston and Hornsby Ltd.
Ogorkiewicz, R. M.	Armour	Stevens 1959
	The Design and Development of Fighting Vehicles	Macdonald 1968
Postan, M.; Hay, D.; and Scott, J. D.	Official History of the Second World War— Design and Development of Weapons	HMSO 1964
Pugh, S. (Ed)	Armour in Profile	Profile Publications 1968
Scott, J. D.	Vickers, A History	Weidenfeld and Nicolson
Singer	A History of Technology	Clarendon
Senger und Etterlin, F. M. von	Die Kampfpanzer von 1916–66	Lehmanns Verlag
Stern, A.	Log Book of a Pioneer	Hodder and Stoughton 1919
Swinton, E.	Eyewitness	Hodder and Stoughton 1932
Williams-Ellis, C. & A.	The Tank Corps	Country Life 1919

The authors have also obtained much invaluable information from numerous articles printed over the years in the following journals:
The Tank – the Journal of the Royal Tank Regiment
Armor – the Magazine of Mobile Warfare
Interavia
The Engineer

Many people have contributed to the production of this book by their specialist knowledge and space does not allow each to be named, but particular mention is due to Master Gunner Ian Hogg, the Directors and Staff of the Royal Armoured Corps Tank Museum, the Armoured Museum at Aberdeen, USA, the Imperial War Museum, and the British Museum. When it came to checking the final draft and giving expert advice the unique experience of Colonel A. Cooper, OBE, RTR (retd) was of vital importance along with the authoritative support of Richard Ogorkiewicz who so kindly wrote the foreword.

Additional illustrations are from the following sources: pages 1–2, British Museum; 4–5, Mansell Collection; 34–5 and 44, Imperial War Museum; 40–1, RAC Tank Museum; 78–9, Ullstein; 101, British Leyland; 152–3, Abbot cutaway from Odhams Press.

Dedication: to the Crews

The Birth of Combat Vehicles

Ever since the earliest days of his fight for survival, man has tried to improve the effectiveness of his weapons, but until comparatively recently he was hampered by having such a limited range of restrictive materials from which to construct them. To make up for these deficiencies in striking power he sought to reduce his personal vulnerability either by wearing armour or by increasing the speed at which he could move. Needless to say, the deficiencies imposed on weapons by materials also caused weaknesses in armour, while natural limitations to motive power — which had to depend on flesh and blood — made startling improvements in speed and endurance almost impossible. Even so, through the centuries, as each new scientific discovery led to modified designs, there was a gradual advance in the military art, not only in technology but also in tactics and organization.

From almost the earliest recorded age — the Third Millennium — men built carts to carry their weapons to and from the battlefield. The onager-drawn wooden-wheeled carts shown on the title page are to be seen on a standard discovered at Ur in Mesopotamia. Thus, in the cradle of civilization, weapons of war occupied a prominent place; but their design did not change very much in style until the Second Millennium. About then, however, there appeared the fast, two-wheeled chariot — probably of Hurrian origin — that dominated the art of making war throughout the Middle East before spreading its influence to many other parts of the known, civilized world. These chariots were used more as fighting platforms than weapon carriers since their crews drove in formation to charge home against cavalry, infantry, and other chariot masses, and employed their weapons while mounted.

Between the years 1100 and 670 BC the Assyrians carried chariot techniques to their highest state of development. Their civilization was based on war and they used their machines to further their all-consuming military aims, treating the spoils and materials of war almost as currency. They used siege engines to break down city walls while chariots worked in close co-operation with cavalry to hold the ring of battle outside; and when rivers barred the path of this mechanized army, goat skins were inflated and attached to the lightweight vehicles to act as pontoons. Theirs was a highly sophisticated, modern army — that went bankrupt when at the height of its powers.

It rather seems as if the decline of the Assyrian armies also heralded the slow eclipse of the chariot, for although these vehicles would take part in many battles for centuries to come — on several occasions after the days of Christ — they became less and less effective against well-organized cavalry and the dense formations of unmounted men which were evolved by the Greeks and Romans. Speed came to be less important and body armour could be made lighter and stronger when methods were discovered to produce iron, and later crude steel, in quantity. Soldiers, particularly those of the mounted élites, came to demand greater personal protection, even though the weight of the extra armour lessened their elusiveness and mobility. Eventually, the mounted, armoured knight wore so much personal protection that even the strongest war horse found difficulty in carrying him about. Indeed, if firearms had not made the knight's protective armour useless when they did, it is likely that the continued up-armouring of the individual man would have had to be stopped in order to prevent over-loading and total immobility!

This constantly shifting balance between armament, armour, and mobility that reached one of its turning points in medieval times, has been the perennial background to the fighting man's environment from the beginning of time until the present day.

Žižka and his Battle-Wagons

1

Even though the battles of the Hundred Years' War, when the long bow and primitive artillery took their toll, foreshadowed the eclipse of the heavily-armoured fighting man, the process of change was slow, partly because firearms took a long time to develop into match winners, partly because old tactical ideas die hard, and, not least, because it is always costly to scrap existing weapons. Not until 1419 did cannon begin to play a significant part in mobile war. It then took a half-blind genius, John Žižka, a member of the revolutionary Bohemian Hussite religious sect, to combine them with fortified vehicles to create an original tactical system that overwhelmed orthodox armies of the day.

Žižka modified ordinary, four-wheeled, horsedrawn farm carts (1), and organized them into formations that foreshadowed the tank force of the 20th century. The battle-wagons, as they came to be called, were modified from ordinary farm carts and thus filled a dual role both in peace and war; this naturally had many advantages for an agrarian minority fighting for survival. Two types were evolved. The first, an infantry vehicle that was defensive in character, carried crews of up to eighteen men and had its wooden sides built up to give protection to cross-bowmen and horses. The second type mounted cannon — named 'snakes' — and conferred an offensive capability on Žižka's army since it enabled artillery to move about in battle instead of being confined only to static sieges.

To begin with even the battle-wagons engaged only in positional battles, locked nose to tail in leaguers with extra protection given by filling the gaps between the wheels, and between each wagon, with heavy boards. By a well-rehearsed drill the leaguers could be formed at high speed into well-nigh impregnable fortresses, deployed by Žižka only on ground of his own choosing. This technique brought fifty Hussite victories in fourteen years, and makes it true to say that, by organizing his army round the battle-wagons, Žižka made a prodigious advance in the art of war in the five years of his command. Many hundreds of wagons were constructed, their crews taught to move at astonishing speed (twenty-five miles in a day is recorded), and to fight defensive battles by provoking the enemy to attack the wagon fortress after it had occupied dominating ground. Yet only three years after the first wagon engagement, Žižka was to be found engaged in a victorious battle of movement at Kutna Hora — not waiting to be attacked, but moving in formation against the enemy, stopping only to fire his guns, and then moving again until the enemy gave way in collapse.

From the time of the Hussite revolt there stemmed a steady interest in war wagons of one sort or another, though the means of propulsion — horses — remained for long the limiting factor.

Yet for generations nobody else developed wagon tactics or employed them to the same effect as Žižka who, by coupling his genius to the fanaticism of the Hussites, created an armoured *corps d'élite* and showed the way to merge several combat functions, both offensive and defensive, in one vehicle.

Early Dreams

Progress was slow during the Middle Ages, but new ideas were far from non-existent and projects for putting newly-discovered sources of power to fresh uses were frequently conceived by the small élite of educated men. The early 14th century witnessed, for instance, the introduction of windmills and with them the gear trains which made it possible to transfer a continuous drive from one direction to another. As is so often the case, a new source of power such as this quickly took the eye of military designers, and thus we find an Italian physician, Guido da Vigevano, making drawings in 1335 of the first known example of a windmill-driven combat machine (2). Its complexity is a tribute to his ingenuity; its fundamental intention — to close with the enemy at least possible risk — was similar to that motivating most other combat vehicle designers, but its mechanical feasibility and the way in which a breeze could be ensured during battle remained obscure.

There were others with similar inspirations. One, Robert Valturio, experimented with a windmill machine in 1472, but also turned his attention to sophisticated chariots fitted with scythes and carrying arquebuses to up-date the old Persian fashion (3). Vigevano and Valturio lived in turbulent times and probably bore arms themselves: nevertheless their projects were far ahead of reality and seem to have been prompted more by a desire to twist strategy and tactics to suit machines than the other way about.

Contrary to popular belief, therefore, Leonardo da Vinci did not design the first 'tank', but his model of 1500 lays greater claim to practicality than those of its predecessors. His notebooks bulge with drawings of machines, gear trains, and weapons, among them the celebrated 'combat vehicle' (4) — its prime claim to distinction being the hand-cranked transmission gear to allow eight men to propel themselves under armour to within striking distance of the enemy.

The vehicle seems to have been intended as an armoured spearhead to break close-packed enemy ranks rather like a battering ram. There are weapon slits in its sides and, therefore, although da Vinci writes of it advancing with guns, these may only have been the personal weapons of the crew — a contention reinforced by his plea that the machine must be followed up immediately by infantry.

As time passed, greater attention came to be paid to fighting from combat vehicles in the manner of Žižka; there is a drawing by the German Holzschuher showing a Land Ship of 1558, but unfortunately he leaves us in doubt as to the means of propulsion he proposed. There were many such suggestions in similar vein, those of the French Ramelli in 1588, the Scottish Napier in 1596, and of Voltaire in mid-18th century being among the most provocative 'paper projects' that remained still-born from lack of a practical source of propulsion.

In 1825, George Stephenson's railway engine gave birth to a compact, mobile power plant, though thirty years were to elapse before a steam-driven combat vehicle was proposed. Then, at last, a Mr James Cowan designed a helmet-shaped, wheeled battle-wagon (5), which was intended to be steam-driven and bristling with rotating scythes to 'mow down infantry'. But Lord Palmerston, despite some lack of restraint in other affairs, thought the idea 'uncivilized' and would have nothing to do with it.

Palmerston could not hope to hold back progress for long, for although Britain managed to remain disengaged from large-scale European wars in the latter half of the 19th century, several large outbreaks occurred elsewhere, and with increasing mechanical violence — notably in America during the civil war. Yet, strangely enough, no armoured vehicles of the Cowan type fought in those conflicts, though evidence of American interest is to be found in Cairo Museum where there is a model, dated 1900, of a so-called 'American 2 gun' battle vehicle (6). And at about the same time Kaiser Wilhelm of Germany proposed a land fortress of his own (7); a fantastic apparition that was meant to be steam-driven and sprouted more guns than many of the warships in his expanding navy.

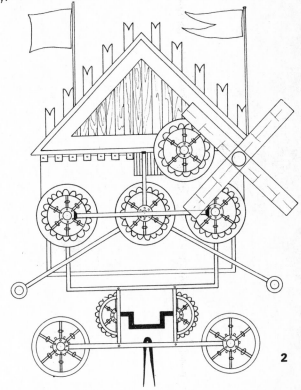

2

3

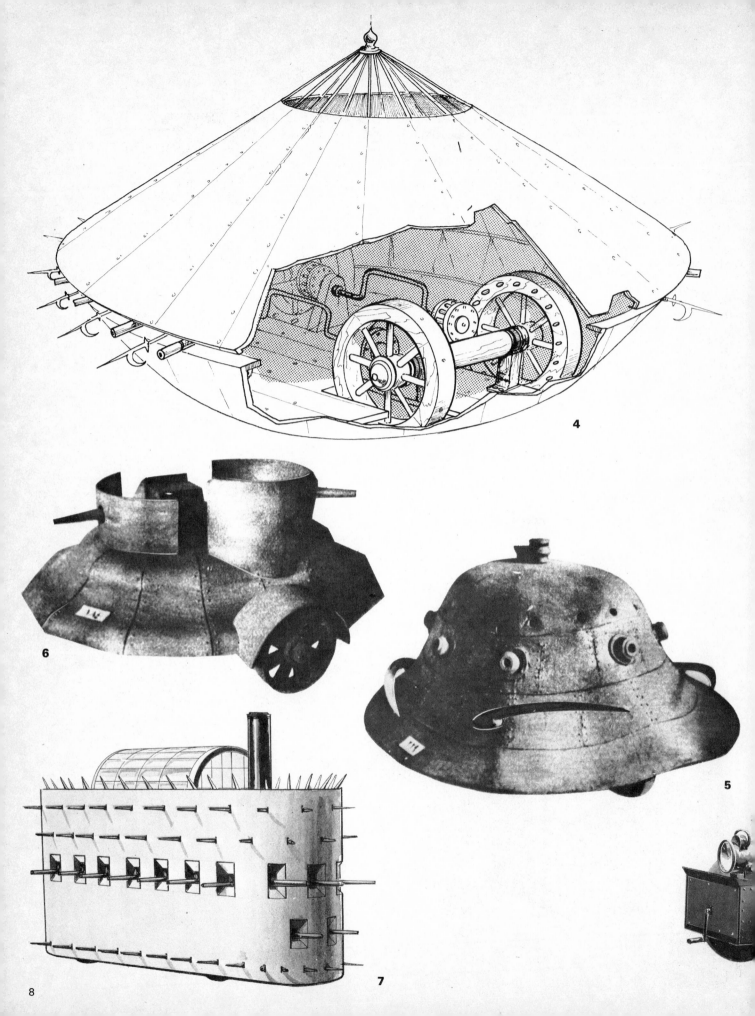

4

6

5

7

8

The Power Breakthrough

In 1885 the long awaited power breakthrough with the invention of an economic mobile propulsion unit took place. An internal combustion engine, running on petrol vaporized in a carburettor (created by a German, Gottlieb Daimler), gave miniaturized power to small land vehicles without needing cumbersome coal or wood fuel supplies like steam engines. From that moment progress accelerated, the advantages of small cheap power plants needing no advocacy — only the expenditure of money on their improvement and manufacture combined with an upsurge of inventive effort. Specially-designed vehicles carried on suspension systems of sufficient resilience to give a smooth ride, free of self-destructive vibration on the rough roads of the day, sprang into existence as far-sighted entrepreneurs and engineers seized their chances.

Fresh ideas abounded. Karl Benz constructed a light, three-wheeled, 3½ horsepower petrol-engined vehicle in 1885, the forerunner of millions of commercial motor cars. In 1899 a de Dion Bouton four-wheeled, petrol-driven motorcycle, mounting a Maxim machine-gun behind a shield (8) was demonstrated by a Mr F. R. Simms, and he followed this in 1902 with a fully armoured War Car armed with two Maxim machine-guns. Four years later, the French firm of Charron-Girardot et Voigt produced a chassis carrying an armoured hull mounting a fully rotating turret (9). And in the same year Daimler entered the military lists with an armoured car of his own [10] (see next page).

By this time a host of refinements had been added to his original engine of 1899 (11), which, setting aside its ignition process by hot tube instead of sparking plug, bears a striking resemblance to a modern power plant.

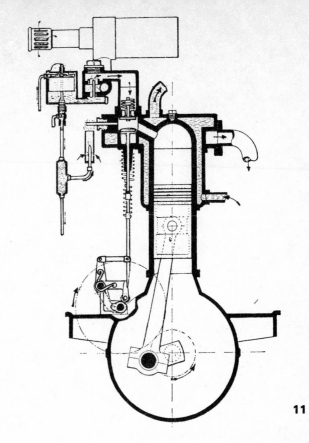

11

Simms (8)
1902

Armament: 1 Maxim machine-gun
Power Plant: 16 hp Daimler

Charron (9)
1906

Weight: 3 tons
Armament: 1 machine-gun
Note: Channels for crossing ditches

8

9

New ideas for combat vehicles were interchanged like wildfire in a world, headed for war, whose communications systems kept pace with an increasing rate of technological improvement. For instance, Charron armoured cars were sold to Russia and in 1906 the German, Ehrhardt, another pioneer of the petrol engine, constructed his own armoured car (12), though he failed to rouse the excitement of the German General Staff (or any other General Staff for that matter). Armies consisted of a great infantry mass, supported by cavalry and artillery, and their plans called for well-developed and reliable railways as the principal form of transportation: therefore an overnight switch to a mobile policy using untried road vehicles lacked realism and appeal. In truth, the new machines, early in development, full of snags, and unreliable, came into prominence while their designers still battled close to the frontiers of technical knowledge — every improvement they made to power or endurance came from the introduction of unique, unproved inventions adapted by the old horse carriage industry whose traditional vehicles usually matched the new power sources more by accident than design. Thus, to make proposals to develop petrol-driven vehicles beyond the requirements of transport into the realms of combat seemed, to conservative minds, to go beyond the limits of sanity. Nevertheless, armoured cars went on being made in a growing number of countries despite a striking lack of encouragement from professional soldiers whose thoughts centred around a staunch belief in the virtue of attack by overwhelming numbers of men and animals. In 1912, however, the Italians employed a Bianchi armoured car (13) at war in the Balkans and again, later, in the Tripolitanian desert — although the début made little impression on other soldiers' imaginations. Indeed, despite a mass of evidence, had they cared to study it, the professional heads of European armies lamentably failed to visualize the shape of the coming war (then less than a decade ahead) and planned battles of self-destruction from which no positive decision, apart from mutual exhaustion, could be achieved using the weapons they piled up in their arsenals.

There is no doubt that this failure to understand was caused, to no small extent, by the immense acceleration in technological progress which streaked ahead of the ability and organization of the General Staffs to acquire and process new knowledge. So small were the technical units incorporated in General Staff departments (due partly to lack of incentive and partly from shortage of trained technologists) that the planners worked without basic data, let alone intelligent technological evaluation of the new machinery which was available. In consequence the daily life of the fighting soldiers was about to be advanced by a series of technical surprises as, one by one, emotional convictions crashed before mechanical sensibility. Regardless of the tenets of recognized strategy (that basic art of getting men to the right battlefield in time) and orthodox tactics (the approved method of using men and weapons on the battlefield), mechanized combat vehicles were about to revolutionize war.

Daimler (10) 1904	*Weight:* 3 tons *Armament:* 1 machine-gun
Ehrhardt (12) 1906	*Weight:* 4 tons, four-wheeled drive *Armament:* Balloon gun 50 mm
Bianchi (13) 1912	*Armament:* 1 machine-gun

10

13

12

Revolution in Striking Power

At about the same time as steam engines were beginning to have a revolutionary impact upon transport (in addition to giving Cowan his idea for a steam-driven combat vehicle) an equally important series of inventions began to increase the quantity of shells and bullets that could be fired both by artillery and infantry. The development of the self-sealing cartridge made it possible to load all types of gun through the breech instead of down the barrel; while advances in metallurgy and improvements in design increased the resistance of barrels to internal pressures so that higher velocities and therefore greater ranges and accuracy could be achieved. Simultaneously special recoil systems were developed to help absorb the extra forces generated by more powerful discharge.

Before the end of the 19th century all the principal armies were equipped with breech-loading guns. Their rifles had magazines with clips containing several bullets, and the first delivery was being taken of belt-fed machine-guns. In fact the first machine-gun had been invented by a man called Puckle in 1718, but not until 1860 did Gatling guns with rotating chambers firing 300 rounds a minute come into practical use. It was the advent of the smaller, belt-fed Maxim gun, however, which marked the greatest step forward and it was machine-guns of this sort that most armies took to war in 1914 (14).

By 1914 the modern breech-loading field guns with compact recoil devices had settled into an almost standard pattern. The British had their 18-pounder, the Germans their 77-mm, and the French their 75-mm (15). Each had a rapid rate of fire with ranges in the order of 6,000 yards. Using the newly developed field telephones observers thus had the opportunity to control the fire of guns which could remain out of sight of the enemy.

Most armies were convinced of the essential need for offensive action to win wars, but still demanded the construction of forts upon which to base their defences — and the modern fort was very tough, made of steel and concrete. To crack these forts, heavy howitzers, firing shells through a high-trajectory, were developed — notably by the Germans whose siege train had no rival in 1914. The German 420-mm howitzer fired a projectile weighing 1,920 pounds — but it also needed great manpower to serve it and demanded a large amount of transport to move it slowly from one part of the front to another. The German 150-mm howitzer (16), on the other hand, was much easier to manage, threw a shell weighing 95 pounds a distance of 8,000 yards and though inaccurate, as was the case with most high-trajectory pieces, was capable of devastating field-works with persistent efficiency.

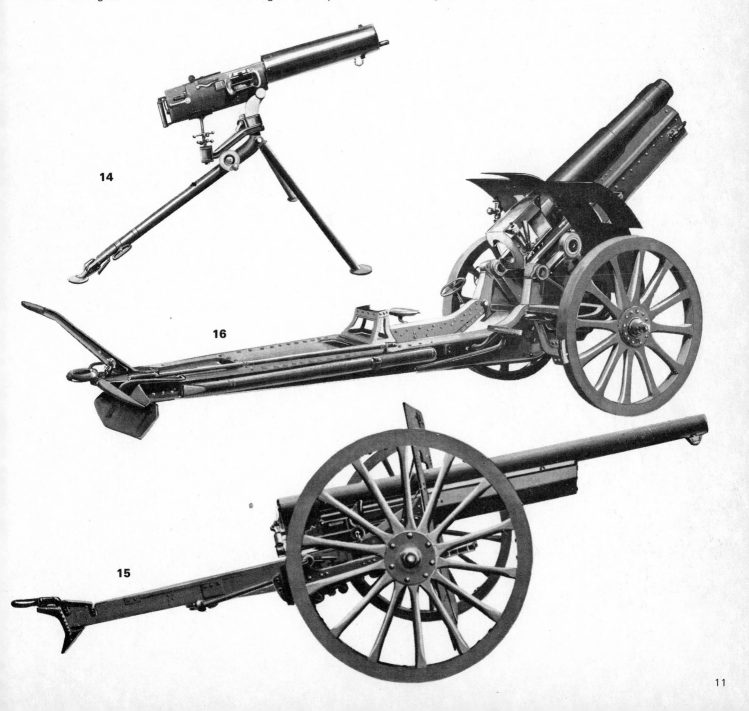

14

16

15

A New Style in Warfare

Industry revolutionized the art of war in the century that followed the battle of Waterloo in 1815. Of fundamental military importance was the widespread building of railways (quite often laid to serve a strict strategic purpose), the increase in firepower, and the rise in available manpower among societies which became better organized with every year that passed. Railways made it possible to move large numbers of men and material to and from battle fronts; conscript armies and the products of rapidly expanding industries came forward to fill the trains. Within a few decades wars escalated into struggles between nations instead of contests between professional armies with limited resources. Whereas, in days gone by, the occupation of continuous lines of fortification had been unusual and confined to short fronts with their flanks secured by natural barriers (leaving the final decisions to the armies that manoeuvred to engage in a single, short-lived encounter), the battles of the late 19th century tended to last longer and to be fought more and more from prepared positions where the defenders held a distinct advantage over their attackers.

In the American Civil War and the various campaigns fought by the Prussians in the 1860s and early 1870s, the greater lethality of massed firepower drove men to take cover behind stockades or in trenches, and this meant that neither infantry nor cavalry could hope to overrun an unshaken, defended position by direct assault. Prepared defences had either to be outflanked or broken down by artillery fire before they could be taken — a process that became progressively more difficult as defensive fortifications became stronger. There were occasions during the American Civil War when a feeling of utter hopelessness began to undermine the morale of infantry who were being slaughtered without achieving positive results — but the powers in Europe, who regarded them- selves as the unchallenged experts in such matters, chose to ignore the lessons taught in America and pointed to the quick success of the Prussian armies against the French in 1870 as proof that man would always prevail over material.

It was much easier for students of war to accept the obvious achievements of a total victory than to examine any of the defeats that had been linked with its accomplishment and which might have given hints of future trends. The defensive successes of the forts of Paris and one or two other French cities, which had imposed a prolonged halt on the Prussians whenever they tried to assault them in 1870, were lost to sight in the euphoria of peace. But the soldiers from the front knew how flesh and blood withered in the face of well-controlled, accurate fire, and that though the railways could bring an almost unlimited supply of men and material to the front, they could not profitably join in that battle when unarmoured. In the Boer War armoured trains added only a slight increase to fighting power in a conflict that offered infinite room for mobility in the African veldt, but which came to a halt when men advanced in the open against concealed marksmen and suffered terrible casualties and some shattering rebuffs. But once again, the pre- liminary victories of the Boers over the British army (that, after all, caused only a few thousand casualties) could be overlooked once the final victory of one vastly superior nation over another had finally been consummated.

Again, in Manchuria during the Russo-Japanese war of 1904 and 1905, a campaign of limited manoeuvre gradually gave way to positional warfare in which entrenched positions imparted supremacy to the defence and a positive indication of the coming dominance of artillery. The Russian defences at Port Arthur were heavily entrenched on commanding ground without a single gap through which the besieging Japanese could pass without resort to a direct assault. Barbed wire had been erected in front of the trenches and was covered by fire from artillery and small arms. To soften up those defences the Japanese employed artillery firing barrages over the heads of their advancing infantry and in due course the Russians were overcome — but the cost in Japanese lives was enormous. Our panorama of the battlefield at Port Arthur gives only an impression of what went on. It marks quite an accurate preview of the sort of battlefield that came into being in Western Europe in 1914.

All the signs of the coming deadlock in warfare could have been read in 1905, yet the most highly industrialized nations — Britain,

France, and Germany — failed to recognize them. The military thinkers of France and Germany preferred to work on the principle that First Class Military Powers, such as themselves, would be exempt from the prolonged slaughters suffered by the Second Class Powers who had already experienced the new phenomena of firepower. And in the early, mobile stages of the first campaign of the First World War in France and Russia in 1914 it looked as if they might be right, for a great German army swept into France and was defeated in a battle of manoeuvre at the Marne while other armies moved with almost untrammelled freedom in the limitless wastes of the Russian Front (as they continued to do for most of the war). But immediately after the Battle of the Marne, in September 1914, the Germans fell back to the River Aisne and dug in with machine-guns on the heights overlooking the river. Their defences proved impenetrable, as did those which spread out on either flank until, step by step, a continuous line of trenches held by rifle and machine-gun fire and backed up by artillery, expanded right and left until they stretched unbroken from the North Sea to the Swiss frontier.

At first only a single strand of waterlogged trenches linking villages and woods was dug, but as greater permanence came to what was, virtually, one enormous siege, both sides (notably the Germans) dug deeper to double and then redouble the trench system. The trench line became a fortified place of abode in which men mostly remained hidden from enemy fire. When they did choose to climb above the surface it was usually only by night but, if by day, under cover of a storm of artillery fire designed to beat down the fire of the opposition. Quite soon each side tried to isolate their trenches from the other by laying continuous fields of barbed wire which, if they were to be crossed, had either to be cut by hand under fire or blasted aside by a volume of artillery fire such as neither could provide in sufficient quantity in 1915. Needless to say, the trenches remained unpenetrated.

So the call went out for more artillery to cut a hole through wire and trenches to enable infantry to advance, break down the trench barrier, and let through cavalry. But guns could not do it on their own. No matter how fierce the artillery fire, it could only give a temporary and limited superiority over short lengths and depths of an entrenched front, and this could be strengthened and rebuilt just as fast as, or even faster than fresh masses of guns could be manufactured (along with millions of shells) and brought into position. Moreover the process of battering by guns took so long that all surprise was lost; the enemy could tell hours, and sometimes days or even weeks, beforehand where the attack would come and be ready to repel it at the outset.

Not even those who advocated the use of mechanical vehicles as a means to carry the fruits of industrialization into combat had accurately envisaged the stalemate, but whereas, at the end of 1914, the Germans were content to adopt a mainly defensive posture on the immobile Western Front and concentrate their offensive efforts on the more open Eastern Front where manoeuvre could always be exploited, the Western Allies simply *had* to attack the trenches in order to end the war and free their territory from the foreign invader. In consequence only the British and French had an immediate need in 1914 to look for a way to break the trench wall. Though they followed the obvious line of approach by saturation with artillery, they also turned to examine other ways by which men could be passed through the trench wall under the protection of armour. In other words, they looked back to the 400-year-old da Vinci solution.

Armoured cars such as had appeared at the beginning of the century were not suited to the task. Their wheels would get stuck in the trenches and become jammed by the wire and, in any case, the low ground-bearing pressures of wheels made it virtually certain that the cars would sink in ground that had been torn up by artillery fire and which quite often, in consequence, had become waterlogged because drainage systems had been destroyed. So, apart from a search for an armoured vehicle driven by internal combustion engines, there had also to be an examination of suitable suspensions and tracks that would allow heavy machines to move across country.

Wheels, Feet, and Tracks

There was no shortage of alternative solutions to enable the weight of a vehicle to be spread lightly and evenly across soft ground: either wide and tall wheels could be employed, as on the big farm traction engines, or chain tracks, as they were called, could be adopted.

As early as 1770 Richard Edgeworth patented a 'portable railway' to carry horse-drawn carriages across the atrocious roads of the day, and from then until 1914 a continuous flow of different devices, intended for the same purpose, had been proposed and built. In 1801, Thomas German patented endless-chain tracks and, gradually, as each new idea suggested others, two quite separate methods were developed – wheels with feet or continuous chain tracks bearing wide plates. Here we concentrate only on the most significant designs, the ones that set a trend and those that entered mass production for industry and agriculture.

A Scotsman, Andrew Dunlop, built a footed wheel in 1861, but in 1882 a design by Fender of Buenos Aires, with its chain track driven by a hexagonal sprocket over a square idler supported on bogie wheels, showed a remarkable likeness to present-day track layouts (17). Fender's ideas were very advanced, for he intended that the shock should be absorbed by the elasticity of the wire chains. Because it was so much ahead of technological feasibility, this engineering project offered a plethora of snags; but also a surfeit of possibilities for the future.

An American, F. W. Batter, had a steam-driven tracked vehicle on his drawing-board in 1888 (18), followed quickly by G. H. Edwards' vehicle of 1890 (19). It was in Britain that footed wheels found most favour; Bramah Diplock's design of 1899 (20) came off the drawing-board and into service with the intention of improving the cross-country performance of agricultural machinery. Indeed, by then, ideas and detailed designs had reached the stage when entrepreneurs could be persuaded to risk their money to make and employ the better-conceived devices. Inevitably, as work grew in volume, new uses and improved methods came to mind.

Nevertheless, except in America where several firms replaced wheels by tracks on vehicles that had to tackle undeveloped land, conversions from existing suspensions were slow and limited. Because his model assumed an early association with combat vehicles, we illustrate Mr Holt's steam tractor of 1906 (21), a simple experi-

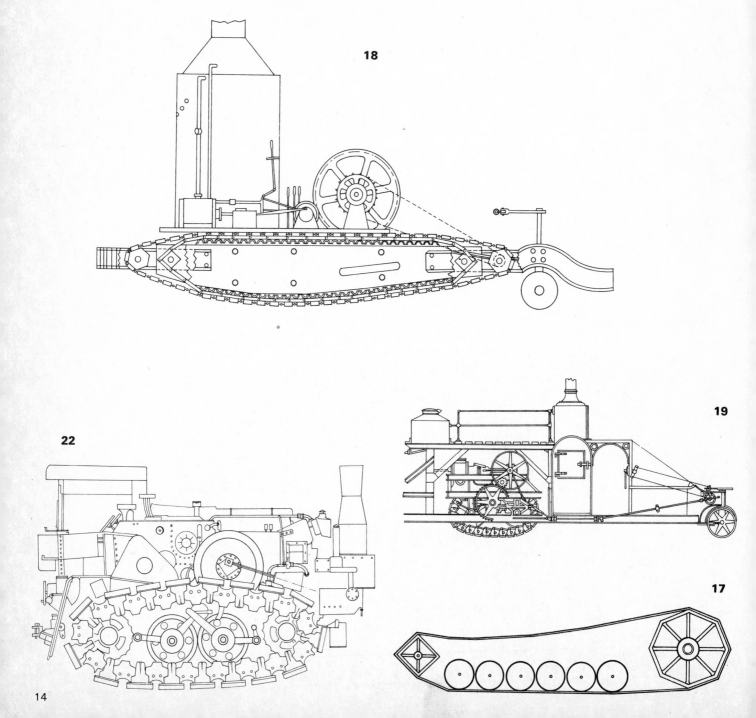

ment whereby an ordinary, wheeled, steam farm tractor had its big wheels replaced by tracks. And when, in 1908, the British War Office offered a prize of £1,000 for a cross-country vehicle that could haul a load forty miles without the need to refuel, the challenge was accepted by David Roberts of R. Hornsby & Sons who had already built a steam, tracked vehicle in 1905 and followed it in 1907 with a petrol-engined version (22) — a full year before Holt put his first petrol-driven model on the road.

Tracked vehicles quickly became big business in America, but not in Britain where the initial urge receded and a suggestion by a Major Donoghue in 1908, to mount a gun protected by armour on a Hornsby tractor, met a brisk rebuff. But from many different kinds of suspension and track linkage tried out through the years in efforts to impart greater flexibility and reliability to rugged machinery, there grew a keen realization that the chain track solution had enormous advantages over the footed wheel. Even Diplock gave up 'feet' and turned to devise his first chain track (23) in 1910 — incorporating elements of the footed principle.

Interest was world wide, though not overwhelming, and so poor was it in Britain that Hornsby's sold their foreign patents to Holt's in 1912. In Austria Holt's representative, Mr Steiner, got the

Austro-Hungarian army interested; but in Germany, his salesmanship suffered the classic rejection — 'No importance for military purposes', the General Staff declared; and in France the soldiers first looked to track vehicles in 1915 only as a means to crush barbed wire. None of the commercial machines had a wide ditch-crossing capability and so, to make a combat vehicle which could cross trenches on tracks, original research had to be started to find a reliable and practical suspension system. But in 1915, combat vehicles of that sort still resided only in the minds of dreamers: and not even the soldiers, up against it at the front, were prepared to give much scope to wild-cat mechanized toys.

Batter (18)	Shoes are of wood
	Steering by front wheels
	Two belts running upon each other
Edwards (19)	Note the complex track links
Pedrail (20)	Feet are of wood, steel, and rubber
Holt (21)	Pin and plate steel track
Hornsby (22)	*Weight:* 8 tons
	Power: 70 hp
	Track: Lubricated pins

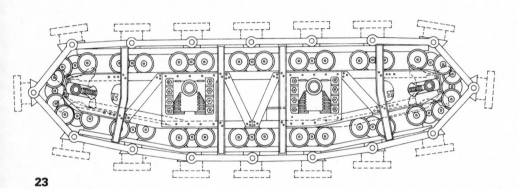

23

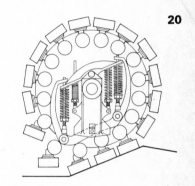

20

21

As we have seen, only armoured cars had become full-blown combat vehicles by 1914, although ideas suggesting how field fortifications might be overcome had been put forward by the score. Memories of a prophecy by H. G. Wells (which incorporated a Diplock footed wheel) went hand-in-hand with traditional concepts generated by adaptations of combat vehicles which had long since been discarded. Inspiration really took flight — but in most minds only after the trench deadlock had come to pass. Apart from Donoghue, only one man — an Australian, called de

Mole — visualized the shape of mechanized combat to come and the means to wage it. In 1912 he filed the design for a fighting vehicle (24) so convincingly similar to those which finally went into service that one wonders why it was never adopted from the outset. But alas for de Mole, his creation suffered the same fate as so many innovations of its kind when a cool, superficial examination in the British War Office consigned it to a frigid pigeon-hole. Yet this vehicle had many features which were superior to the machines that were eventually produced, for although de Mole's definition

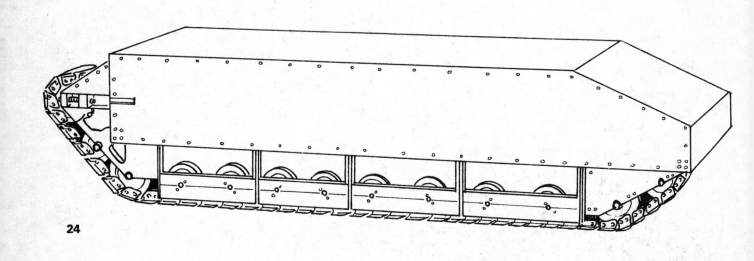

24

25

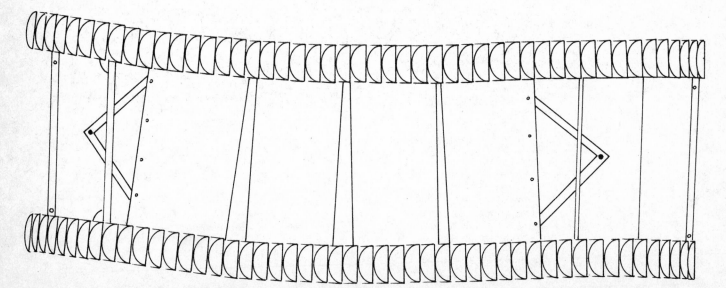

of armament remained vague, he had grasped the importance of all-round armoured protection, high ground clearance to avoid bogging, and the need for tracks — the fundamental technological combination. Moreover his tracks were steered by 'bowing' (25) — a device some ten years ahead of its time. Indeed, it was de Mole's fate to be too far ahead of his time just like Fender.

In fact, the first combat cars in use with the British were those belonging to the Royal Naval Air Service in Belgium. They were only armed with machine-guns and, later, 3-pounder cannon, but experience soon told their exposed crews that armour was as essential as guns. So, first, they hung boiler plate and then armoured plate to the sides of the cars, and even then they went into action without overhead protection, as can be seen on this large Rolls-Royce armoured car (26) (see next page).

Nevertheless, vehicles of this kind dominated the actions in which they fought — so long as the roads stayed open. It was even admitted by an infantryman that one armoured car possessed the value of an infantry company in open warfare. So, as early as 1914, the thought was sown that, perhaps, one day, armoured vehicles would break out of their narrow tactical limits into the wider realms of psychological and strategic importance.

Let us therefore examine armoured cars before the flood tide of 'tracks' engulfs the field of combat vehicle invention, and recall that, in 1915, those closest to the struggle to build a trench-crossing vehicle thought first of wheels as the solution.

The British Royal Naval Air Service, which had employed armoured cars so boldly in support of the soldiers in the early, mobile stages of the German invasion of Belgium, produced innovators in the search for better combat vehicles. Deprived of their mobility by the trenches, airmen found time to experiment, to pass on their knowledge, and give birth to some weird creatures in addition to highly-successful weapons. A Sizaire-Berwick armoured car driven by a 110-hp aeroplane engine propeller to supplement its 20-hp engine (27) to help cross soft sand in the desert, symbolized the influence of grounded airmen when married to the exuberance of youth — but it made no practical impact. The Rolls-Royce armoured car of 1914 (28), however, was more durable and could still be found in the thick of action over thirty years later, in between having fought in countless wars and survived without radical modification.

Stung by the discovery that the Germans already possessed an armour-piercing bullet, the builders of the Rolls-Royce settled on a working compromise between the need for speed, matched to armoured protection, and the ability to carry an impressive armament. It was discovered that a German bullet would penetrate a one-inch board sandwiched between two ordinary $\frac{1}{4}$-inch steel plates, and that it took 12 mm of armour plate to stop penetration from point-blank range. Not being prepared to give up too much speed by increasing weight, the sailors settled for 8 mm of armour and hoped their own firepower would keep the Germans from getting closer than a range of 500 yards. Thus, from the very beginning, the sailors struggled with the classic compromise between armour, mobility, and firepower, giving their Seabrook armoured car of 1915 (29) a 3-pounder gun and again sacrificing armour protection in order to retain superior hitting power.

Nothing like this enthusiasm spurred on the Germans, whose designers were retarded by the policy of a General Staff which held rigidly to the doctrine that the war would be won by men — not by material. Indeed, for some time, the German General Staff easily held off its critics by supplying such dynamic organizational and tactical innovations to the battlefield that they were able to defeat their opponents and win convincing victories without the use of unconventional weapons.

Nevertheless, Ehrhardt persisted with his earlier work and produced an armoured car in 1915 (30) which had a strikingly high silhouette — quite the opposite of the compact, aggressive lines of the Rolls-Royce — and Daimler also built a Panzer Wagen (31) of similarly unwieldy proportions. Both cars saw action, mostly on the more open eastern fronts, where their presence came to be tolerated by cavalry patrols, particularly when Russian machine-guns closed the battlefield to horses. Italy, too, as she came into the war on the side of France and Britain in 1915, remembered her Bianchis of 1912, and encouraged Lancia to build a new armoured car (32). The seeds of tactical armoured warfare were being sown broadcast, but it was from the New World, still at peace, that the most striking hint of future strategic possibilities came.

Colonel R. P. Davidson was head of the North Western Military and Naval Academy at Lake Geneva, Wisconsin, USA, when, in 1915, he led a column of combat vehicles from Chicago to San Francisco, running to a carefully planned and executed schedule. Since 1898, Davidson had built experimental weapon carriers with the aid of his students, who performed crew duties each year during a long proving trek. In consequence, by 1915, Davidson had acquired extensive experience of petrol-driven vehicles backed by many thousand miles' running on the poor quality American roads.

On 10th June 1915 Davidson set out on his most ambitious journey with a force comprising eight Cadillac cars of different vintage, each representing an essential element of an almost comprehensive armoured force. The most important vehicle was the fully armoured car (33) — the first ever built in America — equipped with a .30-inch machine-gun and capable of 70 mph on a good road. Davidson led the force from a reconnaissance car from which vision could be extended by the use of a periscope; communications were established from two wireless cars, their sets fed by telescopic antennae; food was prepared in a kitchen car, cooked in electric ovens powered by a Delco generator; there was a hospital car, a quartermaster's car, and, of special interest to aviation enthusiasts, an unarmoured balloon destroyer car mounting an upward pointing Colt machine-gun.

The column was controlled by strict military and mechanical discipline, the crews picked from the best cadets whose previous work on the vehicles had taught them how to cope with almost any breakdown or emergency. All along the route they gave demonstrations of their versatility, the capabilities of their machines and the possibilities of mechanized warfare.

Naturally, the newspaper publicity accorded to Davidson's column created useful benefits for Cadillac, while Davidson seems to have concentrated more on pushing the need for America to set about improving the quality of her nation-wide road network: the future of armoured warfare took second place in his mind.

Indeed, Davidson, a modest man who loathed waste, was no great propagandist, and so this remarkable innovator of armoured vehicles has passed from view, his work swept out of sight by the sheer enormity of the revolution brewing in Europe.

Sizaire-Berwick 'Wind Wagon' (27)
 Armament: 1 Vickers machine-gun
 Power Plant:(a) 20-hp Sizaire
      (b) 110-hp Sunbeam Aero Engine
      (for use in desert)

Rolls-Royce 1914 (28)
 Weight: 3.5 tons
 Armour: 8 mm
 Crew: 3
 Armament: 1 Vickers mg

Seabrook (29)
 Weight: 10 tons
 Armour: 8 mm
 Crew: 6
 Armament: 1 x 3-pdr
     4 x Vickers mg

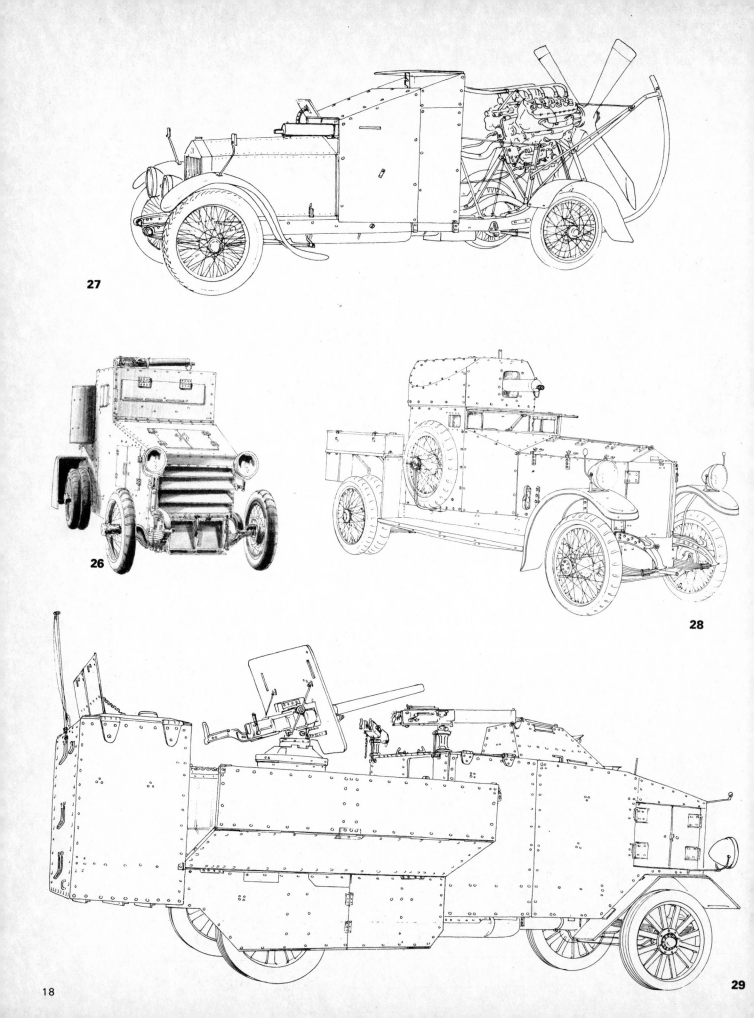

27

26

28

29

Ehrhardt 1915 (30) 5 x mg
Daimler Panzer Wagen 1915 (31)
Lancia 1915 (32) 3 x mg
Cadillac 1915 (33) Armoured Car/Balloon Destroyer

30

32

31

ARMOR·
BATTERY

33

Birth of the Tank

The need to create a fighting machine of some sort or another and as quickly as possible, overrode all other considerations in 1915, and drove the pioneers to prodigious efforts in exploring numerous possibilities. Fortunately for the armoured idea, the size of the challenge attracted men of vision, energy and determination, the names of Winston Churchill, Ernest Swinton, Albert Stern (**below**), Murray Sueter, Tom Hetherington, William Tritton, and Walter Wilson appearing highest in the list of British champions, and that of Jean Estienne top among those who worked, quite separately from the British, in France. But because haste was the order of the day to help save lives in breaching the trench wall, little time remained for deep research and the perfection of designs: only by adapting existing components, to meet the soldiers' rough specifications, could fighting machines be got ready to take part in the great British offensive in 1916 – and even then they could not be in time for the start.

34

35

The pioneers followed two lines of enquiry, the first, a variation on the Big Wheel theme, was to be mounted on 40-foot-diameter wheels driven by an 800-hp submarine diesel engine, armed with three twin 4-inch gun turrets and to weigh 300 tons – a veritable Land Battleship. Work began on a wooden mock-up (34) known as the Hetherington Big Wheel – and came to an abrupt end in June 1915 when it could be clearly seen how vulnerable such a giant would be and how long it would take to build even if the wheel was reduced to 15 feet.

The second line of enquiry looked at tracked vehicles of which three types were immediately available for experiment. Pedrail (35), the only pure British contender, underwent development, was rejected because it grew too heavy, but became subjected to further, abortive, examination as a cross-country flame-thrower carrier. Next, there was the little triple-tracked Killen-Strait tractor, of American derivation (36), whose principal use in war might have

been only as a wire cutter, but whose prime role in the experiments became that of an ideal demonstration device used to enthuse those who doubted the potential of tracked vehicles.

The third prospect was a Bullock Tractor (37) embodying Holt-type tracks. Two were linked together and performed better than anything else, but still well below what was needed because they were not large enough to cross wide gaps or to function reliably in badly-broken ground. Nevertheless, by July 1915, tracks had won official favour and the investigation had narrowed into a search for a robust version capable of crossing a 5-foot ditch. The soldiers' demands for payload and armament were less precise. An early request asked for fifty armed men to be carried behind 8 mm of armour along with various guns ranging from the naval 2-pounder Pom-Pom to the 6-pounder Hotchkiss gun: they settled in due course on the latter supplemented by numerous machine-guns.

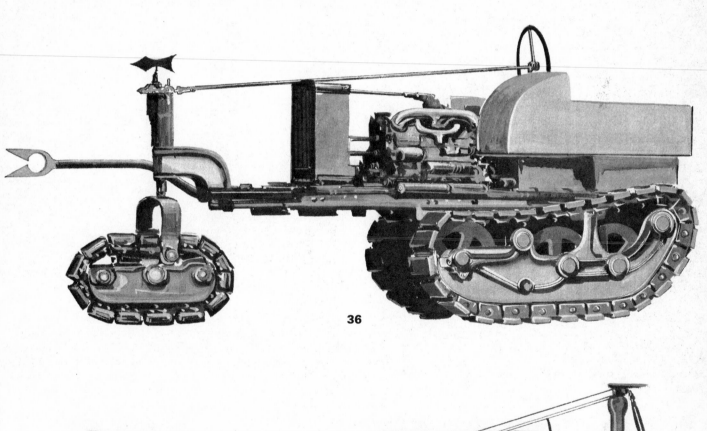

36

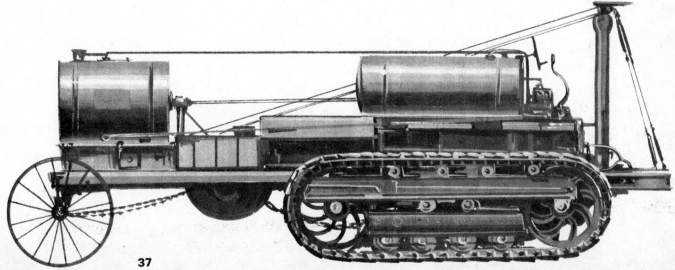

37

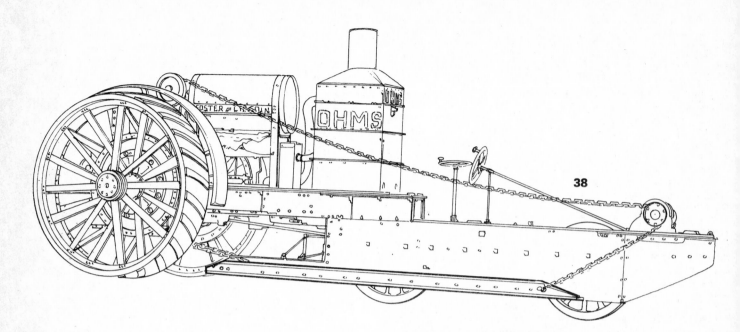

The most critical problem lay in the search for a suitable track. In parallel with work directed towards the construction of a heavy gun tractor, Mr W. Tritton of Foster & Co, Lincoln, had already built a 105-hp trench-crossing machine (38) along with other cross-country devices (including the mock-up Big Wheel). When it was decided to build a pilot, tracked model in July 1915, the final request went to Fosters who, with the help of Major Wilson, merged the results of earlier trials into one machine. Complicated concepts such as 'Elephants' Feet' (39) and Sueter's Articulated Proposal (40) were dropped because a relatively simple solution was in demand. Yet these complex machines were typical of the mass of ingenious ideas generated by an urgent situation. They are far too numerous to show here, but at that time nothing could safely be rejected without investigation.

In the final analysis, the operational model had to be simple and robust for short-term employment in a limited role. People envisaged combat vehicles like these advancing only a few miles, helping to breach the trenches, and then being left behind once the open had been reached and troops fanned out into a final, war-winning battle.

Tritton received the order to construct the first 'armoured' vehicle on 29th July 1915, along with instructions to make best use of whatever material lay at his disposal. Some 'armour' could only be boiler plate, the engine the same 105-hp Daimler as that used on his trench-crossing machine, driving through the same sort of transmission to Bullock tracks — the latter still being in transit on the

39

40

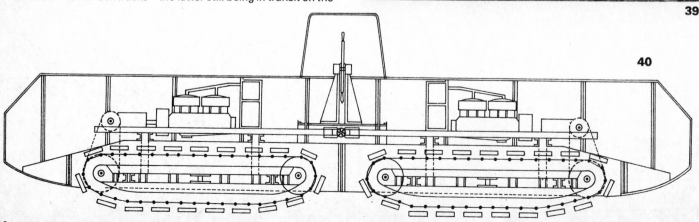

high seas from America when design began. It had been decided to mount a 2-pounder Pom-Pom in a fully rotating turret, along with several machine-guns firing through portholes; but in the event only a mock-up turret was made since, even while the vehicle was under construction, other more advanced types were envisaged and began to overtake the original.

Early in September the Bullock Track Machine, later known as the Tritton No. 1 (41), ran and immediately demonstrated that, although on the right lines, it suffered from severe track weaknesses in that it failed to cross a 5-foot gap and ran off its tracks all too easily. Nothing could stop the inventors now. Within a few days of the failure of Bullock track, a new pressed steel plate (42) had been designed and proved on the test bed. As Stern wrote, 'This was the birth of the Tank.'

It should not be thought that the rapid progress made by Fosters represented an easy passage of armoured vehicles up the path to war. Vested interests opposed the pioneers at every step, for only a few enlightened people understood the nature of the experiments and fewer still could envisage strange, as yet unmade, armoured monsters playing a decisive role in the sort of campaign which had upset every pre-war military calculation. Immersed in unyielding, conventional thoughts, the British commanders resented the least attempt to divert essential materials from the support of the infantry and artillery massed assaults they were preparing. Not entirely without logic, they saw no reason to submit men's lives to even greater chance at the behest of amateurs and the whim of untried machines.

Lacking further guidance from front line soldiers, those directing the war effort in 1916 found it difficult to commit industrial effort to the manufacture of vehicles whose every detail threw unheard of loads on an already overloaded economy. Men of strong views had to be persuaded in a hurry of the effectiveness of ungainly and unproven machines — and industry had to learn to mass produce equipment which stretched its knowledge to the limits.

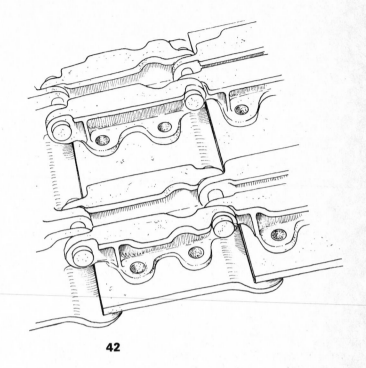

42

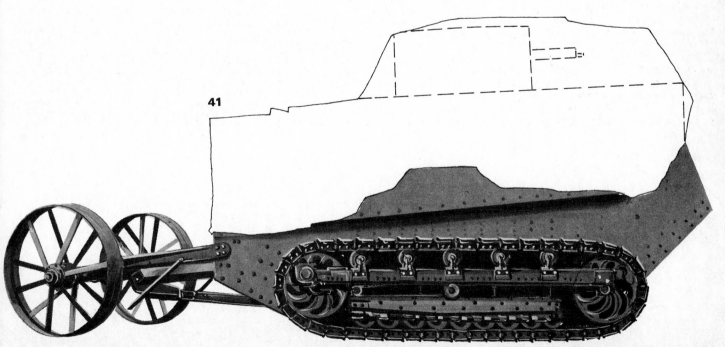

41

While Tritton No. 1 underwent its trials, preparations were made to modify it primarily to test the new pressed steel track. This model looked very like No. 1, dragging behind it the wheels which were meant to aid stability and assist steering but which, in fact, created more hindrance than help. Neither Tritton No. 1, nor the modified vehicle, known as 'Little Willie' (43) ever acquired armament although a ring to receive a mock-up turret was incorporated on the top of their hull. Little Willie was a project study to demonstrate the feasibility of the soldiers' requirements. Having done that she (or he!) went on to do service as a training vehicle to teach the first operational drivers.

From Swinton came the basic battlefield requirements that guided Tritton's and Wilson's designs. Swinton asked for a speed of 4 mph, for a trench-crossing capability of 8 feet and the ability to climb a 5-foot parapet, for a 6-pounder gun, since it could fire high-explosive shell (whereas the 2-pounder could not), and for an armour thickness of 10 mm. Confronted by these stiff requirements, the designers had to recast their original layout and yet continue to employ the components evolved during the summer if they were to produce a fighting machine by the turn of the year.

The need to cross broken ground and 8-foot ditches overrode all other considerations and it was this which persuaded Wilson to go for a radically new approach by carrying the track over the top of a high hull. By so doing any possibility of mounting a cannon in a rotating turret vanished, since the combination would be too high. As a compromise (and all combat vehicle design comes to that) the guns were mounted in 'sponsons', one on either side of the hull – thus inhibiting the vehicle's overall fighting capacity.

Little Willie first ran on 3rd December 1915, by which time the battle model (44) – at first called 'Centipede', then 'Big Willie', and finally 'Mother' – stood almost complete. She ran on 16th January 1916 and showed beyond doubt that the specification had been satisfied and that the pioneers' claims were justified. But the call for haste had enforced many undesirable features. Of the eight man crew, no less than four were needed to help drive, one as co-ordinator or commander, one to change the main gears, and one to control each track as 'gearsman'. Because only the 105-hp Daimler engine was available, the power to weight ratio for a 28-ton machine was pitifully low at only 3.7 hp per ton – and would have been much less had the thicker armour desired been hung. In action it was found that 10 mm of armour would not keep out the German armour-piercing bullet and, of course, a direct hit by a high explosive field gun shell was, more often than not, totally disruptive. Moreover, the problem of working and drilling thin armour plate was new to British industry and, at first, raised serious production difficulties.

But the Tank had been born, and christened 'Tank' as a measure of deception to deflect enemy attention from her real purpose and nature. It is a name which, as will be seen in due course, has led to many misunderstandings and misrepresentations.

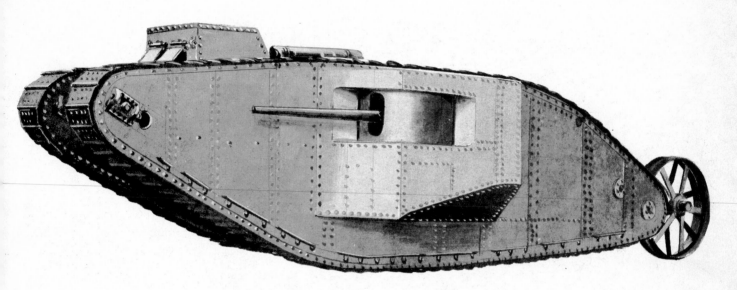

44

'MOTHER' OR MARK I (44)

Weight:	28 tons
Power Plant:	105-hp Daimler Petrol Engine
Crew:	8
Length with Tail:	32 feet 6 inches
Width:	13 feet 9 inches
Height:	8 feet 2 inches
Armour:	10 mm
Speed:	3.7 mph
Armament:	2 x 57 mm (6 pdr)
	4 mg
Trench-crossing:	10 feet
Range:	23 miles

The first fighting tanks went into action during the last phase of the Battle of the Somme on 15th September 1916 and were Mark Is, almost identical to Mother. Their dramatic impact on friend and foe won only marginal successes, but their very appearance sufficed to ensure for themselves a second chance in action.

The early tanks played only a subsidiary role in the infantry assault and suffered many set-backs. Ill-co-ordinated crews had to overcome the most appalling difficulties, four of them trying to drive and four others endeavouring to fire five or six guns in the general direction of an elusive enemy. The noise and heat were oppressive, so the men would have preferred to wear next to no clothing, but had to remain covered as protection against hot working parts, the danger of fire, and the 'splash' thrown off when the armour was struck by enemy projectiles. Engine starting was a laborious, cranking business and the automotive parts required constant lubrication and maintenance, often when on the move – though the considerable spare space then had advantages. Riding in a pitching and rolling, unsprung, enclosed cabin called for the utmost care to maintain a footing while glass vision blocks and open slits in the sides gave only limited arcs of view, making it difficult for commanders and gunners to pick and fire at fleeting targets. Intercommunication came by touch and hand signal, for a shout could not overcome the clamour of the engine and tracks: yet each change of direction was a team effort, when it required shifting of the main gears, and locking of the differential and braking action by a steering 'gearsman' – each by a different person.

The first Mark Is were called many names, not all of them complimentary, but officially those fitted with 6-pounder guns were described as 'Males' and those with five machine-guns 'Females'. So 'Mother', with her 6-pounder guns, changed sex again a few months after birth.

25

France joins in

46

45

Quite independently of the British, the French army, prompted mainly by Colonel J. E. Estienne, set about devising tanks of their own. Wire-crushing tractors were tried and rejected in 1915, but later that year, Estienne, an artilleryman, proposed transporting a gun, protected by armour, close to the enemy lines. Just like the British innovators, Estienne grasped the vital need for haste and how essential it would be to employ whatever components came immediately to hand: he had seen Holt tractors used by the British to tow guns and adopted them forthwith as the carriage for an armoured box mounting a 75-mm gun. Trench crossing and the perils of moving across broken ground were not tackled with anything like the same thoroughness as in Britain—and so, in due course, French tanks of poor cross-country performance and with limited fighting capacity, came into being — but in larger numbers than in Britain.

The first orders for 400 went to the Schneider Company in February 1916, and shortly after that another 400 were ordered from the Compagnie des Forges d'Honecourt at Saint Chamond. Like the British, the French tried hard to keep their work secret, but seem to have been more successful than their allies in resisting attempts to launch the new machines prematurely into action. Not without disgust, therefore, the French came to hear of the first, minor British tank attack in September 1916 when they, themselves, could not be ready in mass before April 1917.

The Schneider (45) first went to war at the Chemin des Dames on 16th April 1917 and contributed very little to a battle that was distinguished by failure and appalling casualties — the grim precursor of mutiny in the French army. The St Chamond (46) had its chance in May — and with no better success for, like the Schneider, it was unreliable and came to grief on rough ground — rather in the manner of the experimental Tritton No. 1. Both machines were abandoned, the French turning to new methods after learning a crucial lesson that a large number of small, cheap machines stood a better chance of combining survival with success than a few heavy, somewhat expensive, and only slightly less vulnerable vehicles. French doctrine thus began to diverge from the British from the start, leading to the evolution of ideas which were to be the pivots of subsequent armoured debates the world over.

Later, the Japanese army bought a few Schneiders and some St Chamonds found their way to Lithuania. The 'Tank Idea' thus spread its influence by commercial as well as military incentive.

	Schneider CA 1 (45)	St Chamond (46)
Weight:	14.6 tons	25.3 tons
Power Plant:	70 hp	90 hp
Crew:	6	9
Armour (max):	25 mm	17 mm
Speed:	5 mph	5 mph
Armament:	1 x 75-mm	1 x 75-mm
	2 mg	4 mg

Divergent trends

Even before the first tank action and at the same time as a host of modifications were being thought up for the existing British Mark I tank, the British began searching for new applications for tracked vehicles. In July 1916 work started on a Gun Carrier (see page 32) – an adaptation of the Mark I to transport a 6-inch howitzer through the shattered trench zone in order to maintain a deep advance within artillery range and support.

But certain characteristics of the Gun Carrier, crossed with Little Willie, can easily be detected in the breeding of a much more ambitious venture launched in June 1916. This was 'Flying Elephant' (47), a design by Tritton aimed at the creation of a genuine heavy tank which would be proof against shell fire. Armour two to three inches thick was to be fitted to what was intended to be an enormous land ship weighing 100 tons, powered by two 120-hp Daimler engines driving inner and outer, interconnected tracks in an effort to prevent bellying (48).

By January 1917, Flying Elephant was almost ready for trials, but, by then, the comparative success of the Mark Is, the promise of modifications being introduced to improve its later versions, the signs of an entirely new concept with a projected light tank, the Tritton 'Chaser', and the soaring cost of Flying Elephant, led to the scrapping of the prototype – a decision charged with significance for the future.

Flying Elephant (47)

Weight:	100 tons
Power Plant:	2 120-hp Daimler
Crew:	8
Length:	29 feet 6 inches
Height:	10 feet
Width:	9 feet 10 inches
Armour:	Sides 2 inches Front 3 inches
Armament:	1 x 57-mm
	6 mg

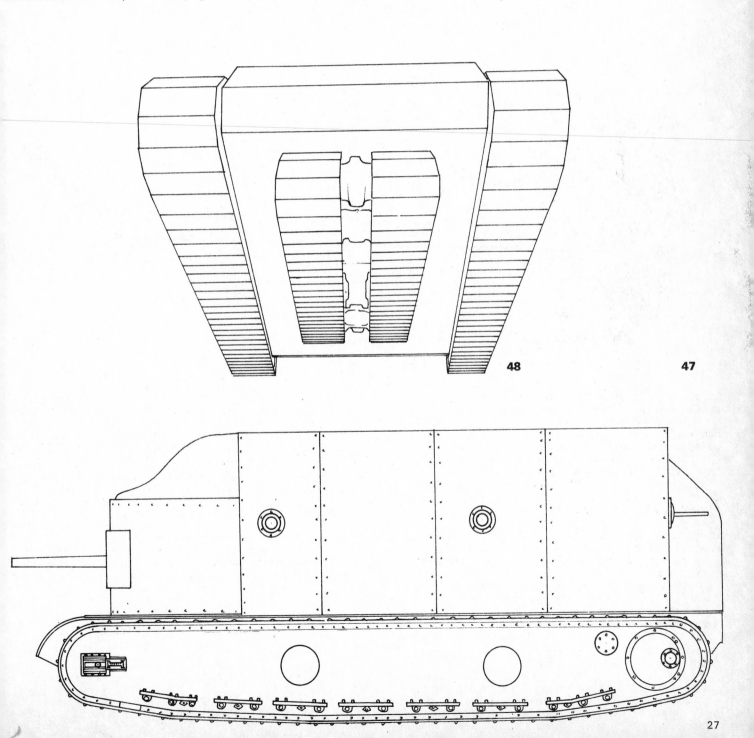

48   47

Graduation in Battle – Cambrai

Tanks, as we have seen, were devised to assist infantry in entering and breaking the enemy trench line. By 1917, however, such was the power of massed artillery, it had become possible actually to subdue the immediate front line for a sufficient length of time to enable it to be occupied with relatively little trouble. In consequence the practice of stationing smaller garrisons in the forward areas and larger ones in the rear was introduced to save the majority of the defenders from the full blast of prolonged bombardments. Trench systems became deeper and more profuse while wire entanglements became thicker and deep ditches were cut to form continuous tank obstacles. Layouts such as these not only went far to nullify the effects of artillery and reduce the chances of tanks' survival when they worked in isolation but also used up vast resources in labour and materials.

Among fortifications such as these, the great Allied offensives of 1917 made hardly any progress at a dreadful cost in lives. Since tanks had yet to show they were anything more important than a bonus to the infantry they were relegated to subordinate tasks such as rolling down the wire and shooting at machine-gun posts. Pleas that the tanks should be used on firm ground that aided their movement and that they should be employed in mass went almost unheard. A proposal by the Tank Corps staff, that originated in the mind of its first genius, Colonel J. F. C. Fuller, called for a large-scale raid by tanks on unbroken ground near Cambrai, but made no impression until the British attacks in Flanders had failed catastrophically. Only then did an assault on a vastly greater scale than that envisaged by Fuller take the fancy of the High Command.

This attack took place on 20th November 1917 with 376 Mark IV tanks. New tactical methods were left in the hands of the Tank Corps staff and, they, seizing their chance, upturned all the old, conventional ideas. They demanded and achieved surprise in time and place by allowing no preliminary artillery bombardment to give warning of an attack; they employed aircraft to co-operate closely in the battle by making low-level bombing and machine-gun attacks; and they persuaded the infantry to match tank deployment with a drill that enabled them to deal methodically and swiftly with each type of enemy defence.

Our diagram (**right**) shows a sector of the German defences guarding Cambrai just as the first wave of tanks has penetrated the front line. British artillery fire is falling on previously-located gun positions in rear while aircraft sweep the battlefield for targets. The leading Mark IVs, having crushed the wire and shot up the foremost German trenches, are making way for others to come onward and drop wooden fascines in the deep ditch before rolling forward to engage the next line of resistance. In order to pass easily through the gaps broken by the tanks, the infantry are following in file, ready to capture the enemy remaining in trenches that have been dominated by the leading tanks.

Out of the picture is the mass of horsemen, waiting in rear, whose task calls upon them to ride through the gap that is being opened towards Cambrai in order to cut the German lines of communication systematically behind this part of the Western Front. Nor can a reserve of tanks be seen to help carry the advance beyond the point when exhaustion has sapped the strength of the assault waves – for there is no reserve and every tank available is coming into action at once.

Nevertheless, this attack tore a wide hole in one of the strongest sectors of the German line, at slight cost to the British and severe loss to the Germans. Because the cavalry barely came into action and, when it did, was stopped dead whenever a machine-gun opened up, the brilliance of the tank victory did away with the fallacy that mobile war would restart once a gap had been opened. The solution of the gapping problem had merely asked the next question of how armoured vehicles were to prosecute the next phase – the exploitation – when cavalry clearly could not.

Disturbing as it may have been to the British military purists, the tank idea as demonstrated at Cambrai did at least point the way to final victory. To the German purists, the defeat came as a doctrinal slap in the face since they had insisted that tanks could be defeated by sound infantry defensive tactics using guns and obstacles – the old concept of men overcoming material was dying hard. But for the Germans it was too late to build a tank fleet of their own in time. They would try and fail – 'they would lose the war'.

SMOKE

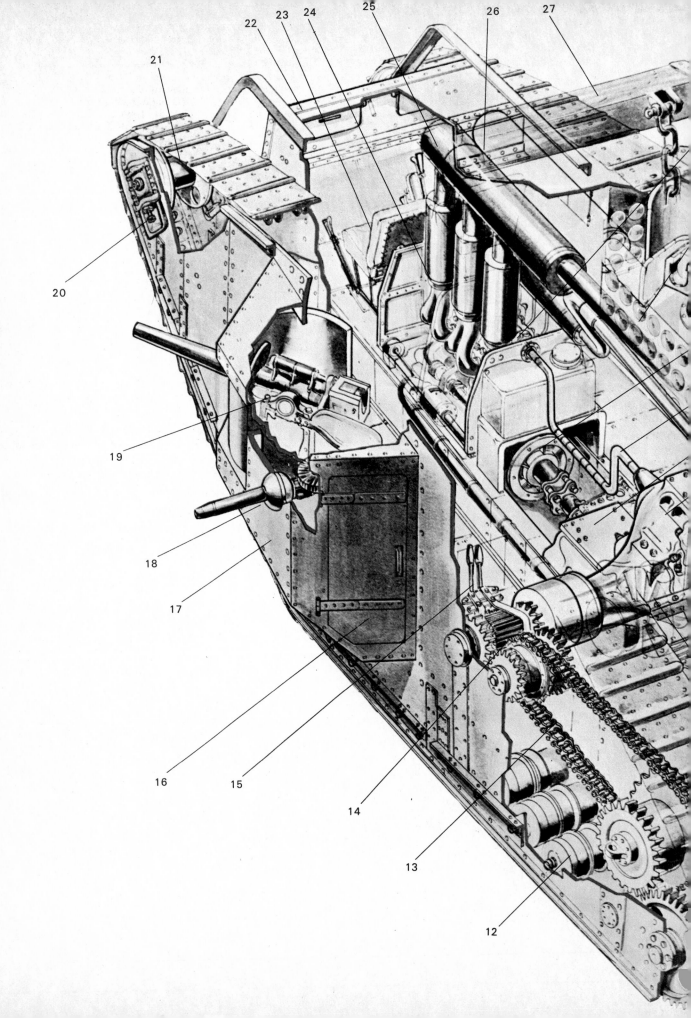

22 23 24 25 26 27

21

20

19

18

17

16 15 14

13

12

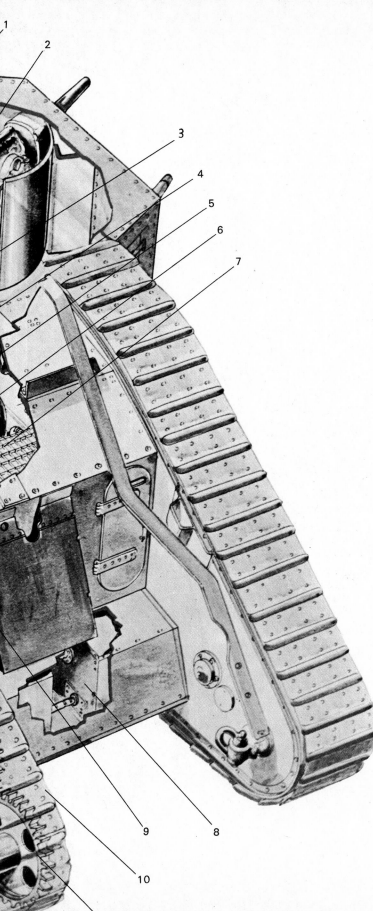

This is the male version of the Mark IV tank (49), which fought at Cambrai, with its two 6-pounder guns and four Lewis machine-guns. It had the basic layout of all the rhomboidal fighting vehicles. In many instances, a new terminology had to be created — some of it of naval origin and some destined to perpetuation even when later designs came out with a quite different shape.

Here is a key to the essential numbered parts:

1 Daimler 105-hp, 6-cylinder engine
2 6-pounder ammunition racks — 332 rounds provided
3 Clutch
4 Starting crank
5 Primary gearbox
6 Differential case
7 Tubular radiator
8 Petrol tanks
9 Cooling fan
10 Pressed steel track plate
11 Final drive and sprocket
12 Unsprung roller bogies
13 Left-hand track driving chain
14 Secondary gears
15 Left-hand gearsman lever for steering
16 Sponson door
17 Sponson
18 Lewis machine-gun in ball joint mounting
19 6-pounder (57-mm) gun mounted on pedestal
20 Track adjusting gear
21 Front idler wheel
22 Front turret
23 Commander's position — he told the driver his course and operated brakes on the secondary shaft
24 Exhaust manifolds
25 Exhaust silencer
26 Driver's position — he operated the clutch, the primary gears, and foot brake and signalled instructions to the secondary gearsmen
27 Unditching beam stowed on guide rails

Partly in sympathy with French policy, the British tended to put numbers and simplicity before outright armour protection and complexity. But, while the trench barrier remained and the Germans seemed set on retaining anti-tank measures that were static and associated with deep ditches covered by artillery fire, the need to maintain a wide ditch-crossing capability stayed paramount. This Female Mark IV (50) had thicker armour (12 mm) than the Mark I, mounted Lewis instead of Hotchkiss machine-guns, incorporated signalling between driver and gearsmen by electric lights, and carried a compass along with various other refinements. The rails laid along the top of the hull could carry a stout wooden beam which, when hooked to the tracks and driven forward, would be dragged down and under the tank to help the tank ride up if it became bogged. These rails could also support the enormous fascines (bundles of brushwood) which, when dropped ahead of the tank into a deep ditch, helped it cross unimpeded – as was done for the first time at Cambrai.

In short, within only a few months of the inception of their inventions, the inventors were heavily involved in the classic mobility, armour, and gun contest, with the constrictions of national economics already beginning to dictate limitations to cost and size. At the same time, they thought of ways to lend the support of artillery to the tanks, realizing that if the tanks penetrated far into the enemy defences they might soon pass beyond the support of guns which could not be hauled by horses through the trench-infested zone. This artillery carrier (51) transported a 60-pounder gun with its wheels removed. Few were built and hardly any were used for their prime purpose, though their employment as supply carriers was important in getting ammunition and petrol to the leading troops, and saved manpower.

50

51

The development of armoured warfare in 1917 and 1918

It is one of the paradoxes of early mechanized warfare that the technologists not only produced the machines but also foresaw their tactical possibilities ahead of the soldiers. Thus the concept of a heavy tank, like Flying Elephant, and light tanks, such as the Tritton 'Chaser', looked well beyond the mere breaking of trench lines even before the first tanks had gone into action. Nevertheless the actual pace of tactical development had to be geared to the speed at which the military leaders and the tank crews could assimilate the lessons of experience. For instance, to have thrown masses of untried tanks all at once into their first action would have been as much of a gamble with men's lives as asking them to walk through barbed wire that had been shelled for the first time by artillery.

So the first tanks went into action only a few at a time; without proper preparation, without recourse to well thought out means of co-operation with artillery, infantry, and cavalry; without adequate reconnaissance of the ground they were to cross; and without a sufficient backing by a workshop maintenance organization. Nothing much was expected from them and very little was accomplished — and so it had gone on throughout the best part of 1917 when scattered parties of tanks played minor roles at the Battle of Arras in April, at Messines Ridge in June, and at Gaza in Palestine. In the sodden ground that screened the approaches to the Passchendaele Ridge, tanks used in penny packets wallowed helplessly in the mire, though on the occasions when detailed care was taken to prepare their entry into action, they enjoyed refreshing successes and helped save many infantry lives. Careful preparation was to be the keynote, and from then on the study of aerial photographs, linked with minute examination of the ground over which the tanks had to pass, led to precise directions which told each crew its exact route and task and left as little as possible to chance.

Tanks were highly vulnerable to artillery fire, even though the relative inaccuracy of field artillery usually called for an appreciable number of rounds to be fired before they could hope to hit the target. Therefore, while the Germans reckoned to base their anti-tank defence upon artillery fire aimed at tanks that moved slowly through a maze of obstacles and deep trenches, the British and French tried to knock out the artillery by counter-battery bombardment and by attacks from low-flying aircraft. Secrecy linked with surprise in the timing and location of an assault were among the principal advantages made possible by tanks. Most movement, of course, took place on railways, since the range and reliability of the early vehicles made it essential that they should run on their tracks only when absolutely necessary, but by moving at night and hiding during the day, the tanks could be assembled close to the front and remain unnoticed until only a short time before action.

Because vision from the early tanks was so restricted, most actions took place by day, and this also allowed the tanks to withdraw for replenishment and repair by night. There were a few attempts at night fighting but these usually ended in chaos and loss. In consequence the German defenders had only to concentrate on defence by day and this they did by moving 77-mm field artillery closer among the front line troops and by encouraging the infantry to attack the tanks with the clumsy and unpopular 13-mm anti-tank rifle, with grenades, and with flamethrowers from close quarters. At Cambrai they also made air attacks on tanks — sometimes with encouraging results.

These were the tactics that had evolved by the time of the Battle of Cambrai when, for the first time, infantry were persuaded to work in close accord with the tanks, conceding the dominant role to the latter. Here too, smoke-screens were used as part of the counter-battery programme so that tanks advancing without warning by the half-light of dawn arrived among a confused and partially-blinded enemy. But, as we have seen, although Cambrai was a tank success, it was not total victory. Co-operation between tanks and the cavalry arm of exploitation had not been catered for and the advance fizzled out. The Whippet tank (see page 37) had not yet arrived and so there was no suitable machine to travel with and to help the cavalry. That was all in the future.

In the meantime, thoughts of further Allied offensive actions in 1918 had to go into abeyance in response to the great German spring and summer offensives. Lacking tanks of their own, the Germans broke the Allied fronts time and again by the novel but still costly combination of short, violent artillery bombardments aimed at the weakest portions of the Allied line and followed up by infantry who by-passed opposition and drove deep into the Allied rear. To help destroy this offensive, the British tended to scatter their tanks in small groups along the length of the front, hidden away but ready to pounce on the enemy when he passed by — like 'Savage Rabbits', as they were known. The underlying intention was aggressive, as tanks inherently are, but their effect was diluted in the same way as the early attacks had been. Yet tanks claimed their successes, notably those scored by the Whippets with their greater speed.

During the German offensive several new facets of armoured warfare were introduced. The Germans started using tanks themselves, first of all manning machines that had been captured from the British but later bringing their own A7V (see page 36) into action until, on 24th April 1918, tank fought tank for the first time at Villers-Bretonneux immediately preceding an action when Whippets charged and played havoc with German infantry. A little later the latest French light tanks, the Renault M-17s (see page 38), came into action for the first time and, by weight of numbers as much as anything else, saturated the German defences — for, given a mass of small armoured targets to shoot at all at once, the distraction proved too much for the German gunners.

By the time the German offensives had been brought to a halt (quite frequently as the result of Allied counterattacks that employed tanks in large numbers) the British and French armies had cleared their minds on the basic principles governing future tank offensives. The Cambrai method to breach the front by the surprise employment of massed tanks along with infantry on a narrow front held good, but it was to be extended to bring in horsed cavalry helped by Whippets, while the presence of such larger numbers of new tanks made possible the preparation of more than one major offensive at once to be launched in close sequence on different parts of the front one after another. In essence, tanks speeded up the whole pace of warfare since they partially replaced artillery and therefore cut down the time needed to prepare for an offensive since there was less need to accumulate as much ammunition as was needed for the prolonged bombardments of old.

On the strategic plane a rain of blows, coming one after the other, threw the Germans off balance and, virtually, brought them to the verge of defeat. Tactically, however, there were limitations to success which held deep repercussions for the future. The German tactic of emplacing 77-mm guns close to the front made the tanks pay a heavy price for their gains, even though the help provided by co-operating infantry brought a high mortality rate to the guns. Simultaneously it was discovered that Whippets working alongside cavalry were hardly compatible: when one could go fast the other could not and vice-versa. Indeed, once a breakthrough had been achieved, as at the Battle of Amiens on 8th August 1918, it was Austin armoured cars (see page 45) running free on roads which scored the most resounding successes in exploitation.

Possibly one of the most important aids to tactical improvement was the mounting of radio sets in tanks to send reports from the forward edge of the battle to headquarters in the rear with unheard of speed. Radio reporting from the front had been almost impossible up to then — which is hardly surprising when it is recalled, for instance, that the bulky British set required nine men to carry it along with its heavy batteries.

So much for the machines and their impact upon the art of war. Do not forget the men who manned them, and remember the extreme difficulties and dangers under which they worked. They were a new breed of soldier — fighting man and mechanic combined — and they had to be imbued with a crusading spirit to overcome the natural prejudices of the older traditional arms with which they had to work in co-operation. If they gave an impression of superiority over the others, it can only be said that there were plenty who despised them as 'rude mechanicals' whose task would be over for good once the war came to an end, for it was a strongly held belief among many orthodox soldiers that tanks were only a temporary expedient made necessary to overcome a passing vogue — the trench vogue — in the evolution of war. To traditionalists such as these there seemed to be a sacred ritual for men to come to personal grips with men — a process that machines should not be allowed to impede.

Tanks get bigger . . .

Casting around for salvation in late 1916, the Germans called upon Mr Steiner, Holt's representative whose proposals they had earlier rejected, to help produce a tank. For, even if the German General Staff persisted in pouring scorn on the landships, they could hardly ignore a weapon which had demoralized German infantry in a few local actions.

In even greater haste than the French, the Germans fastened a steel box on top of Holt tracks and, like Schneider and St Chamond, created a vehicle that was thoroughly unwieldy. Indeed, the vast A7V (52) seemed to draw inspiration from Kaiser Wilhelm's fantasy of an earlier decade, turned out top heavy, underprotected by poor-quality armour plate, sprouting guns all over, and manned by an immense crew, eighteen strong. Furthermore, to make confusion doubly confounding, the crews were recruited from three separate agencies — artillerymen to man the cannon, infantrymen the machine-guns, and mechanics to drive and maintain the vehicle. Thus, unlike their opponents, the Germans created factions within a vehicle which could only function efficiently on team work so that when one of their machine-gunners complained he had been 'let down by the artillery' he was, in fact, merely complaining about the crew of his tank's 57-mm gun.

Meanwhile one fundamental improvement in the next British tank, Mark V (53), encouraged team spirit still further; for although eight men were still carried, only one was needed as driver since the epicyclic gear train devised by Wilson had disposed of the need for gearsmen. Now the Commander took sole responsibility for directing every activity without becoming personally involved in a separate crew function. This, when added to better vision devices and the improved cross-country performance made possible by the introduction of Ricardo's 150-hp engine (the first designed specially for a tank), engineered a combat vehicle of greatly expanded fighting power. This, the first one-man-driven tank—here is his position (54) — was the combat vehicle used most frequently by the British Tank Corps during the final battles of 1918.

	A7V (52)	**Mark V (Male)** (53)
Weight:	32 tons	29 tons
Power Plant:	2 x 100 hp	150 hp
Crew:	18	8
Armour (max):	30 mm	12 mm
Speed:	5 mph	5 mph
Armament:	1 57-mm	2 57-mm
	6 mg	4 mg

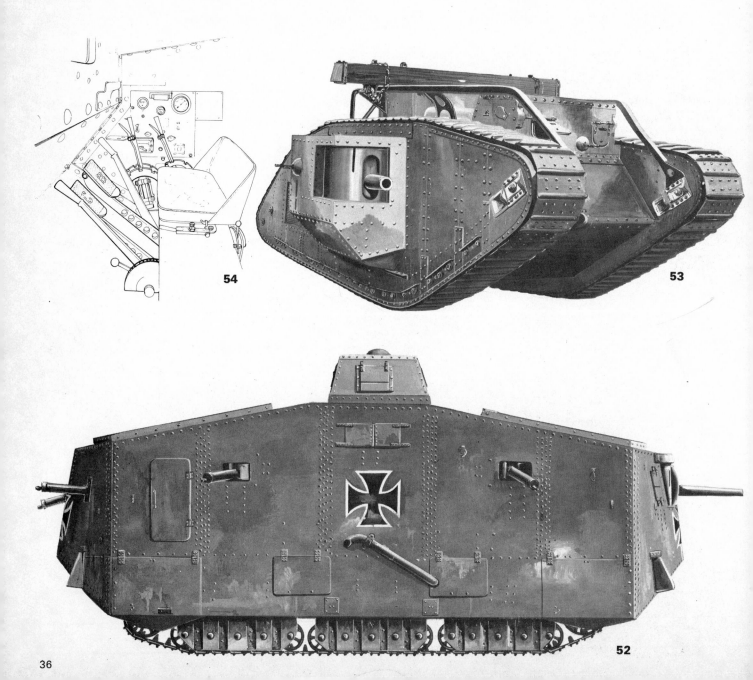

54

53

52

. . . and also smaller

No sooner had the British demonstrated the feasibility of armoured, tracked fighting vehicles than they set out to improve the existing machines and also to develop a light tank. Based on its prototype (the Tritton Chaser) Medium A, or Whippet (55) as it came to be known, started down the production line in 1917, an engineer's solution to the cavalry's insoluble problem of how to exploit the breakthrough. This was the horseman's armoured substitute which earned for itself the simile of 'Cavalry Tank' whose first actions helped to stem the great German offensives in 1918. But not until August at Amiens did it demonstrate conclusively that the day of unarmoured cavalry had passed. Yet, this first British light tank was riddled with disadvantages; the driver had the complicated task of combining the speeds of two separate engines to alter pace and course, and the commander, with one gunner to help, had to plan his action as well as fire four machine-guns covering an arc of 360 degrees from a fixed box instead of from a rotating turret. The range of only forty miles was not good enough for a tank which had to penetrate far into the enemy lines — and the practice of carrying spare petrol tins outside the armour was suicidal. The Germans, desperate in their efforts to catch up in a race already lost, copied anything the British made for all they were worth, and set to work

in June 1918 to build their own Whippet, calling it LK II (56). But, too late though it was to intervene in battle before the war ended, LK II at least gave birth to a doctrine upon which a later generation built with skill.

LK II, slightly better powered, more heavily armed, and easier to handle than Whippet, died at the hands of the Treaty of Versailles which, in 1919, forbade Germany to make or possess tanks. But Sweden took over a few, rechristened them M-21 (57) and these, duly modified, became the founders of Swedish tank technology — reinforced when, later, the German firm of Krupp took a large holding in the Swedish armament firm of Bofors.

	Whippet (55)	**LK II** (56)
Weight:	14 tons	9 tons
Power Plant:	2 x 45 hp	55 hp
Crew:	3	3
Armour (max):	12 mm	14 mm
Speed:	8 mph	10 mph
Armament:	4 mg	1 57-mm or 2 mg

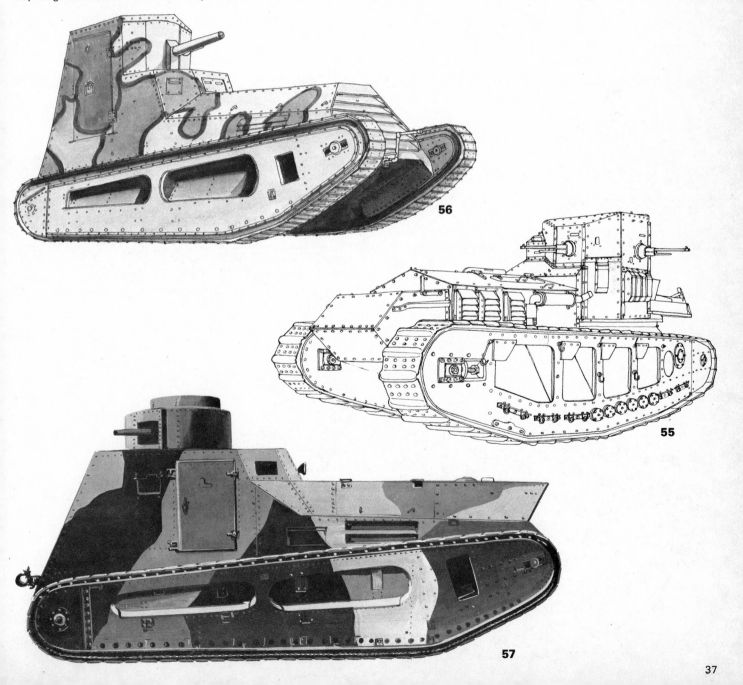

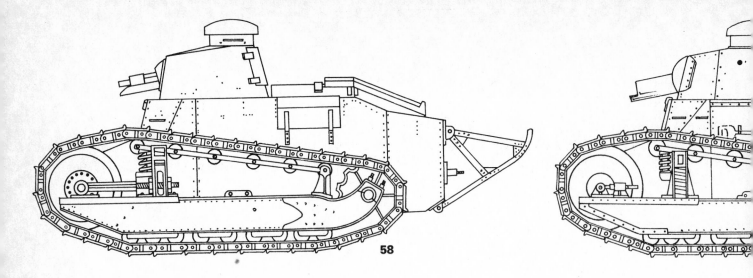

58

In France, as elsewhere, opposition to tank construction followed close on the heels of failures with the early machines and on the inherent conservatism of the traditionally-minded fighting soldiers. Estienne, a gunner himself, had actually intended to sponsor 'artillery carriers' in the first place — but in 1916 turned his attention to an 'infantry' version, in the shape of a small, two-man, tracked vehicle to transport an armoured machine-gunner into the enemy's midst. Part of the appeal of this miniaturized model sprang from its cheapness and the fact that the motor industry could produce it rapidly in mass. At Estienne's instigation, the firm of Renault designed what came to be known as the M-17 or FT (58) — the forerunner of a breed which dominated French armoured policy for the next two decades, as well as imposing a strong influence on the policies of other nations while they studied mechanization. The French made a cheap fighting vehicle with a strong sales appeal — the fact that it was highly vulnerable (despite the relative protection given by small size), detracted not in the least from its commercial attraction, though the first wooden idler wheel may have been symbolic of an incorrigible habit of governments buying on the cheap even when men's lives are at stake.

Let it be understood, however, that Estienne never lost sight of the need for a heavy tank to support the infantry carriers and the infantry marching with them. But if the post-war views of the German General Ludendorff meant anything, the small armoured machine-gun carrier merely extended the power of the essential infantryman — that of the mobile man, machine-gun in hand. In 1917 dreams such as these lay beneath the mire of the trench nightmare where the tiny Renaults worked at a severe disadvantage when driven across badly disrupted ground.

In April 1917 America came into the war and found herself in desperate need of all sorts of materials to expand a small peacetime army to the size and competence necessary to engage in full-scale European War. Both Britain and France could sell her a few tanks — the Americans looking enthusiastically on the Renault M-17 and deciding to lay down a production line of their own. But production lines of that sort cannot be built overnight: on this occasion even American industrial organization failed — only ten of their Renault M-1917 (59), of which nearly a thousand were eventually built, reached France and none in time to see action. Nevertheless the attempt, along with other armoured developments, marked the birth of the American tank industry.

In the meantime the French had up-gunned the M-17 with a short 75-mm gun and christened it BS (60). Later still, an M-17 captured from the White Russian armies presented the struggling

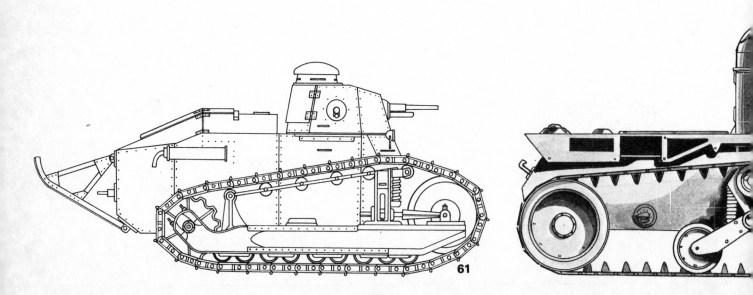

61

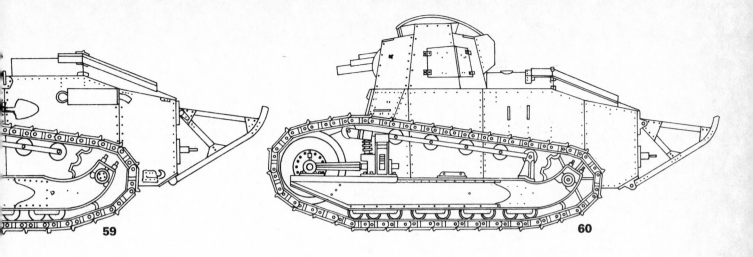

59   60

post-revolution Russian nation with its first Renault for use as a pattern for a Russian-built model, christened 'Lenin' (61). Very few were built — perhaps the name showed the tank for the prestige project that it was.

The vogue of the light vehicle found great favour with the Americans, principally because their thriving, indigenous automobile industry could be better adapted to making small, simple vehicles, using car components, than replicas of the big British tanks. Logically enough, the Ford Motor Company, when asked to convert its mass-production line to making tanks, came out with a lightly armoured two-man machine-gun carrier powered by two Model T engines (62). Yet apart from the obvious advantage of presenting so small a target, the battle-worthiness of a thin automotive 'shield' of this sort could only remain in doubt since, in the end (although 15,000 were ordered) only fifteen were made and not one went to war.

At the same time a brilliant, maverick American inventor, J. Walter Christie, who had already designed several tracked artillery carriers, made a light armoured fighting vehicle (63), whose superficial resemblance to the Renault tank was instantly belied by its original design. This vehicle was intended to move either on its tracks or wheels, and at the same speed, forward or reverse. Quite

deliberately Christie aimed at an engineering breakthrough by increasing power, speed, and range in one leap far beyond anything achieved up to that moment. But, of course, he paid penalties since his ideas developed so fast that nothing could be proved, with the result that incipient unreliability plagued this model. Nevertheless, the mark of an inspired inventor who thought deeper into the mystique of mobility than many soldiers had been made. For the next two decades or more he was to set new trends.

	Renault M-17 (58)	Ford M-1918 (62)	Christie 1919 (63)
Weight:	6.7 tons	3.4 tons	13.5 tons
Power Plant:	39 hp	2 x 22.5 hp	120 hp
Crew:	2	2	3
Armour (max):	22 mm	13 mm	25 mm
Speed:	5 mph	7 mph	7 mph
Armament:	1 37-mm or 1 mg	1 57-mm or 1 mg	1 57-mm 1 mg

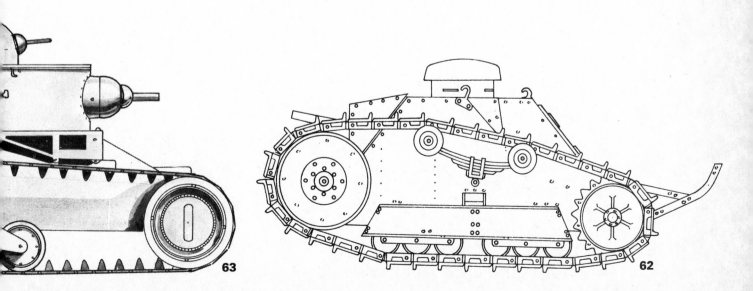

63   62

Primitive communication Systems

There had not been enough time to supply the first tanks with remote, internal communications for the crew, let alone the means to permit vehicle to talk to vehicle or any of the other battlefield participants. Tank interiors were dimly lit by only a few small festoon lights or through vision chinks in the armour. Tanks entered battle to a preconceived plan: if changes involving discussion and orders had to be made, the commanders had to dismount, often under fire, and hold a conference before going on. Quite frequently, commanders actually led their vehicles on foot or horseback – with great bravery since, the moment a tank hove into sight, it invariably became the target for every sort of enemy fire. Towards the end of the war voice pipes were fitted in a few tanks along with fire directive aids, but these never saw action.

At first, external messages passed either by pigeon (64) or by semaphores (65). Neither was reliable: the former did not always 'home' and, anyway, tank crews had a tendency to overfeed their messengers, inducing a cosy malaise in the erstwhile birds of war: the latter could not always be picked out in the smoke of battle and were often shot away. Co-operation with the infantry and cavalry was most difficult of all; many a man outside spent fruitless time hammering on a tank's armour to draw attention to his desire to pass a message inside. Nobody doubted that radio offered the best solution, but the existing sets (66), as already mentioned, were extremely bulky, could transmit slow, morse-keyed messages only, demanded extensive aerial displays, and were somewhat unreliable because they had not been designed to withstand the shocks of a ride in an unsprung tracked vehicle. However, both France and Britain exerimented with radio tanks from an early stage – the French carrying out a radical modification to the Renault M-17 (67), the British fitting a set into a Mark IV (68) where there was plenty of room and adding an extensive mast and aerial array. Neither machine could be used in the forefront of combat, but acted instead as specialized headquarters vehicles charged with the task of keeping the course of a battle under observation and thus acting as a reporting agency. In so doing they filled an important role for, up to then, contact with leading infantry had been by means of runner, light, and smoke signals – using the telephone only when conditions permitted and enemy fire had not cut the cables. A trial had once shown that cable had to be buried 9 feet underground to resist the effects of shell-fire, so the boon of wireless, if it could be made to work, had not to be underestimated.

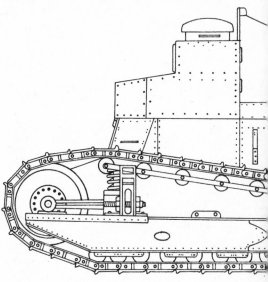

Moreover, as the possibilities of tank attacks ranging further and wider became evident, the need for better mobile direct communications at the front became almost mandatory. General Elles had led the attack at Cambrai in person in order to encourage the crews with the knowledge that he was sharing their dangers, but his direction and influence on the course of the battle once he entered the hull of the tank 'Hilda' was no greater than if he had been the most junior tank commander. Yet, had he been able to divert tanks from one success to another as the battle changed in fortune at various moments throughout the day, the magnitude of the victory might have been even more resounding than it was. A reliable voice radio was required. It would be over ten years before one came into practical use.

68

64

67

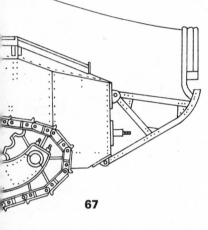

66

65

The Rise of the Giants

The success of the big British rhomboidal tanks encouraged other industrial nations to build still larger ones themselves: as offensive weapons they carried a prestige value and, in some respects, were the deterrent of their day. The fact that nobody managed to produce an accurate, high velocity anti-tank gun before the end of the war lent credibility to these bulky giants and certainly revived interest in the manufacture of tanks with armour thick enough to resist a direct hit from a field-gun's shell. As will be seen (on page 52), the French decided, rather late in the day, to produce a heavy tank of their own to supplement the light Renaults — but up to the end of the war they had to make do with improved British Mark Vs.

Ahead of current practice, for the first time, the Germans laid down their own giant — the 'K' tank (69) — a cumbersome monster of 150 tons with no military application or political future under the Treaty of Versailles which forbade them the use of all offensive weapons including tanks.

A joint Anglo-American project, dating from early 1918, gave birth to the last of the big rhomboidal machines — the Mark VIII (70) — all 37 tons of her driven by a 300-hp engine and shaped on the assumption that even wider anti-tank ditches would be met, thus requiring an even greater trench-crossing ability of 15 feet. But already the trends of war were changing in response to revised artillery, infantry, and tank tactics. As trench lines were reduced to impotence by tanks, battles reverted from slogging matches and gradually took place in greater depth with far more room to manoeuvre. Natural obstacles such as rivers and canals, that had to be crossed by bridges instead of fascines, now became the 'backbone' of tank defences, while infantry positions tended to gather in knots rather than lie strung out in line.

To overcome water obstacles the designers attached a bridge to the final Mark of Mark V — the lengthened Mark V** (71) — and later tried out a mine-bumping roller on the same tank to deal with the advent of anti-tank mines.

Mark V**, as can be seen, was much bigger and more powerful than any previous British tank and had rather better ventilation than the earlier Mark Vs. But the attachment of special devices to assist tanks overcome natural and man-made obstacles opened up

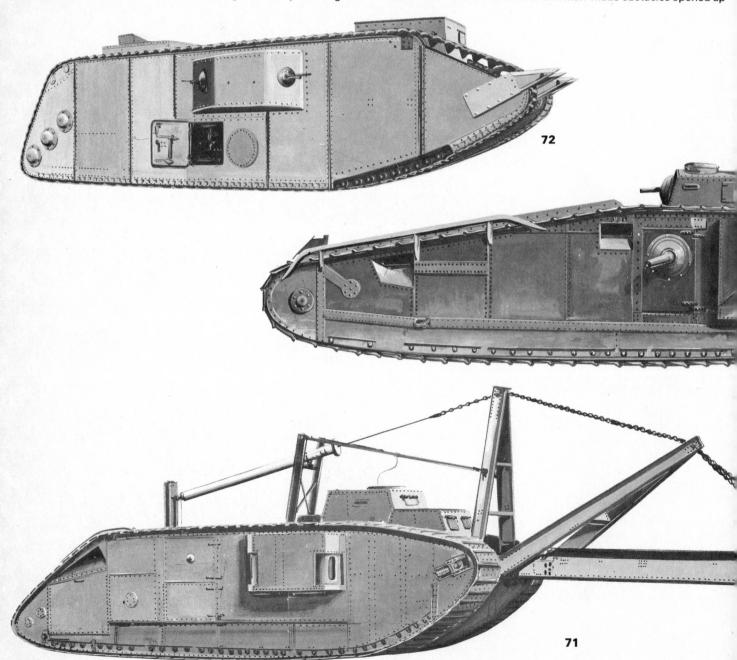

72

71

a new department in tank design, as improvements to defences threw an increasing demand on additional and costly gadgets to allow tanks to live on the battlefield.

Another special tank was the American Steam Tank (72) — powered that way because it was originally believed that a steam jet would give added impetus to the tank's main armament — a flame-gun. This sort of armament also came into being to solve a particular battlefield problem, that of burning out the pill-boxes with which the Germans covered their main lines of defence. Only one steam tank was ever made, but it was the forerunner of many flame-throwing tanks to come in a later generation.

Tank technology was a new and expanding science, still only mistily defined in 1918. Throw-back projects could readily appear which, with the benefit of hindsight, now make us gasp. Perhaps the Italian Fiat 2000 (73) of 1918 provokes that reaction, for she is like the clumsy German A7V — so top heavy and vulnerable. Yet this 40-ton AFV incorporated several modern features — armour 20 mm thick, a fully rotating turret with a cannon, and a single engine giving 240 hp — in every respect typical of Italian engineering enterprise.

	German K (69)	British/US Mark VIII (70)	British Mark V** (71)
Weight:	150 tons	37 tons	35 tons
Power Plant:	2 x 650 hp	1 x 300 hp	225 hp
Crew:	22	8	8
Armour:	30 mm	16 mm	12 mm
Speed:	5 mph	6 mph	4.6 mph
Armament:	4 x 77-mm	2 x 57-mm	2 x 57-mm
	7 mg	7 mg	4 mg
			or
			6 mg

	US Steam Tank (72)	Fiat 2000 (73)
Weight:	44 tons	40 tons
Power Plant:	2 x 250 hp	240 hp
Crew:	8	10
Armour:	13 mm	20 mm
Speed:	4 mph	5 mph
Armament:	1 Flame-thrower	1 x 65-mm
	4 mg	7 mg

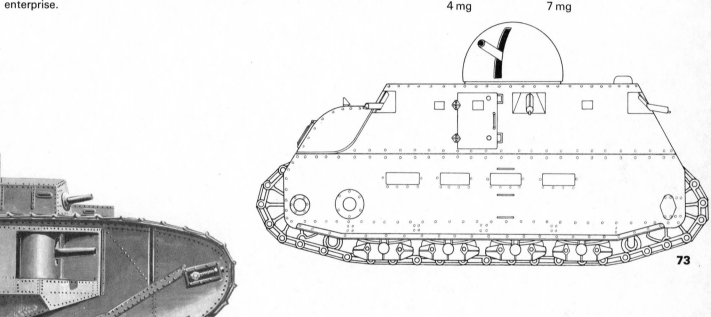

73

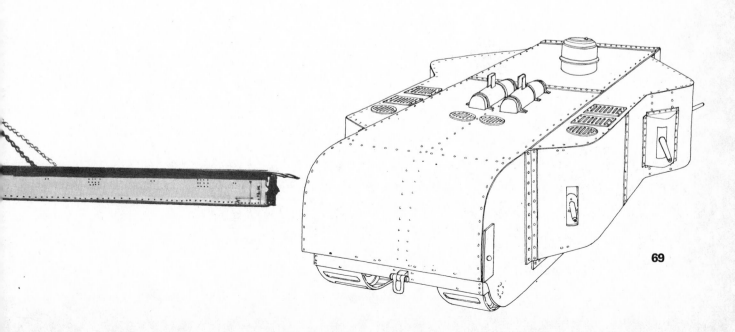

70

69

Crew Clothing

The early tanks became very hot inside due to poor ventilation and the fact that the engine was usually in the middle of the crew compartment. Hence crews tended to wear as little clothing as possible – with serious consequence in the event of an outbreak of fire. Nevertheless they were encouraged to wear certain items of special clothing.

The chain-mail face mask (74) was designed to protect the wearer from white hot particles (called 'splash') which flew about when the armour was struck by bullets. Like the leather helmet (75), which was introduced as protection against injury to the head on crew compartment projections, the face mask was not worn very often by crews who preferred to be as unencumbered as possible.

Respirators (76), however, had always to be ready for wear since poison gas was frequently used in the First World War and could be hard to detect when sucked into the crew compartment and mixed with all the other vehicle smells.

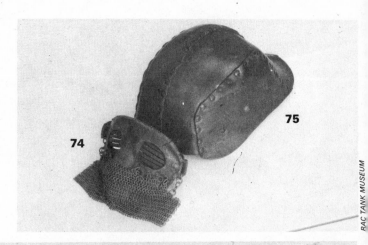

74   75

RAC TANK MUSEUM

76

IMPERIAL WAR MUSEUM

Ways to High Mobility

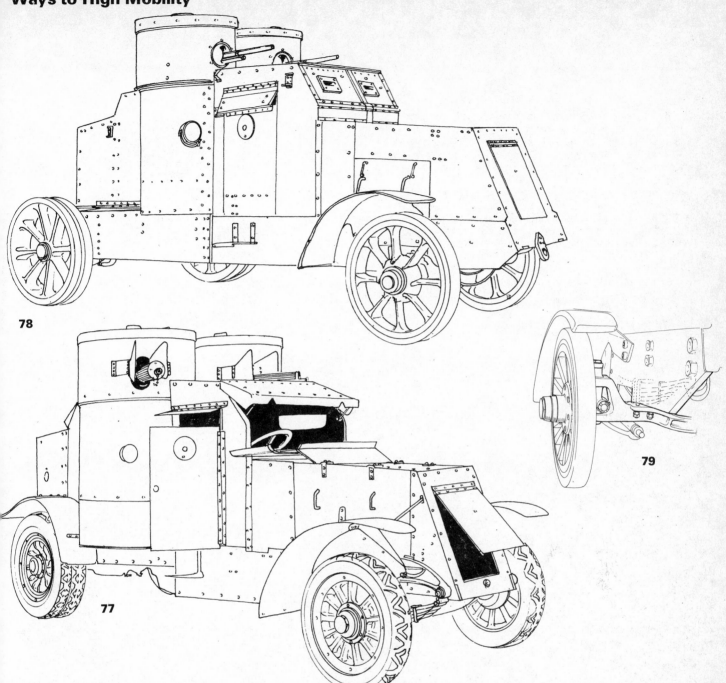

78

77

79

The loosening of the trench manacles once again set free armoured cars to roam the open road in the combat zone — and it says something for British foresight that they had a number of new machines ready in 1918 to supplement the work of the Whippets after the breakthrough at Amiens. The firms of Austin (77) and Peerless (78) had built armoured bodies on to existing lorry chassis (the former in response to a Russian order) — bone-shaking, robust vehicles carried on solid tyres with a leaf-sprung suspension (79), the very narrowness of the tyres reducing cross-country movement to a minimum.

The most striking feature of these armoured cars (which later performed in many theatres of war, including the North-West Frontier of India where they took part in the Afghan War in 1919 in addition to numerous tribal skirmishes) was the twin, tub-shaped machine-gun turrets. Those laying down the specifications dwelt on the necessity to fire in two directions at once, saying that, in any case, a single turret might not be able to traverse quickly enough to engage targets which appeared successively from different quarters. The concept reappeared in the next decade closely associated with a predilection for carrying as many machine-guns as possible. But it was endemic at a time when gunnery techniques

took low priority during crew training, the commander's difficulties in controlling his gunners being of less concern than getting the driver to go in the right direction. So long as fire could be sprayed in the general area of the target most people were satisfied — and this was a tactical habit that would last for years to come.

However, the return of armoured cars to an effective operational role at the end of the war had its advantages, for these hardy machines were to be the spearhead of peacetime, quasi-military police organizations — a cheap and quick way of applying minimum force to a host of insurrections and small wars. And in peacetime it has usually been low cost which has decided choice when it has come to equipping armies.

	Austin (77)	**Peerless** (78)
Weight:	4.14 tons	7 tons
Power Plant:	50 hp	40 hp
Crew:	4	4
Armour (max):	8 mm	10 mm
Speed:	35 mph	18 mph
Armament:	2 mg	2 mg

Strictly in association with the need to unglue or outflank the trench barrier, many strange plans and devices intended to help armoured vehicles and increase their mobility came into being. The Germans had always been sensitive to the prospect of Allied maritime raids behind their front on the Belgian coast or even deep into the Baltic, and the British later justified these fears when they raided Zeebrugge and Ostend in 1918. But a far more ambitious operation, aimed to land in strength on the sea front around Middelkerke, had been planned for 1917. The proposed site for the launching had a steep esplanade, however, making it necessary to build special tank transportable ramps (80) that were pushed ahead to be laid to help the tank climb off the foreshore. Track grip had also to be improved by attaching wide 'spuds' to the normal tracks of Mark IV tanks (81). This first method to help land tanks from the sea came to naught – but, like nearly all the special devices hatched in the First War, was to find profitable employment in the Second.

A large armoured infantry-cum-supply carrier, the Mark IX (82), did not see action either, although this Trojan Horse could carry 30 men or 10 tons of stores and tallied closely with the original concept of a landship, indicating the advantages that infantry might have shared with tanks when moving in unison. But as an experi-

mental model, Mark IX did important service in 1919 when, with huge cylindrical pontoons strapped to its sides (83), it was made to float. Large paddles were fixed to the tracks to provide propulsion and the experiment amply proved the feasibility of an idea and demonstrated how armoured vehicles could be made waterproof. To those who ordered this work it had seemed inevitable that, although tracked vehicles had largely conquered soft ground and trenches, the new mobility which grew from their impact held forth promise of undreamed-of sweeps, deep into enemy territory, which could only be accomplished if speed and momentum were maintained. Visions of this kind, rising in the minds of the leading military prophets, saw far beyond the bounds of a trench-girt battlefield, looking instead to constant motion by armoured cross-country vehicles capable of overcoming every natural or man-made obstacle.

Mark IX (82)

Weight:	27 tons unladen
Power Plant:	150 hp Ricardo
Crew:	4
Armour:	12 mm
Speed:	3.5 mph
Armament:	1 mg

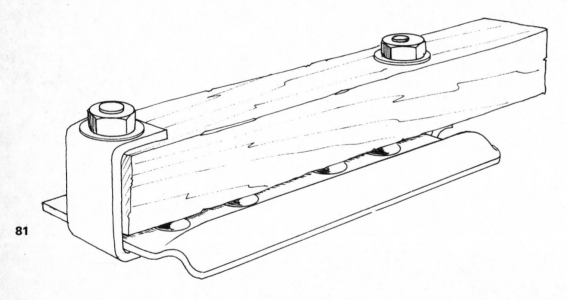

81

80

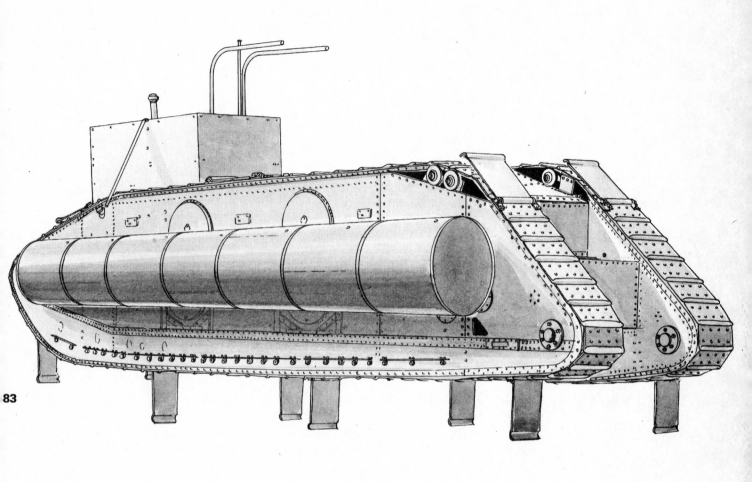

83

82

Plan 1919

Throughout the winter of 1918 and in spare moments between the crises brought about by the German spring offensive, Fuller (**below right**) and the British Tanks Corps Staff hunted for a formula that would elevate tank tactics from the direct art of tactical breaching to the plane of strategic decision. The ultimate proposals, drawn up by Fuller into what he described as 'a kind of military novelette', was entitled 'Plan 1919' – and was to lay the foundation of every future use for armoured formations up to the present day.

While Fuller witnessed, day by day, the convulsions of the Anglo-French armies as they fell back in retreat, it occurred to him that nothing was more conducive to defeat than the collapse of an army's nervous system. But horse and foot armies could move neither with enough speed nor sufficient endurance to penetrate as far back as the headquarters that were the centres of control, and aeroplanes could neither destroy those headquarters by bombing (though they could help disrupt them) nor land troops in sufficient quantity for an assault. In practice, up to then, orthodox attacks had rarely penetrated beyond the gun-line.

Tanks alone – provided a new machine with the capability of Medium D (see page 50) could be built – might achieve the purpose, which was nothing less than the wholesale reduction of the enemy forces, by a surprise stroke aimed at the enemy's centres of communication, followed by the systematic destruction of his unco-ordinated and bewildered formations.

Our diagram (**far right**) shows the standard configuration of the battle area as laid out in 1918. Fuller proposed that a 90-mile-long front should be selected for assault and the enemy persuaded to reinforce it with some four or five armies *by allowing them to see* preparations for an offensive. This snaring of the enemy, in itself, was revolutionary to the day, though not unknown in the distant past. When all was ready, Fuller envisaged fleets of Medium D's moving without warning, 'at top speed by day, or possibly by night, directly on to the various headquarters lying in the primary tactical zone'. He thought these headquarters could be found and marked by aircraft and he demanded that aircraft should mount an all-out attack on supply and route centres.

Once the Mediums were loose in the rear and enemy headquarters either destroyed or dominated, Fuller believed that the enemy reserves would begin to lose their cohesion for, 'Bad news confuses, confusion stimulates panic.' Careful timing would then decide when the next phase should be launched, depending upon enemy reaction for, 'As soon as [his] orders and counter orders have been given a little time to become epidemic', a tank, infantry, and artillery attack would be pushed through to a distance of 10,000 yards among the gun-lines in the secondary tactical zone. Total disruption could then be expected followed by a pursuit with a force consisting of 'all Medium tanks available and lorry-carried infantry'.

In the method to be employed to break a front of 90 miles with relatively small forces Fuller invented what he called 'The Morcellated Attack'. On the assumption that one tank in attack was probably equal to 400 infantry (and bear in mind that Fuller was an infantryman himself, so he had no partisan axe to grind), he expected a vast initial economy in manpower to be achieved by machines which would redouble their effect by attacking relatively narrow sectors of the selected 90-mile front, with heavy tanks, and then fanning out to pulverize from flank and rear the sectors that had been by-passed in the initial assault.

Fuller only mentioned the horsed cavalry 'to propitiate the horse worshippers', though he saw even less future for them than for infantry of whom he wrote, that, except for gaining the secondary zone with the heavy tanks, '. . . on their feet [they] will be next to useless'. They would have to be motorized to assist in tactical penetration, operate where tanks could not, occupy ground conquered by tanks, and protect rear services. 'Therefore', he wrote, 'their tactics will be defensive, and their chief weapon will be the machine-gun.' Likewise he suggested that heavy artillery would disappear after the first day's fighting 'and will be relegated to its original position in the siege train', while horsedrawn field artillery which could not hope to keep up with a tank advance would have to be replaced by tractors. Indeed it was to aeroplanes that Fuller looked for the greatest assistance both in reconnaissance, supply, and attack upon the enemy. Typically he suggested how: 'The German Western GHQ should be dealt with by dropping several hundred tons of explosive upon it: that, at least, will neutralize clear thinking.'

Although this almost inflammatory document arrived too late to be put into practice before the war ended in November 1918, it set ideas whirling in the brains of those who read it. A few with open minds found it stimulating, but the many who clung pathologically to outmoded ideas were deeply offended and – worse – frightened. The fierce debate between the new and old schools that went on between the wars found its genesis in 'Plan 1919'.

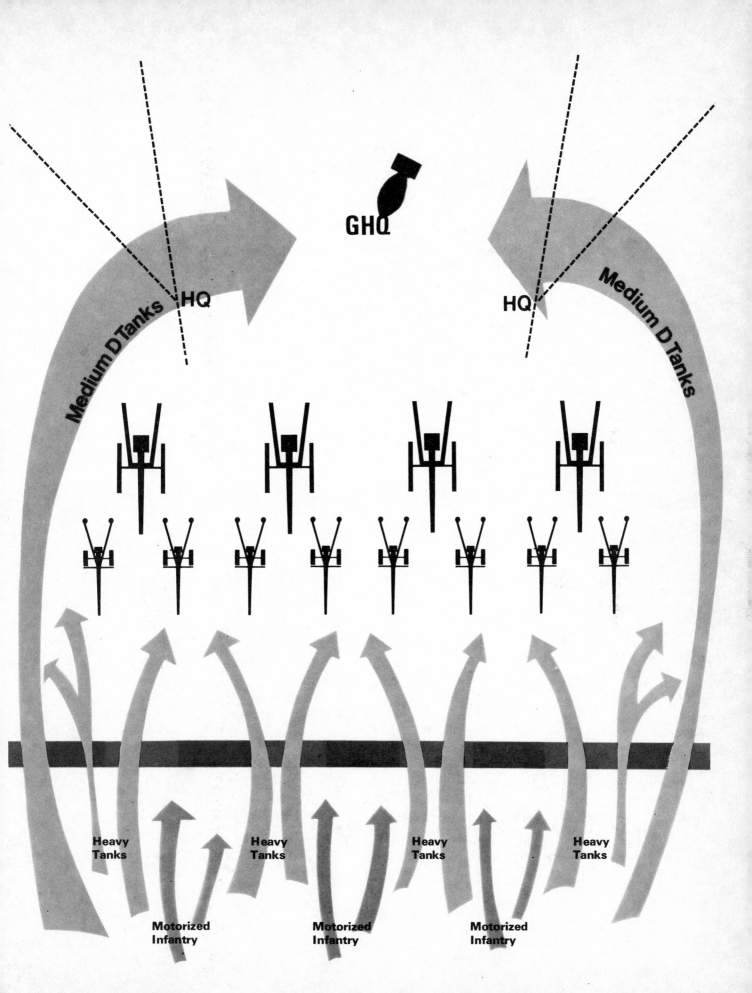

GHQ

HQ

HQ

Medium D Tanks

Medium D Tanks

Heavy
Tanks

Heavy
Tanks

Heavy
Tanks

Heavy
Tanks

Motorized
Infantry

Motorized
Infantry

Motorized
Infantry

Quite naturally Plan 1919, urged on with all the enthusiasm Fuller could muster, had enormous influence on British tank design and put it on a different basis from that of other nations. Yet Fuller's scheme drew its inspiration from what the designers had shown to be possible: he merely grafted his ideas upon the roots they had planted — it was a team effort. Nevertheless, Fuller made his impression not only because he was an intellectual with a highly fertile mind, but also because, with his collaborators, he moved in a new environment where his fluency of expression found ample room to expand in a world where brand new problems could often only be solved by devising a new language.

The Whippet tank possessed neither the endurance nor the speed compatible with serious long-range penetrations demanded by Fuller. Medium B (84), over which Fuller had little influence, took shape in 1917 but failed to improve very much on Whippet due to unreliability and too short a range for its prospective task. Its engine compartment was also cramped and inaccessible. In December 1917, in response to the Tank Corps' firm specifications, Medium B was followed by Medium C (85) which was little more than an enlarged B. No better armoured or armed, slightly faster and with a longer range, it still fell well short of Fuller's desire for a machine with a speed of 20 mph which, on its own, would be the equivalent of a squadron of horsed cavalry. His dream almost came

true with the next offering — Medium D (86) — which had a range of 100 miles, a speed in excess of 20 mph, and an inherent ability to float and move at $1\frac{1}{2}$ mph in water. But the war ended before either Medium B or D passed beyond the experimental stage, though the running models of D which came into being after the war showed just what sort of revolutionary vehicle this was.

The designer of Medium D was Lieutenant-Colonel Johnson, an engineer whose fascination with mechanical problems, to the occasional exclusion of practicalities, is exemplified by the highly desirable but extraordinarily complex cable-sprung track and its successor, the 'snake track' (87); its resemblance to the 'bowed' de Mole track is of more than passing interest. Johnson's work put Britain far ahead in the field of tank technology, for steering and suspensions were the least developed aspects of tank design up to then — little progress having been made since Tritton evolved his first track in 1915. Medium D was a versatile machine with revolutionary steering (like de Mole's tank the flexible track could be bowed to help change direction, thus saving the loss of power caused by 'braking' the track) and this helped give the crew a smooth, sprung ride at more than twice the speed of any other tracked fighting vehicle. But haste in design and development left multiple scars of unreliability. Work on Medium D rapidly fell behind schedule, and this delay proved fatal to its future.

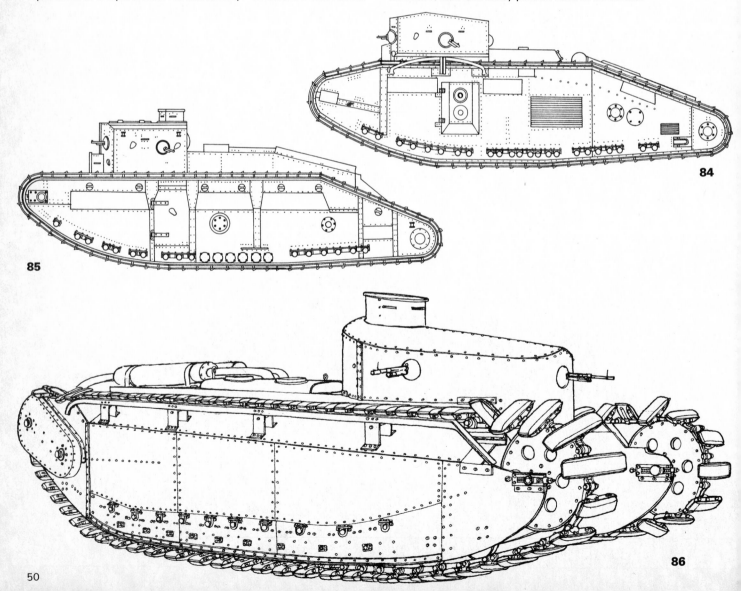

84

85

86

Vickers Spread Their Influence

It was War Office peacetime policy to experiment on those tactical operations which seemed most likely to be affected by the war's last-minute inventions. Armoured forces and long-range penetration of the 'Plan 1919' type came high in this category, but without possession of the right kind of vehicle these experiments hung fire just as peacetime economies cut off money at source. Indeed, an economy measure of 1923 shut the official British Department of Tank Design (killing Medium D), and this left the firm of Vickers Ltd in undisputed possession of the British tank-building industry. In 1921, the War Office had asked Vickers to produce a cheap, reliable tank in competition with the 'official' Mediums. The result appeared as the Vickers Light Infantry or No. 1 Tank (88) — a machine, not dissimilar to Medium B, which met only a few of the specifications, but which promised, to the delight of the Treasury, a potential for cheap development, a thriving export market, and an attractive military configuration. Gone were sponsons and in their place was a rotating turret. Out too, were elaborate suspensions and tracks — their substitute a simple, plate track round coil-sprung bogies. Early complexities in design (notably from the hydrostatic transmission) led to initial setbacks, but this vehicle lived up to its promise and founded a world-wide generation of versatile fighting vehicles.

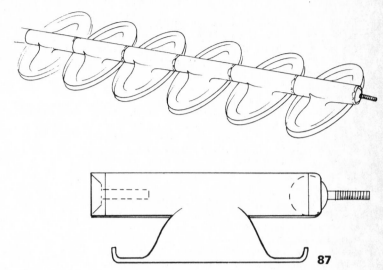

87

	Medium B (84)	C (Hornet) (85)	D (86)	Vickers No. 1 (88)
Weight:	18 tons	20 tons	20 tons	8 tons
Power:	100 hp	150 hp	240 hp	90 hp
Crew:	4	4	4	4
Armour (max):	14 mm	12 mm	10 mm	8 mm
Speed:	6 mph	8 mph	25 mph	30 mph
Armament:	4 mg or 40-mm and 3 mg	4 mg or 57-mm and 3 mg	3 mg or 57-mm and 3 mg	1 47-mm 2 mg

88

More Giants

In the true spirit of experiment, the 1920s and 1930s brought a large crop of designs, some sound and some outlandish, in response to a deluge of ideas. Each design was usually turned into one or more expensive prototypes, but only rarely was the order given for production to start. Among those that got no further than prototype stage were the heavy tanks of France and Britain.

Lacking a heavy tank of her own to support the swarm of light Renaults, the French planned in 1916, and started development in 1918, of a 70-ton model, of which ten, called 2C (89), were produced by 1923. Speed gave pride of place to armour and armament, yet 45 mm of plate is only just proof against a medium-sized shell and the turreted 75-mm gun hardly justified such a large carriage — although, later, a 155-mm was introduced. Char 2C is, perhaps, most celebrated for her shape and the publicity conferred on her by enthusiastic Press comments which outlasted her obsolescence. She gave rise to a hundred rumours of 'super heavies' but, in fact, never went into action.

Little need be said of the British 'Independent' (90) of which only one was made in haste in response to a General Staff requirement in 1924. She traded armour for pace (20 mph) and managed with a smaller crew than 2C; but the lower priority accorded to armour protection came almost by default since the specification merely asked that the armour should be 'as thick as possible'. In a country whose people never wished to fight another World War, a tank of Independent's dimensions and cost had no place. These big machines were leftovers from the trench-bound days, when great track length alone could ensure the crossing of wide gaps. Nevertheless they had a special prestige, propaganda value, which is the prerogative of giants, such as battleships. Several nations toyed with monsters like this but in peacetime, with no major war in sight, costly armoured vehicles of strictly offensive application held few attractions apart from supplying attenuated tank design teams and automotive industries with valuable information from research and development — a good example of which was provided by the work that went into Independent's hydraulic braking system. So great was the combined weight and speed of this tank that special test gear had to be constructed by the makers of brake linings in order to assess the reliability of new materials. Thus did tank technology contribute to future commercial road safety.

	Char 2C (89)	**Independent** (90)
Weight:	70 tons	32 tons
Power:	2 x 250 hp	398 hp
Crew:	13	8
Armour (max):	45 mm	29 mm
Speed:	9 mph	20 mph
Armament:	1 75-mm	1 47-mm
	4 mg	4 mg

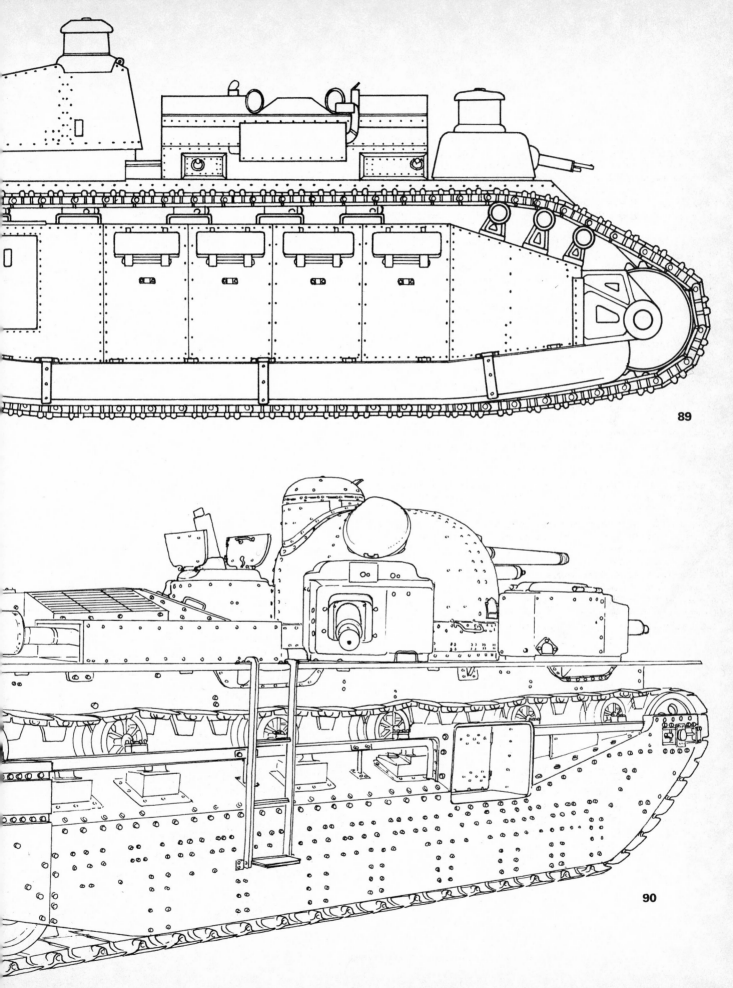

89

90

The Vickers' Monopoly

For more than a decade the world's tank designers drew their inspiration from developments in France, the USA, and Britain. But France had ended the war with a horde of cheap vehicles and saw no need, at first, to manufacture radically new types apart from the 2C; while the USA soon isolated herself from warring Europe and blighted her armoured forces by incorporating them with the infantry arm which took no particular interest in them. Only in Britain, where eager commercial instincts drove Vickers Ltd, and enthusiasm inspired a few rabid Tank Corps officers (who saw in war-machines a way of economizing in manpower and lives), did fresh designs flourish and actually enter production – thus initiating what might be termed the 'Vickers Monopoly'.

Although Vickers No. 1 did not satisfy the British army, a revised version offered such great improvements at relatively low cost that it became a source of attraction to foreign buyers and a relief to the Treasury. This was Vickers Medium (91) – the final Mark II model of which is shown here.

In 1922, Vickers were searching diligently for new business during the first post-war economic recession, so their designs reflect a stringent frugality – a motive which is renowned for undermining the expensive operational demands of soldiers – and Medium proved no exception to this rule. Its armour, a mere 6.5 mm (later 8 mm), was thinner than that of the original 'Mother' – and the latter had not been bullet-proof – while having the petrol tank located within the crew compartment posed a dreadful hazard: the 47-mm gun could not fire a satisfactory high explosive shell and six machine-guns were beyond the capability of a five-man crew. Medium, however, was fast and proved reliable, the air-cooled Armstrong Siddeley engine eliminating many snags inherent in water-cooled types with the advantages of a specially designed power plant, that suited the peculiar environment of armoured vehicles as opposed to the improvisation common to an adaptation of an ordinary commercial type. The sprung bogie suspension was another important advance, for not only did it give a far better cross-country ride at speed, it also helped reduce wear on tracks and sprockets that up to then were prone to break due to the use of inadequate materials.

The crew is the prime element which turns an armoured vehicle into a fighting entity, and in this respect the configuration of Medium was fundamentally important since it established the layout of a turret that encouraged teamwork by improvements in manual efficiency and the enhancement of morale in action.

Another of Medium's attractive features was the ease with which it could be converted to other roles – becoming father of what, in modern parlance, is called 'A Family of Vehicles'. The turret – so like that originally fitted on to the 1914 Rolls-Royce armoured car – could be left off and the hull adapted for use as an artillery tractor, a command vehicle, a bridgelayer, or, as shown here, an infantry machine-gun carrier (92). But Medium's surest claim to distinction derives from its dominant role in British field trials to establish the future employment of armoured formations. It never actually went to war itself (although it more than once saw active service as a static pill-box), but it helped show the way to shape a thousand armoured battles to come.

Medium II (91)	
Weight:	13.5 tons
Power Plant:	90 hp
Crew:	5
Armour:	8 mm
Speed:	18 mph
Armament:	1 47-mm
	6 mg

VICKERS MEDIUM MARK II

1 47-mm gun
2 .303 machine-gun
3 Driver's hood
4 Steering levers
5 Change speed lever
6 Brake levers
7 Armstrong Siddeley 90 hp V8 engine
8 Ventilator fan
9 Track adjusting wheel
10 Driver's seat
11 Clutch
12 .303 Vickers machine-gun
13 Gearbox
14 Suspension unit
15 Driving sprocket
16 Bevel gearbox
17 Epicycle
18 Plavet brake
19 Driving pinion
20 Exhaust
21 Boiling vessel (crew modification)
22 Two fuel tanks
23 Commander's cupola

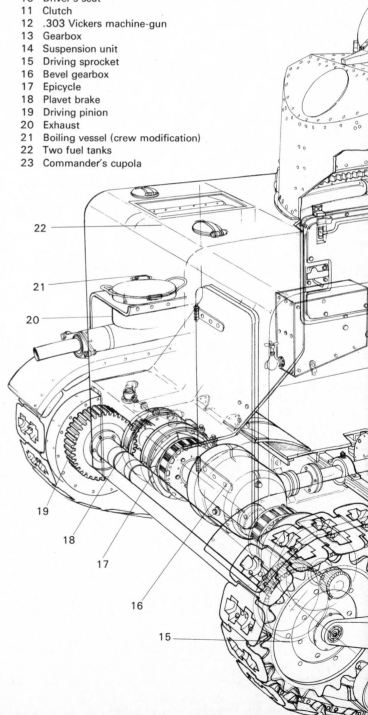

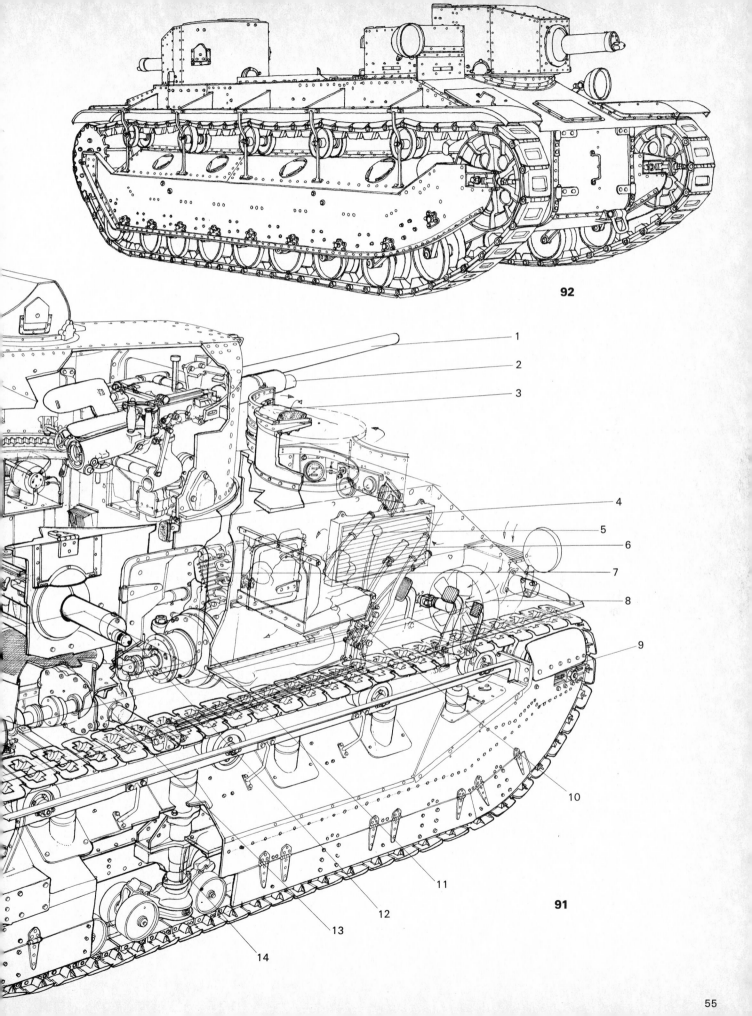

92

1
2
3
4
5
6
7
8
9
10
11
12
13
14

91

The world-wide sales drive by Vickers to exploit their fighting vehicles laid the foundations of several foreign emergent armoured forces. Quite often a special model would be tailored to the needs of a specific nation or as the pilot for that country's own manufacturing line: and, not without reason, other nations came to buy what suited another, if, in so doing, they got a bargain. This was the case with Vickers' Medium 'C' (93) which had been produced in response to an order from Japan when that country began to establish its own tank industry. In fact, the Japanese had started the construction of a heavy tank of their own, but ran into trouble from lack of experience and had no option but to adapt French and British models in order to hasten development and rescue their inexperienced designers.

One Mark 'C' (an offshoot of the Medium and Independent) went to Japan in 1926, and the Japanese modified and redesigned it until 1929 when it appeared as Type 89A (94). It bore a strong resemblance to its parent but benefited from thicker armour, a reduction in the number of machine-guns and crew, and the addition of a stronger suspension and a tail to help obstacle cross-

ing — all this set against loss in speed. In effect the Japanese had converted a fast light tank into an infantry support vehicle — a reflection of all subsequent Japanese armoured policy in which tanks were usually regarded as no more than a helpmate to the traditional arms — not as an arm of decision in their own right.

Meanwhile the first home-produced Japanese tank had crawled through the development stages — the example which appeared in 1932, called Type 92 (95) and running on 34 bogie wheels, looking not unlike a centipede! But with only 15-mm armour protection it hardly justified the nomenclature of Heavy Tank and, in due course, faded as the Japanese tended to lighter designs more in keeping with their maritime strategy aimed at weak opponents.

Vickers, meanwhile, had not stood still. Besides selling Mark 'C' to Eire, they had made a number of different vehicles for the British army and, in 1928, introduced an outstanding new model — their significant light 6-tonner (96) that incorporated twin, almost archaic, turrets but, in recompense, a host of original features which, within a few years, were to infiltrate the schemes of nearly every tank-seeking nation. Apart from its feeble armament, 6-

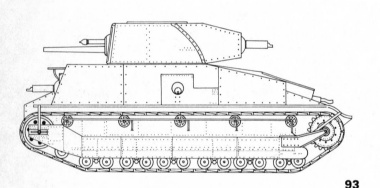

93

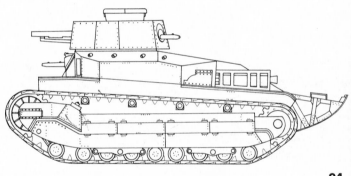

94

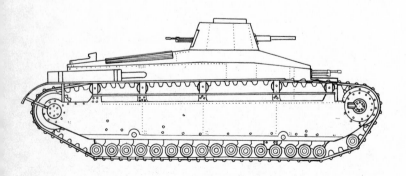

95

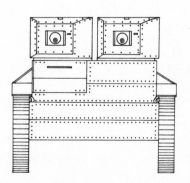

96

tonner combined speed and protection in admirable proportions along with an unprecedented all-round reliability. Much credit went to the specially designed Armstrong Siddeley engine as well as to a new suspension arrangement that dramatically improved the cross-country ride — until then, a notably uncomfortable experience in small tracked vehicles. Another major improvement came with the introduction of a manganese steel track, for the old plate-tracks had rarely lasted much longer than 20 miles, whereas 6-tonner could travel for 3,000 without a change. In terms of mobility this sort of reliability counted heavily since, on active service, even a sub-standard fighting unit that kept running was better than a superior one broken down by the roadside. And, in any case, 6-tonner had room to spare for up-gunning with a single turret (97), called 6-tonner B.

The Russians forthwith adopted the 6-tonner, renamed it T-26A (98), and set up their own production line. Later, in obsolescence, it came to play a part in the early battles of the Second World War until overwhelmed by vastly superior vehicles of later design.

In the meantime the USA also experimented with Vickers

	Mark 'C' (93)	Japanese 89A (94)	Japanese Type 92 (95)	Vickers 6-ton A (96)
Weight:	11.6 tons	12.7 tons	26 tons	7.2 tons
Power Plant:	165 hp	118 hp	290 hp	87 hp
Crew:	5	4	5	3
Armour:	6.5 mm	17 mm	35 mm	13 mm
Speed:	20 mph	15 mph	14 mph	20 mph
Armament:	1 57-mm 4 mg	1 57-mm 2 mg	1 37-mm 2 mg	2 mg

	Vickers 6-ton B (97)	Russian T-26 A (98)	US Medium M1 (99)	US Light T1 E4 (101)
Weight:	7.4 tons	8.6 tons	21 tons	8 tons
Power Plant:	87 hp	91 hp	195 hp	150 hp
Crew:	3	3	4	4
Armour:	17 mm	15 mm	25 mm	16 mm
Speed:	20 mph	19 mph	14 mph	20 mph
Armament:	47-mm 1 mg	1 37-mm 1 mg	1 37-mm 2 mg	1 37-mm 1 mg

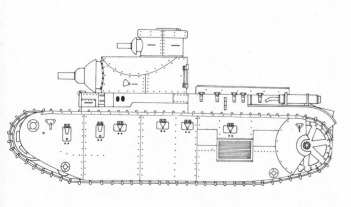

97

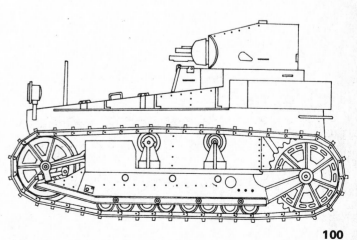

98

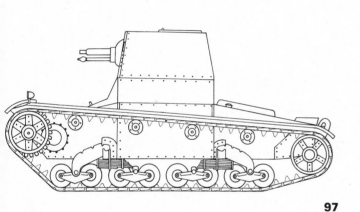

99

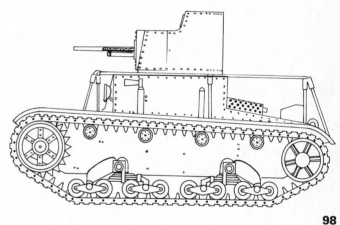

100

projects. Within the confines of their infantry corps' strictures, they examined a refinement of the British Medium 'D' that was crowned with a rotating turret mounting a 37-mm gun and called Medium M1 (99): they then rebuilt the concept into a still heavier vehicle, Medium T1 E2. But the Americans could not make up their minds on the sort of armoured fighting vehicles they really wanted, and in 1926 swung away from mediums towards the light types.

The early American light tanks were no more successful than those of Japanese origin – the Light T1 E1 of 1929 (100), bearing a strong Vickers look, set the trend and demonstrated a miserable lack of inspiration. Then in 1931 the Americans imported a Vickers 6-tonner Model B with its single turret and 47-mm gun and this they developed and tried out as T1 E4 (101) while the Russians did similar things to the same model, giving it a 45-mm gun and a radio set, and calling it T-26B (102). But the most significant trends were in outlook, for while the Americans only experimented in a half-hearted way, the Russians began to form a large armoured force along with the industrial knowledge to expand and support it.

Meanwhile, since 1919, the Germans had not been allowed to possess offensive weapons at all – and that included tanks. Smarting under these restrictions, the enforced contraction of her frontiers, and the imposition of an upper limit of 100,000 on the manpower of her army, Germany turned to the theoretical study of armoured forces, seeing in them the weapon most responsible for bringing about her recent defeat. Only through subversive activities could progress be made. By clandestine design and construction they made two variations on the Vickers theme of which Leichter Traktor (103) bore a close likeness to Medium and LK II. Built in secrecy and mostly run in Russia under a secret agreement, this AFV merely acquired experience for a cadre of designers who, quite soon, were to build tanks for the most competent armoured army ever raised in peacetime.

Meanwhile, Vickers 6-tonners crossed still more frontiers – the Polish 7 TP (104) of 1932 being only one of a number of examples, even though bought by misconception for employment in the role of medium tank. Indeed, it is ironic that, at the time when this design was being sold world-wide, the British army put it aside, after trial, in favour of less effective lighter machines.

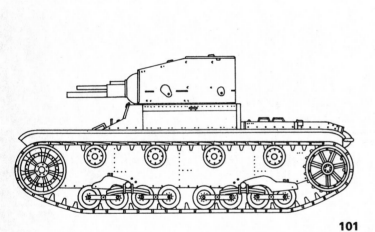

101

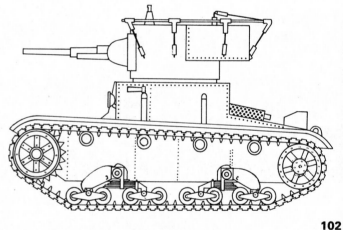

102

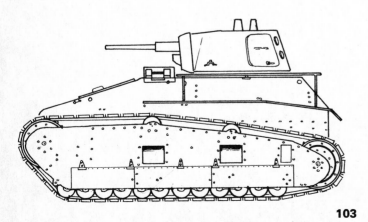

103

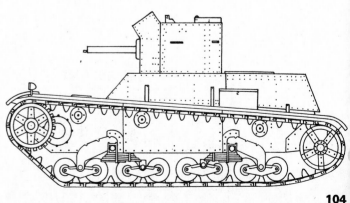

104

Competition from France

France, the other principal contender for tank export markets, lagged behind in the development race while variations on the original design of her early Renault M-17 were reproduced broadcast. Wherever a new version appeared it usually included some innovation of technical interest, exploiting the Renault as a useful test bed.

Most attention was focused on improving the suspension. Fiat of Italy cleaned it up without improving its resilience to any marked extent, in their 3000 A (105): the high speed attained was at cost in wear and tear to crew and vehicle, but their long 37-mm gun symbolized an awakening interest in guns of higher velocity with an armour-piercing capability. The Russians, copying the French and Americans and substituting an advanced, sprung bogie suspension in place of the more rigid original, doubled the speed of their T-18 (106) to 10 mph without reducing armour or increasing power plant. In fact, in the field of suspensions and tracks, as much if not more progress was made in the 1920s than in any other period – and the Russians were among the first to appreciate its significance.

Because France's experiments with novel tracks and suspen-

sions were inhibited by the insistence of her General Staff on tanks remaining tied to infantry pace, her armoured vehicles evolved less radically than those of other nations. If tanks were not to go faster, more attention had to be directed to improving armour and armament. Nevertheless, French efforts to promote better springing and rubber tracks bore fruit in NC-27 (107) with improved cross-country performance at medium speeds. Yet when the Japanese bought some and called them NC-31s (108) for comparison with Vickers' products, the decision in favour of Vickers showed that the Japanese had little doubt which nation was making most progress and offered the best terms.

Complacent in victory and secure in the knowledge that their large army dominated Europe by size and, above all, reputation, the French military leaders relaxed their technical vigilance in the 1920s, declining to integrate unorthodox thinking with the lessons learnt in the last months of the First World War. The doctrine of the Ubiquitous Infantryman as the decisive arm in battle, helped by, but not dependent on, other arms, held its ground in the military academies – an attitude, let it be understood, in which

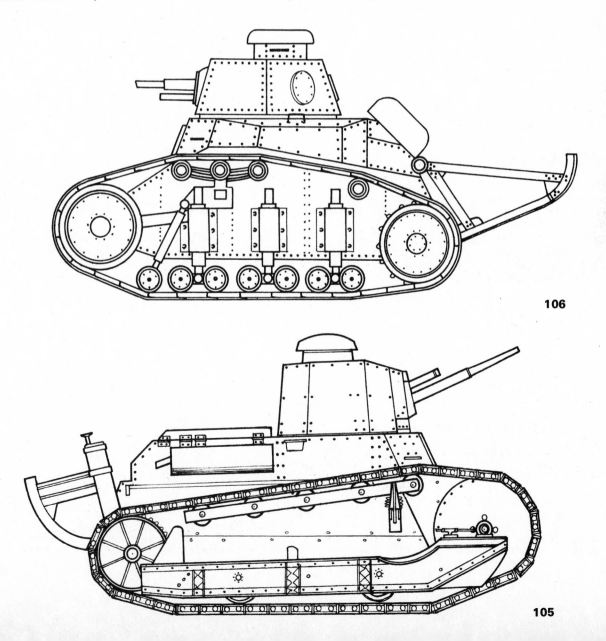

106

105

nearly every other military hierarchy concurred. Inevitably the shape of new armoured vehicles came to be tailored to infantry doctrine whereby men walked accompanied by slow-moving fighting vehicles whose task was to fire a mass of machine-guns, supplemented by a few light anti-tank guns. Armour was made just thick enough to resist the most advanced high-velocity guns known to belong to potential opponents. Horsed cavalry, which had ended the war in decline as a decisive battlefield element, reverted to its traditional employment in reconnaissance and as a screening force, supplemented by light, faster AFVs whose protection was felt to be compatible with small size and whose light armament could be used only as a last desperate measure to help escape from danger. Heavier guns, when mounted in AFVs, merely acted as a substitute for artillery should all else fail.

With this prime infantry role in mind, the French started work in 1921 on their next main battle tank – Char B (109) – a fascinating combination of cross-country agility (see the similarity to early

British practice with the all-round track), heavy protection, and mixed firepower using the little one-man turret and the short 75-mm gun slung between the tracks. With such thick armour, Char B was pre-eminent among heavy tracked vehicles and in 1940 was to set German gunners a pretty problem. But imagine the dilemma of its commander, whose task included giving orders over the radio and to the crew (not one of whom worked in the turret alongside him), co-operation with other armoured vehicles and with walking infantry, in addition to a personal search for enemy targets at which to fire his own 47-mm gun unaided. Think, too, of the difficulty of aiming the 75-mm gun which could be elevated and depressed by the gun layer but had to be traversed by turning the tank. Complexities such as these went far to cancel out the other virtues that had been built into Char B.

In 1930, on the eve of the International Disarmament Conference, the French at last decided to build a new tank to replace their ageing Renault M-17s. The NC had shown one way in which

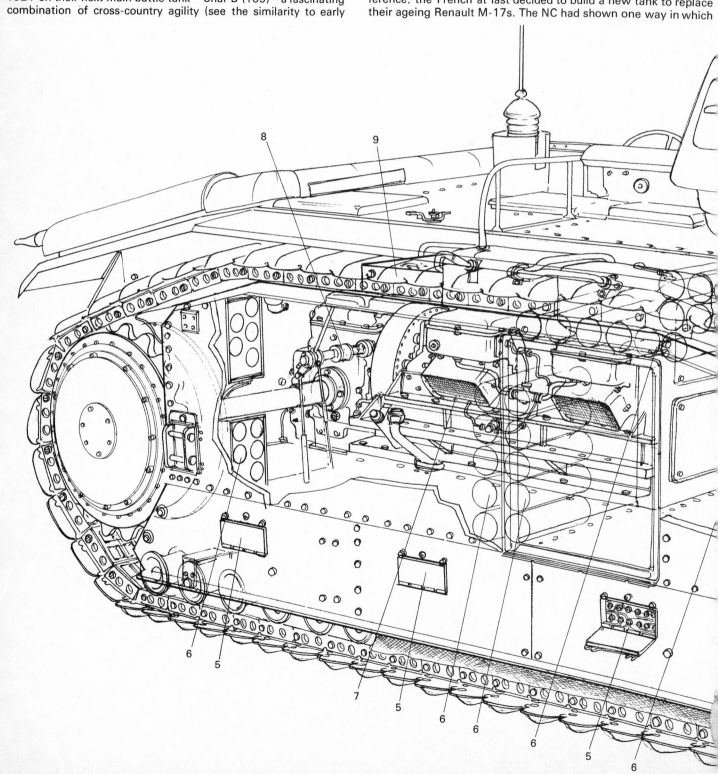

60

CHAR B

1 Commander/Gunner's cupola
2 47-mm gun
3 Driver's position including gun-laying equipment
4 75-mm gun
5 Grease points
6 Ammunition racks
7 Renault 6-cylinder water-cooled engine
8 5-speed gearbox
9 Fuel tank

it might be done, at the price of an increase in weight, but the D-1 series which finally evolved seems to have suited neither the infantry nor the cavalry concept of operations. D-1 lacked sufficient armoured protection for the former and appeared too conspicuous for the latter: like so many compromises it satisfied nobody.

Yet again the French had used a one-man turret in the D-1 series, stationing the other two members of the crew in the hull, the first to drive and the second to operate the radio and man the second machine-gun. D-1 (110), however, led to the improved D-2 (111) in 1932, the year in which D-1 showed its paces during the critical, early French experiments with armoured formations that prefaced the creation of their first 'Division Légère Mécanique' (DLM) in 1934. The DLM, by confirming the French way of cavalry armoured warfare, also demonstrated why even this sort of formation, with its primary reconnaissance characteristics, had to be equipped with something more effective than a light AFV armed only with a machine-gun. Hence D-2 prompted the need for the

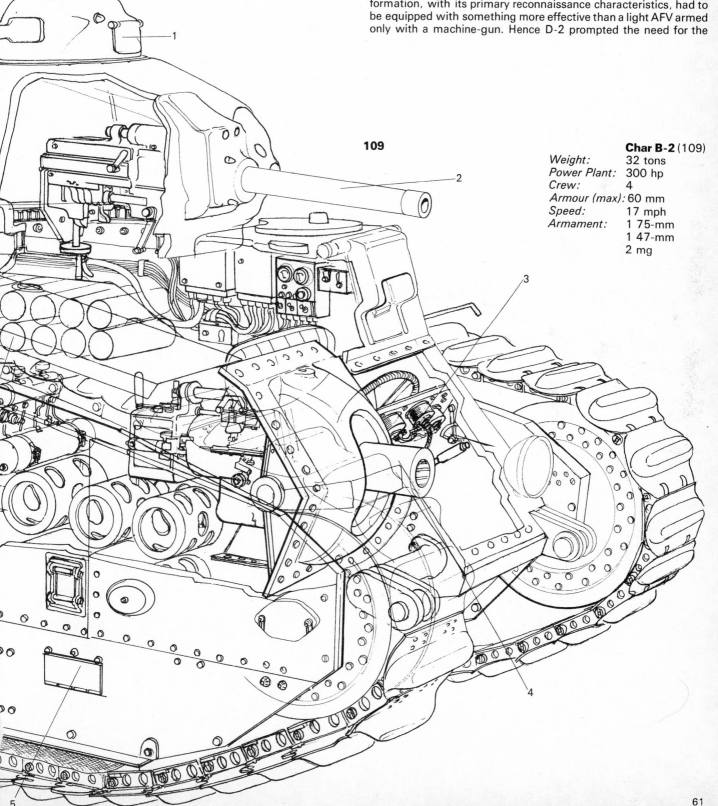

109

Char B-2 (109)

Weight:	32 tons
Power Plant:	300 hp
Crew:	4
Armour (max):	60 mm
Speed:	17 mph
Armament:	1 75-mm
	1 47-mm
	2 mg

introduction of better successors that were to be either of the same bulk or significantly smaller. Needless to say it was the latter type that was adopted — emerging in two forms under the auspices of the firms of Renault and Hotchkiss — culminating in R-35 (112) and H-35 (113) which, in effect, were miniaturized D-2s or, put another way, greatly improved M-17s. These were to be among the prime fighting machines which went to war with the French army in 1939 as part of the cavalry-orientated DLMs.

From the technical angle both these AFVs were distinguished by the use of cast hulls and turrets (somewhat expensive and not quite as resistant to shot as homogeneous armour plate), and the employment of 'Cletrac' steering whereby, instead of braking one track to steer, the drive was transferred from one track to the other via a differential and the gearbox, reducing loss of power when steering and improving overall cross-country performance. However much the concept of small machines with a one-man turret may have been seriously open to question, the technical improvements to achieve it were praiseworthy. No matter how unimaginative French strategic and tactical employment of their tanks was to be, the creative imagination of their designers and engineers was of high quality.

	3000A (105)	**T-18** (106)	**NC-27** (107)	**NC-31** (108)
Weight:	5.5 tons	5.5 tons	8.5 tons	9.5 tons
Power Plant:	55 hp	35 hp	60 hp	75 hp
Crew:	2	2	2	2
Armour (max):	16 mm	16 mm	34 mm	34 mm
Speed:	14 mph	10 mph	12 mph	12 mph
Armament:	1 37-mm	1 37-mm	1 37-mm	1 37-mm
		1 mg	1 mg	1 mg

	D-1 (110)	**D-2** (111)	**R-35** (112)	**H-35** (113)
Weight:	12 tons	20 tons	9.8 tons	11.4 tons
Power Plant:	64 hp	150 hp	82 hp	75 hp
Crew:	3	3	2	2
Armour (max):	30 mm	40 mm	45 mm	34 mm
Speed:	11 mph	14 mph	13 mph	17 mph
Armament:	1 37-mm	1 47-mm	1 37-mm	1 37-mm
	2 mg	2 mg	1 mg	1 mg

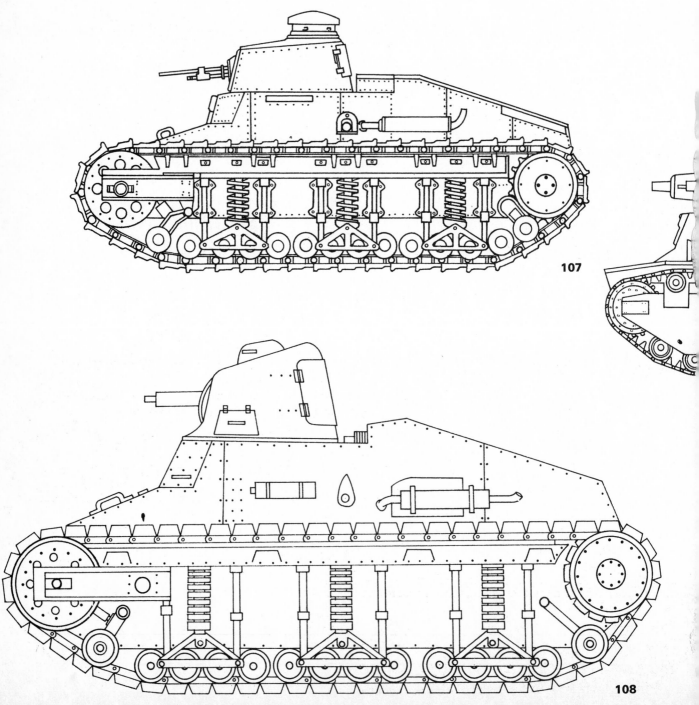

107

108

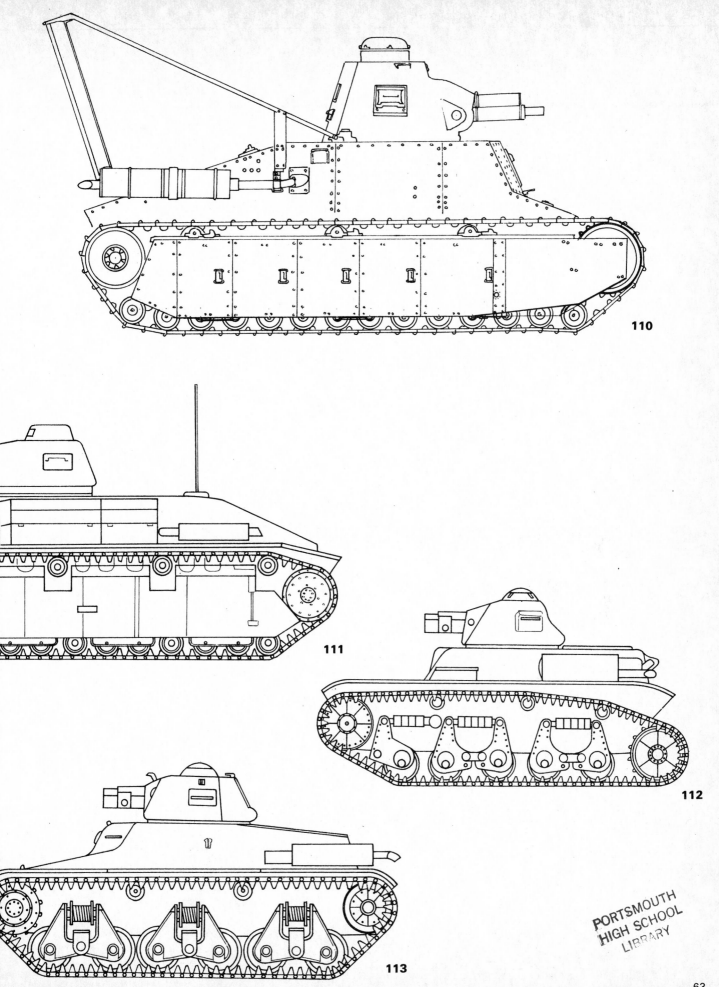

110

111

112

113

The Machine-gun Carriers of Britain

In the 1920s only in Britain did the idea of establishing armoured forces as a decisive arm in their own right take root – but it cannot be said that a great deal of enthusiasm was to be found even there – though it must be remembered that because Britain's principal defence commitments were directed to the maintenance of order on the fringes of her Empire, the study of general war in Europe could not hope for priority at a time of financial stringency. In any case, many pundits suggested, 'even if tanks are still needed in the next war as in the last, it will not be long before they are knocked out by the new and improving anti-tank defences'. Talk of armoured forces acting in isolation merely led to accusations that the armoured enthusiasts visualized an 'All Tank Solution' as a suspect panacea to save heavy infantry casualties.

When the German General Ludendorff had concluded that the infantryman of the future would be a machine-gunner, he partially reinforced the concept behind the French Renault M-17s, themselves little more than machine-gun carriers, and in 1925 the same impulse inspired two Britons to make separate approaches towards the same solution. Major Gifford Martel, backed by the resources of the motor manufacturer, William Morris, and John Carden, working in the garage of a Mr Loyd, built machine-gun carriers that were cheap and easy to mass-produce. Martel preferred a lightly armoured, wheel-cum-track solution, while Carden concentrated on an unsprung tracked suspension. Both aimed to offer the option of fighting mounted or dismounted. Martel's first model carried one man (114), the second two, and the third, made in conjunction with Crossley's (115), reverted to one man, put the engine in rear, introduced a more sophisticated suspension, and reduced the armour to 6 mm.

The light, tracked weapon carriers nearly all had similar dimensions:

Weight:	3 tons
Power Plant:	20 hp
Crew:	1 or 2
Armour:	10 mm
Speed:	25 mph
Armament:	1 mg

The lead in development passed rapidly to Carden and Loyd, who took to running tracks on sprung rollers and then tried out a wheels-cum-track solution while, in the meantime, they got the British Army deeply interested in their vehicle's potential for reconnaissance as well as a weapon carrier. By so doing they blurred the original concept, for the army called Carden-Loyd's carriers 'tankettes' and thus gave an impression that the Tank Corps and not the infantry had a vested interest in them. In practice, carriers extended the range and safety of infantrymen, giving them a golden opportunity to raise their speed to that of the cavalry or tank arm of decision by acting as part of the team which could be formed round the 'Capital AFV' – the tank. This was the essence of the 'All Armoured Idea' which few really understood and most preferred to revile under the name of 'The All Tank Idea'.

Carden-Loyd's Mark III (116), because it lacked all-round armour or 360 degree traverse for its armament, bore no resemblance to the Tank Corps' image of a 'Capital AFV'. The same applied to Mark V (117) or Mark VIa (118). Steadily these versatile and simple little infantry carriers were improved under the genius of Carden and, for lack of anything better available, played an important role in reconnaissance and protection duties to the main force of medium tanks during the first armoured force experiments in 1927 and 1928. For, in the absence of a genuine light tank, the British Tank Corps had no option but to man carriers themselves instead of leaving the job to the infantry.

Carden-Loyd was bought out by Vickers-Armstrong in 1928, and this infusion of new capital hastened the development of rationalized vehicles. In future the engines were to be Ford and the transmission, with the addition of an extra low gear, that of the famous Model 'T'. Track life was a persistent problem – hence the temporary resort to the wheel-cum-track solution – but gradually this was rectified and track life raised to over 600 miles.

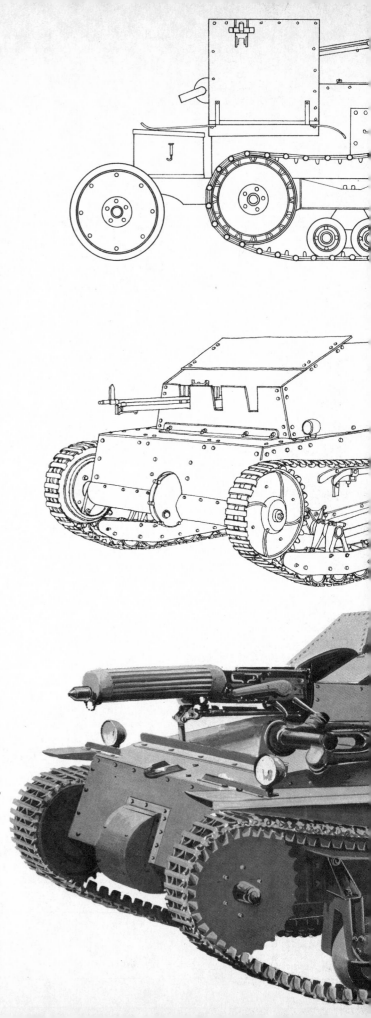

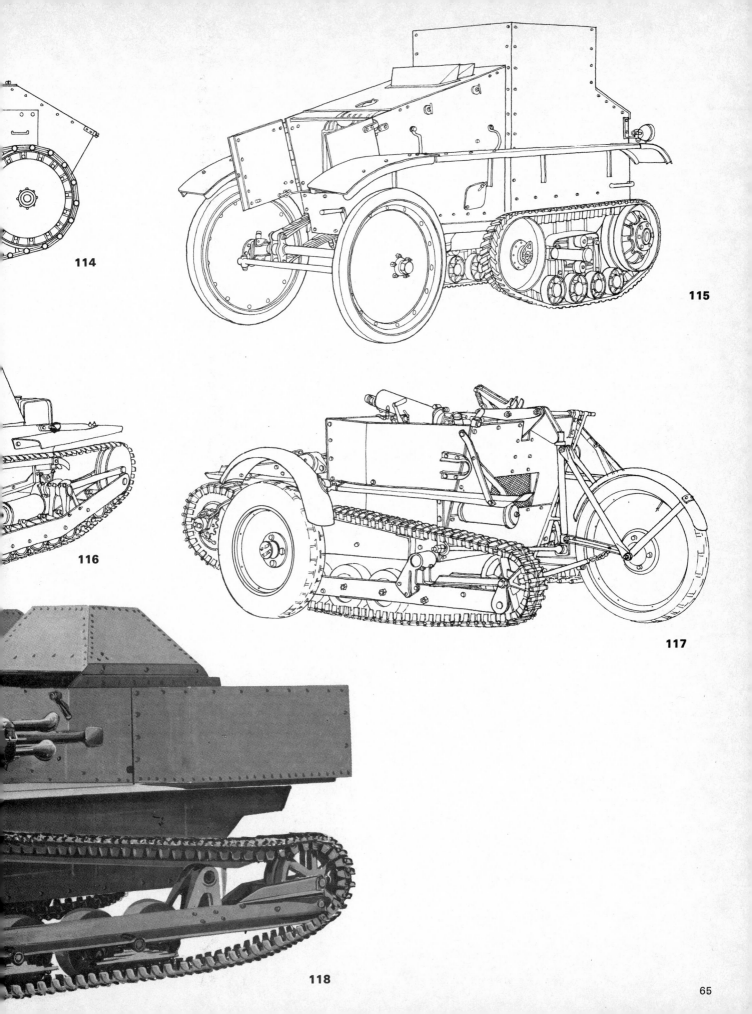

114

115

116

117

118

Well behind in thought and action, the infantry did not begin their armoured experiments until 1931, only to abandon them in 1933 because senior officers felt the infantry would not be able to keep up with 'tank pace' and also from their repulsion at involvement with petrol engines. It became common-place to refer to almost any armoured tracked vehicle as a 'tank' and to associate the protagonists of all-armoured mobile formations (usually members of the Tank Corps) with an ambitious minority who were accused of wishing to destroy the traditional arms and substitute an 'All Tank Army' in their place.

Inevitably Carden-Loyd carriers grew into genuine light tanks (see pages 84–85), while foreign purchasers came forward to buy the basic vehicle prior to adapting it in their own factories to suit

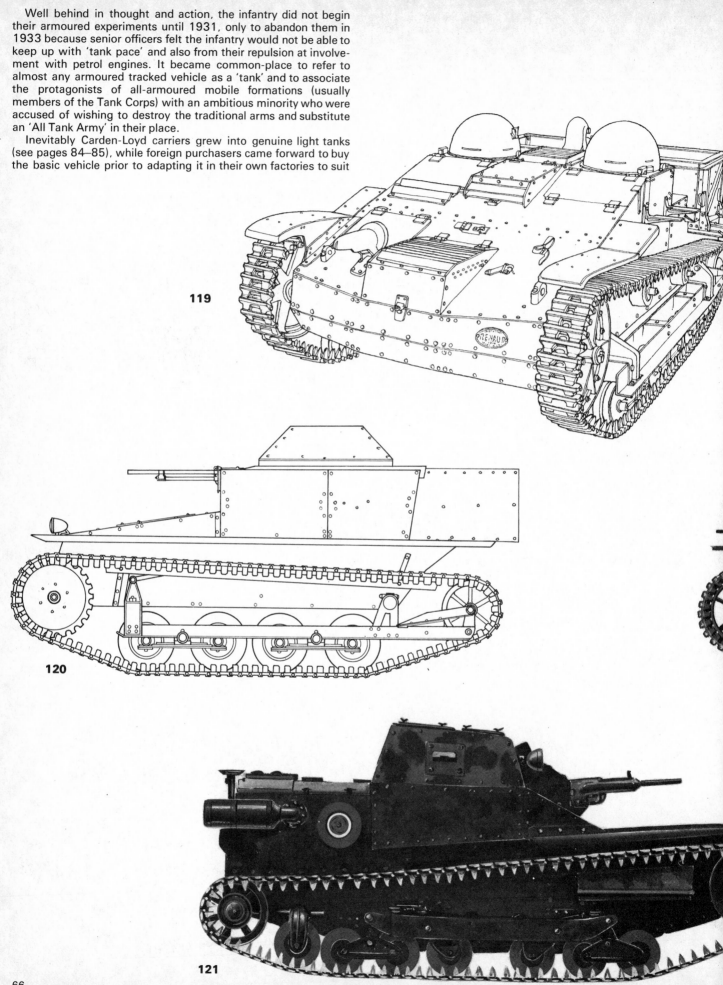

their requirements. France's UE (119), Russia's T-27 (120), and the Italian CV-33/5 (121) came closer to the weapon carrier concept (although frequently referred to as tanks): Poland's TK-3 (122) and Czechoslovakia's Skoda MU-4 (123) got nearer to the 'tank' ideal without completely crossing the line — even were it possible to define so vague a boundary.

In Britain the weapon carrier at last returned to the infantry's favour in 1935 with the introduction of the Bren Carrier Mark I (124) (a fighting vehicle the Germans were often, later, to report as 'tank' in battle) intended by infantry to be solely a means of enhancing fire support although frequently and instinctively called upon to rescue foot soldiers who had become pinned down by the firepower of modern weapons.

122

123

124

Walter Christie and His Ideals

The main trends of armoured vehicle fashion could be detected long before the experimental almost hand-made phase of the 1920s had given way to the mass-production phases of the 1930s. Two schools of thought predominated: the slow, infantry-paced one which preferred protection to mobility and firepower, and the faster, more mobile school, with precedence given to cross-country agility, in which the designers had been given a comparatively free hand in proposing gun and armour characteristics — to the detriment of both. Emphasis fell upon automotive, transmission, and suspension components to the exclusion of armour and armament which converted a mobile machine into a fighting vehicle. In those days, when army officers with technical leanings were often despised, it was frequently left to designers with the drive of Walter Christie to persuade soldiers to enter the future. But while Christie's products gave priority to agility, and several could even cross water or move on roads after discarding their tracks, their fighting qualities came last. His basic ideas can be clearly spotted in the Amphibious Gun started in 1921 (125) (its sides were packed with cork to increase flotation), of which, typically, only one was made since Christie thrived mainly on ideas and built prototypes to order without getting personally involved in the practicalities of production.

True mobility, he reasoned, demanded constant motion, but in land warfare, water obstacles whose bridges had been destroyed were bound to intervene: therefore fighting vehicles had to dispense with bridges and become inherent swimmers. But in 1921, Christie saw no immediate hope of lengthening the abysmally short life of contemporary tracks. Furthermore, tracked vehicles burnt more fuel while their steel track links caused severe damage to roads — and the roads of the early 1920s were not by any means as durable as today's highways.

So Christie offered armies the option of running their armoured vehicles on tracks or wheels with a subtle arrangement whereby the track had only to be removed to achieve the second state. Vickers, on the other hand, simply took a tracked vehicle and attached retractable wheels, investing their first wheels-cum-track experiment (126) with an air of uncertain faith in a requirement that had not been clearly stated. Later, when they attached another retractable undercarriage to a Medium (127), the wheels being raised and lowered from a power take-off attached to the gearbox, the arrangement was still not a success. Clearly external devices such as these would be vulnerable to fire and, in any case, the whole balance of the tank was upset. Ansaldo of Italy also made a practical investigation into wheels-cum-track in 1925 (128), with a less Heath Robinson device than Vickers' but still without any result. Both projects then foundered as attention focused on Christie.

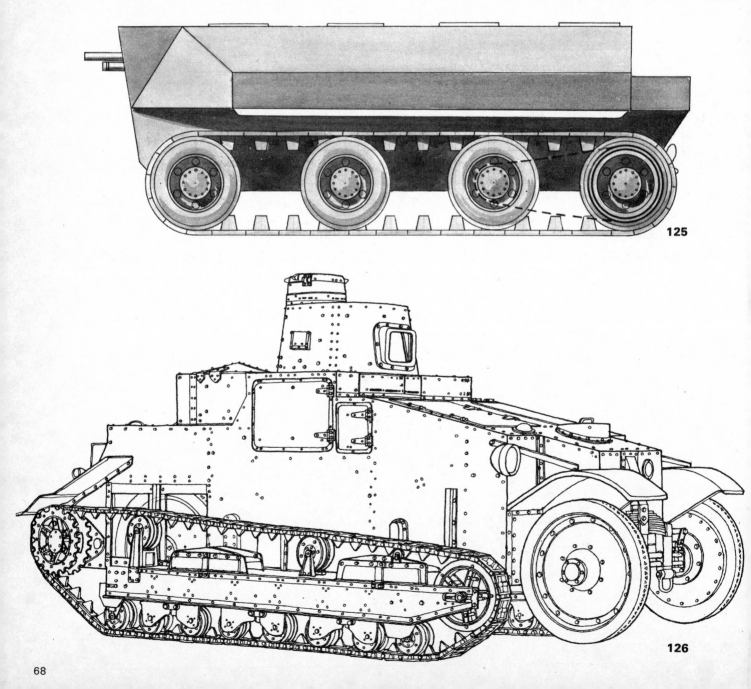

125

126

In 1928, Christie achieved a breakthrough in transmission and suspension design by incorporating a practical wheel-cum-track drive with chain link from sprocket wheel to the rear bogie. Along with a completely original hull and suspension layout, he located each solid rubber-tyred bogie wheel at the end of a crank, pivoted in the hull and sprung by a vertical coil spring; thus he conferred free, cushioned, independent movement which gave a smoother ride than ever achieved before. Powered by an ex-aeroplane engine — the Liberty — Christie's M-1928 (129) ran at record speeds for a tracked vehicle, but its uninspired layout of armament coupled with incipient mechanical unreliability marked it simply as a project study in which a fundamental fault marred the 'wheeled' part of the concept. For although M-1928 took only 30 minutes to discard the tracks, the high pressures under the narrow rubber tyres were such that the tank would only run on wheels when on a road surface. Yet the tracks on Christie's tanks were not very satisfactory, either, for he had concentrated on demonstrating high speed on hard ground, while in softer ground the flat, shoed tracks with its inadequate guides lost traction and either came off or broke.

Christie, realizing better than the soldiers the limitations as well as the potential of M-1928, declined a purchase offer by the United States Army and turned to devizing an even better model. In 1931 it appeared — his M-1931 — or T-3 (130), as the US Army called it when they bought three for $34,000 each (less armour, guns, engine, and radio) while Poland also ordered two, but defaulted on the order. Of greater significance, however, Russia took a pair and thus gave M-1931 an international reputation unlike any previous American design: indeed, with its sloped armour, which reduced the effectiveness of high-velocity shot, it looked years ahead of its time — in fact, the legitimate parent of generations of battle tanks.

Christie's notions next, quite literally, took flights of fantasy, for having solved, as he believed, the problem of fast cross-country movement (at the expense of amphibious capability), he aimed to make an airportable machine which could fly over obstacles and land, if necessary, deep in enemy territory. This led him to go to extraordinary lengths to save weight in M-1932 (131) on which the hull consisted of a double skin enclosing the springs; the wheels and the inner hull were made of duralumin; and the 750 hp Hispano-Suiza aeroplane engine, which gave a road speed on tracks of 36 mph or 65 mph on wheels, enabled the tank to leap a 20-foot gap from a 45 degree ramp. Consideration of a helicopter rotor to lift the vehicle over gaps (long before helicopters had been proved feasible) gave way in favour of attaching conventional aerofoil surfaces to the hull, using the tracks as a powered undercarriage and transferring power to the propeller at the critical moment of take-off. This vehicle Christie also sold to the Russians — whereupon it disappeared from view for ever — but interest in airborne AFVs has never slackened and today the issue is more alive than ever.

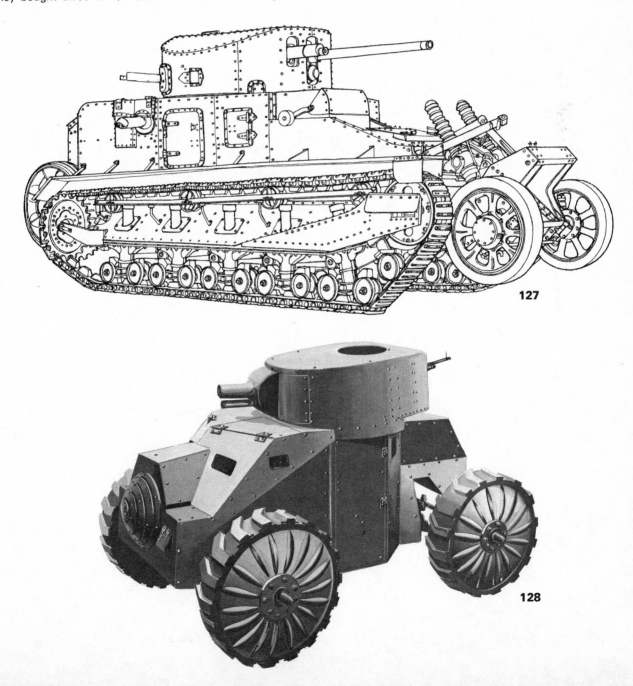

127

128

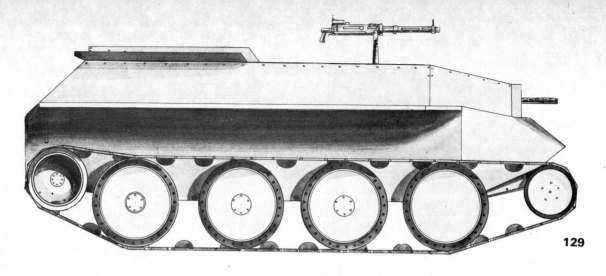

129

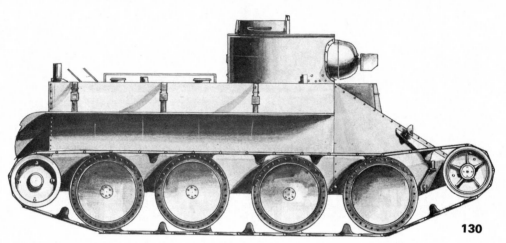

130

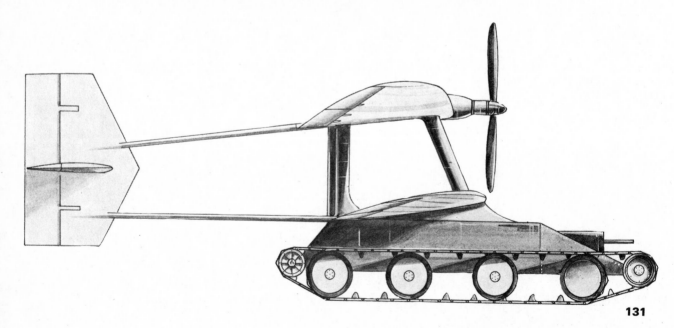

131

	M-1928 (129)	M-1931 or T-3 (130)	M-1932 (131)
Weight:	8.6 tons	10.5 tons	5 tons
Power Plant:	338 hp	338 hp	750 hp
Crew:	3	3	3
Armour:	13 mm	16 mm	13 mm
Speed: Tracks	26 mph	25 mph	36 mph
Wheels	50 mph	50 mph	65 mph
Armament:	2 mg	1 37-mm 1 mg	1 37-mm 1 mg

Suspensions

The concentrated attention given to suspensions and tracks between the wars by no means exhausted the subject since there had always to be more developments to keep pace with every increase in weight and speed, and a good cross-country performance helped by a low track to ground pressure was still desirable. 'Mother' had a ground pressure of 12.8 lb per square inch: but Vickers Medium had fallen to 9.5 and Christie T-3 still better at 9.

Here are five different suspensions which, in their day, were trend-setters:

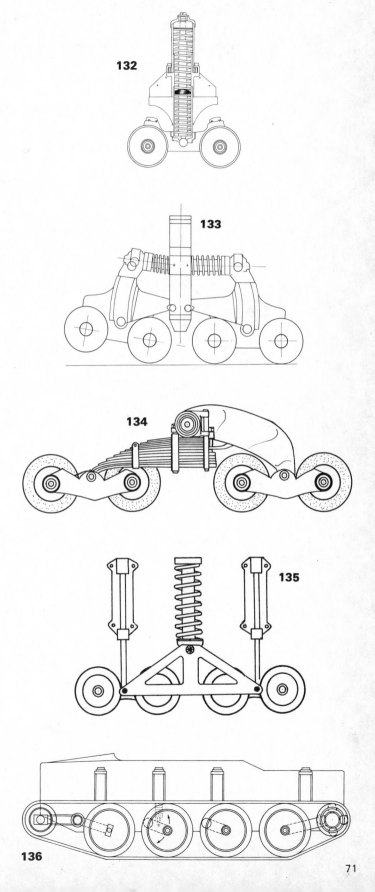

● The Vickers Medium used what is known as a Unit Sprung type of suspension (132) in which pairs of bogies were fixed to a vertical cylinder containing a coiled spring. This arrangement, though reliable, gave rather a jumpy ride. Nevertheless the same type of unit found its way on to later Vickers' tanks, though not the Medium C or the 6-tonner which were the forerunners of other tanks all over the world.

● Vickers Medium C had four separate units (133) — the first an independent, sprung bogie, the remainder of three trains of double bogies each with four rollers — each pair of bogies being attached to the other by a crank with a central compression spring. A later development of this suspension came into use on the celebrated Matilda II, and something similar was also to be found on the French H-35s and R-35s (see page 63) — the so-called 'scissors' suspension.

● The Vickers 6-tonner made use of yet another arrangement (134) whereby eight bogies were suspended from two units, each unit consisting of a bogie set attached to an arm with another set running free at the end of a leaf spring. As already mentioned, the track that went with this suspension was the extremely hard-wearing manganese-steel type whose life could be longer than that of the tank itself.

● The suspension employed on the Renault NC — double bogies supported by a central coil spring (135) — was important, not only because the Japanese bought and adapted it for integration with some of their own designs, but also because it became the basis of suspension for the coming generation of French D tanks.

● Each tank-manufacturing nation was watching the others' inventions with almost as much care as their own. With so much to learn about a subject and so little money given over to research and development, nobody dared ignore the slightest suggestion of another designer's improvements. This is why the big-wheeled Christie suspensions were regarded with such interest: its defects were obvious, but no engineer could ignore the possibilities. Here is the early Christie wheel (136) pivoting on an arm sprung by a single coil but without shock absorption. The amount of vertical wheel movement was considerable and at speed the track whipped about to an extraordinary extent — adding to the drama that Christie always engendered to publicize his ideas.

New Vehicles and Gathering Forces

As an economically prostrate world entered the 1930s in a financial blizzard, international relationships became as disturbed as the currencies they seemed unable to control. Germany stirred in protest against the restrictions of the Versailles Treaty, but from the 1930s onwards it was Russia who possessed more AFVs than any other nation. This sudden eruption into prominence of Russian mechanized forces bears testimony to the lively, revolutionary thread of her political doctrine, yet the underlying theme of Russian armoured philosophy actually copied the reactionary infantry and cavalry technique, as practised by the French army, whereby tank units were permanently attached to infantry formations and denied much freedom of action.

Unlike the French, however, the Russians continued to experiment with armour as an independent arm of decision by forming a number of one hundred-strong tank brigades, grouping them along with infantry and artillery components, into so-called Mechanized Corps. These were the Russian equivalent of what, in Western terminology, came to be known as mobile or armoured divisions. But the Russian mechanized corps continued to be hamstrung by having to practise as a sort of cavalry screen, bound by tactical demands to charge opposition at speed rather than to stand off and make best use of the protection afforded by armour and the firepower of their guns — an attraction towards superior speed that may well have persuaded the Russians to investigate Christie's designs.

As already stated, the Russians bought two chassis and began serious development. Three years later BT-5 (137) was coming off the production line in quite large numbers. Outwardly a true Christie, she incorporated many improvements including an excellent lightweight, 350-hp diesel engine (originally designed for air-

ULLSTEIN

137

138

craft), the 45-mm gun, and a crew of three. Speed had come down, yet the title Bystrokhodyne Tank (BT), standing for Fast Tank, was apt, and in this capacity it composed the striking element of the new Russian mechanized corps. Its operational début was not long delayed when, in the hands of Spanish government troops during the Civil War, it was matched for the first time — somewhat inconclusively — against German tanks of the type that would soon spearhead Panzer divisions.

But already a still more efficient type — BT-7 — was on its way, better protected by sloped armour along with an all-round improvement in reliability and crew compartment arrangements. Weight was up and range down, reflecting concern on the part of the Russian General Staff at the increasing threat imposed by modern anti-tank weapons. Few shots had been fired in anger, but already the classic gun versus armour race was in progress.

The Germans, as we have seen, had already conducted a few clandestine experiments to the mutual benefit of the Russians and themselves. With their 'Grosstraktor' (138) they partially copied yet another Vickers design, the 'Independent', but drew not a little inspiration as well from A7U — a prototype which had grown out of A7V (see page 36). Unlike its light cousin, Leichter Traktor, Grosstraktor was to undergo extensive development, but the central stream of German armoured doctrine that bubbled away under the impulse of Major Guderian (**left**) and men of his temperament, turned aside from heavily armoured, ponderous vehicles in the quest for nimble, lighter, and less conspicuous AFVs, particularly if the latter could be made to carry almost as powerful an armament as their bigger brethren. In any case, Germany's needs during the early stages of rearmament — particularly mechanized rearmament in

1933 — had to be concentrated primarily upon vehicles that could be easily acquired and manufactured quickly in large numbers for experimental purposes in order to train a new generation of soldiers.

An adaptation by the firm of Krupp of a Carden-Loyd vehicle, suitably disguised under the name 'Agricultural Tractor', came secretly into service in 1934 and eventually came to be known as Panzerkampfwagen I (PzKpfw-I) (139). Intended only as a training machine, she eventually went into battle in Spain and, in due course, spearheaded the Panzer divisions which overwhelmed Poland in 1939 and France in 1940. Later still she extended her usefulness in many other guises until long after her first task had lapsed. PzKpfw-I could never be described as a battleworthy vehicle, but it was 'Father of all the Panzers', the machine which converted Adolf Hitler to the idea. For all her small size and weak armament she bore the title of tank with enough conviction to subjugate unprepared enemies; and let it not be forgotten that, in her day, the mere sight and sound of an aggressively handled AFV had repercussions on morale which far outweighed other considerations.

	BT-5 (137)	**PzKpfw-I** (139)
Weight:	11.2 tons	5.5 tons
Power Plant:	350 hp	57 hp
Crew:	3	2
Armour:	13 mm	12 mm
Speed:	36 mph	22 mph
Armament:	1 45-mm	2 mg
	1 mg	

139

Germany persevered with a few derivatives of Grosstraktor in accordance with the wishes of the conventionally-minded element of their General Staff who continued to pin their beliefs on the need for armour to work closely with infantry. In due course PzKpfw-V (140) came to life out of Grosstraktor, but it takes many years to establish a brand new industrial technique and the task is made no easier when so complicated a project as this is used at the start since so much time is wasted overcoming problems which, with more experience, might be avoided. The similarity of PzKpfw-V to 'Independent' is apparent, but already the signs of an original configuration can be detected in the shape of the turret – a shape which was to reappear on numerous, operational successors of different nations – including the British A-6.

Far more sophisticated than PzKpfw-V, or any previous Medium, the Vickers A-6 often known as the '16-Tonner' (141) came from Vickers in 1928 – their private challenger in the competition for a successor to the Medium. But the timing of her début was unfortunate since Medium still had a few years' life left in her, the economic blizzard was in sight, and the peaceful spirit born of the Treaty

lish the real battlefield effectiveness of armoured vehicles vis-à-vis other means of waging war. Instead there raged a hot debate lost amid the clouds of highly charged emotion generated by the aftermath of 'Plan 1919'. It is an immutable rule that when neither side in a military argument is sure of its ground, both will resist the performance of controlled experiments that might prove one or the other wrong.

Yet A-6 E3 was a fine example of the tank builders' art which solved many problems, consolidated new trends, and asked fresh questions by the possibilities it opened up. The turret layout with its central position, for instance, gave all-round vision to the commander, simplified his job, and became standard practice in German medium tanks; at the same time the ability to traverse the turret gun quickly from side to side re-emphasized the superfluity of the two sub-turrets. But 14 mm of armour matched with a 47-mm gun with a muzzle velocity no better than 1,750 feet per second was not compensated by obvious good cross-country performance and layout. With reasons (if only negative ones) the Treasury officials turned down their thumbs on A-6.

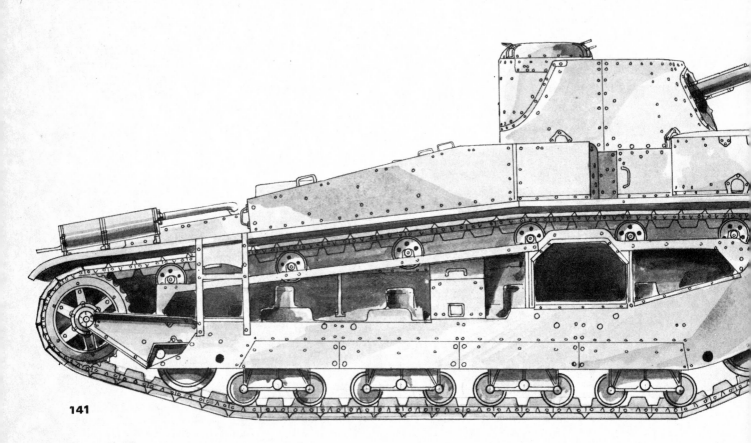

141

of Locarno was about to be capitalized by an International Peace Conference. It is scarcely surprising, therefore, that A-6 got no closer to production than PzKpfw-V. Nevertheless, she made a most suitable test-bed for a number of advanced ideas of which the most important, undoubtedly, were the Ricardo 180-hp diesel in A-6 E2, and the experimental Wilson epicyclic gearbox (precursor of practical regenerative steering such as was introduced in later, wartime tanks) mounted in A-6 E3.

The advantages of a diesel engine in an AFV had long been appreciated: reduced risk of fire, increased range, and greater reliability compensated for its tendency to give off clouds of smoke, when starting up, with ensuing tactical disadvantages. The loss of power caused when steering has been remarked upon, but the Wilson gearbox did much to dispense with this loss even though its incorporation in a production tank had to wait another decade. For let it be acknowledged that financial controls (which play their part in getting value for money) were against A-6. She cost £16,000 (a big sum in those days) and her value lay wide open to doubt since scientific, operational studies had never been undertaken to estab-

A-6 had a competitor – the A-7 (142) designed and made at great cost and labour in a ridiculously long time by the official Tank Design Establishment at Woolwich Arsenal. It took four years to get her on show and she arrived too late for the selection race, but even so she had her purpose, since from her came the twin AEC diesel engines and the suspension which, one day, were to act as the power plant and running gear for the celebrated Matilda II (see page 98), while the stationing of a single bow machine-gun alongside the driver heralded the demise of sub-turrets.

	PzKpfw-V (140)	A-6 (141)	A-7 (142)
Weight:	35 tons	18 tons	14 tons
Power Plant:	500 hp	180 hp	250 hp
Crew:	6	6	5
Armour:	70 mm	14 mm	14 mm
Speed:	21 mph	30 mph	25 mph
Armament:	1 75-mm	1 47-mm	1 47-mm
	1 37-mm	3 mg	2 mg
	5 mg		

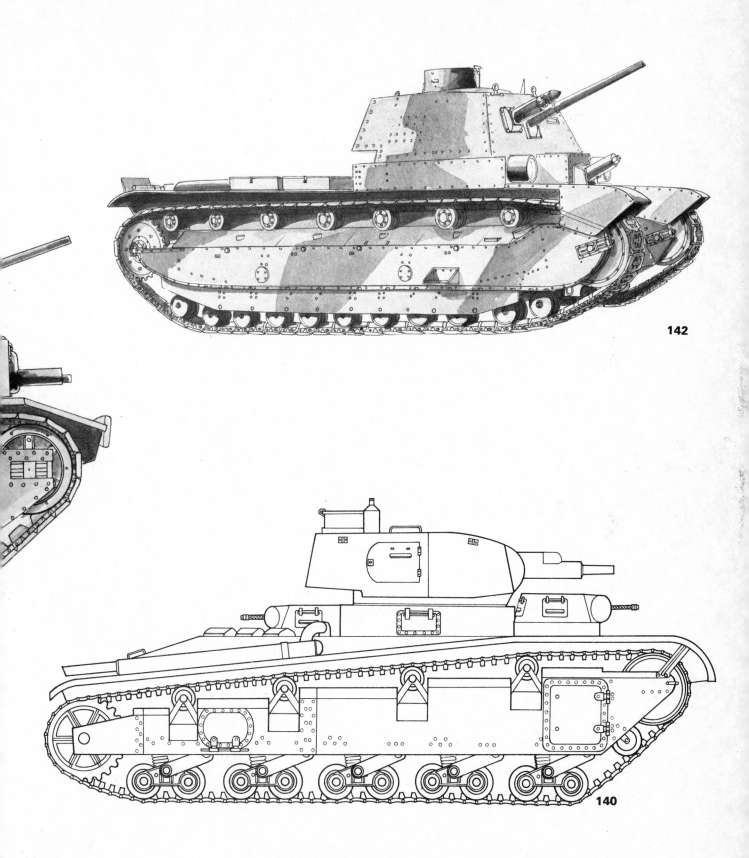

142

140

Throw-backs and Freaks

The state of confusion into which international politics were plunging the world in the early 1930s may well have originated from the same chaotic economic state that flung tank design into disarray. The spirit of experimentation without an ultimate discipline to convert experiments into production had given birth to numerous tank throw-backs and freaks. Later it will be seen how fighting vehicle design settled down to a fairly standard pattern, but in 1932, all sorts of shapes and sizes were being sketched on the drawing-boards to appear in solitary and costly prototype.

A throw-back of 1930 was the United States Medium T-2 (143) with its striking resemblance to the Vickers Medium. Placed alongside the rakish Christie models which had already made their début, it looked really antiquated. What few concessions it made to progress were increased armour thickness and a much more powerful engine than Medium's, but the old, vertically sprung suspension was hardly compatible with a speed of 25 mph on the road and

15 mph cross-country, while hand-traverse of the turret could only condemn the crew to a desperately slow engagement of targets. Only one was made.

Less orthodox in appearance, but bearing the Christie stamp, the US Combat Car T-2 (144) paid more attention to the needs of reconnaissance than combat and was the forerunner of the breed of scout cars and half-tracks with which the American and many other armies were to be equipped in the Second World War. This vehicle possessed additional interest, however, in the use of aluminium indicating persistent attempts to keep down weight.

Yet another strange-looking development of the wheel-cum-track arrangement was made by the Swedish firm of Landswerk (145) in 1931. In this design there was a clear intention to achieve a better performance for the wheeled version than had been the case with other wheel-cum-track models. The employment of balloon tyres instead of solid rubber and the separation of the tracks from the wheels show how the Christie influence was thrown off in favour of the Vickers concept. Indeed this vehicle firmly demonstrated central European trends, its turret and sloped armour, for instance, foreshadowing configurations that were later

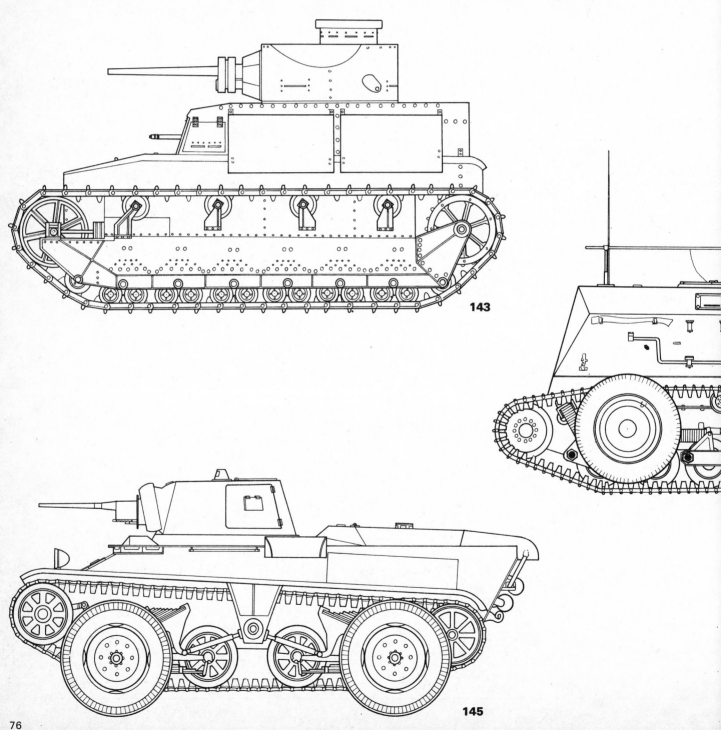

143

145

to become standard in German tanks and those produced by the Czech firm of Skoda. German industry was comparing notes with others on the verge of expansion under Hitler's rearmament programme and badly needed vehicles and know-how as the start to its initial investigations. The German army actually acquired a few wheel-cum-tracks named SdKfz-254 (146), but its real interest lay in tanks along with armoured cars of German design and in any case there was no time or spare manufacturing capacity for extremely complex vehicles that might be difficult to build and maintain. Germany had to face the fact that the crews who would man the, as yet, unbuilt fighting vehicles would come from a population that was still relatively unfamiliar with mechanical vehicles: it was dangerous to expect too high a standard of driving or maintenance from them at first.

So long as armies were prepared to equip themselves with relatively simple vehicles which did not demand the services of heavy industry, quite small nations could construct fighting machines that were economically sound. The Schofield armoured vehicle (147), made in New Zealand, is a good example and showed what might be achieved by maintaining sobriety in design and keeping to simple armour plate. In the long run, however, only the big industrial nations with great foundries were going to survive in the race to produce tanks that were battleworthy in the face of a mounting threat by anti-tank weapons. In 1935 the time had come, like it or not, for the nations to enter an arms race in which armoured fighting vehicles were to be of prime importance.

	Medium T-2 (143)	Combat Car T-2 (144)	Landswerk 30 (145)
Weight:	16 tons	8 tons	11.5 tons
Power Plant:	312 hp	167 hp	200 hp
Crew:	4	3	3
Armour:	19 mm	13 mm	14 mm
Speed:	25 mph	30 mph wheels	45 mph wheels
		20 mph tracks	20 mph tracks
Armament:	1 47-mm 2 mg	2 mg	2 mg

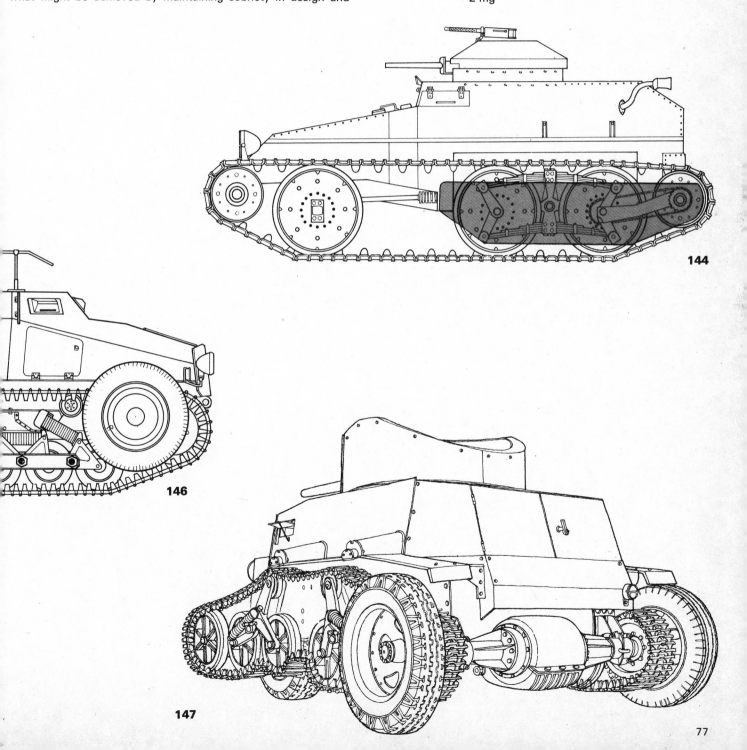

144

146

147

The Rise of Armoured Divisions

Ever since the Armistice of 1918 overtook the British 'Plan 1919', Fuller and his collaborators had schemed to run trials with armoured forces to show the feasibility of their wartime inspiration. The British army had never before suffered casualties like those of the First World War and thought it imperative to find some way of reducing bloodshed in the future, the more so since the Royal Air Force proposed settling all future conflicts by aerial bombardment alone, without calling on land forces. But peacetime inertia, natural resistance to change and a total absence of suitable vehicles, all helped to delay a start until 1927. That year, a hotch-potch force of Medium tanks, Carden-Loyd carriers, armoured cars, and mechanized infantry and artillery demonstrated how, even in a peacetime exercise, a mechanized force could paralyze a horse and foot army. Yet radio — the essential element by which a mechanized force commander could maintain contact, receive information, and match his orders to the speed of his units — was absent at the lower levels.

Much later, in 1931, crystal-controlled radios became available, and this prompted a further experiment which used tanks and carriers alone to demonstrate the practicability of one man, in the forefront of battle, controlling far-spread sub-units by voice radio. This was the prime aim of the exercise, but the absence of infantry and gunners inspired renewed fears among the traditional arms that the tank soldiers were planning an All Tank Army. So when next a British tank brigade assembled in 1934, its activities attracted almost as much restrictive suspicion as constructive interest. Yet the 1934 exercise merely went on where those of 1931 had left off, raising the level of study from battalion to brigade level as the essential forerunner to combined exercises with infantry and artillery in association with the tanks.

That autumn the British temporarily brought together the essential components of what they called a Mobile Division — a mixed force of infantry in wheeled vehicles and a few tracked carriers, motor-towed artillery, armoured cars, and the vital Tank Brigade which was its *raison d'être.* There were dreadful deficiencies, there being virtually no bridging equipment to help cross rivers and only a few aeroplanes to supplement the information gathered by the armoured cars and light tanks. Furthermore, the exercise, in which the armour was pitted against the old-fashioned conventional forces, was so planned that the Mobile Division fought in a constant and unnatural state of disadvantage. For all that, it exhibited beyond a shadow of doubt what might have been achieved if 'Plan 1919' had been put into action and what would happen in the future when mobile or armoured divisions came into their own against an outmoded opponent.

The other armies of the world paid close attention to the British experiment and none more than Germany's. There, encouraged by General Seeckt and Colonel Lutz, Major Guderian and his colleagues had studied mechanization throughout the 1920s and were spurred on by the priority which Hitler gave to the re-equipment of the army with high-quality manpower and equipment put at the disposal of armoured forces. The first Panzer (armoured) divisions came into existence in 1935 as a prime element in rearmament, and at first, with their separate tank and infantry brigades, looked remarkably similar to the British Mobile Division. But soon the grafting of an additional reconnaissance unit with armoured cars and motor-cyclists, of field artillery and anti-tank gun units, and a number of half-tracked, armoured infantry carriers in lieu of unarmoured trucks, turned this force into a unique and powerful weapon capable of executing almost any operation of war without external aid except that of aircraft for reconnaissance and bombing.

Unlike the British, the Germans regarded Panzer divisions as self-sufficient, versatile formations capable, on their own, of breaking a front as the overture to deep penetration. The Panzer divisions were to be the spearhead of the marching army and the tank brigade was to be its armoured tip — each division capable of its own 'Plan 1919'. At first the tank brigade contained no less than

560 PzKpfw-I tanks, but the substitution of new medium tanks, as they came into service, gradually reduced this number until, by 1940, the division's tank strength had fallen to 320. By then, too, infantry units had been increased so that their number almost matched the number of armoured units, although each element still moved and operated as a separate entity.

Frequently there has been misunderstanding concerning differences between early British and German practice. It has been said that the British armoured enthusiasts thought only of using tanks to the exclusion of infantry and artillery. Yet in 1934, within the embryo British Mobile Division on its first outing, a tank battalion was peeled off from the armoured brigade in order to accompany the infantry. And while the Germans had used battle groups in the First World War that were composed of mixed teams of infantry, machine-gunners, and field artillery and had extended this unit, informally, to Panzer divisions, they too were perfectly liable to use their tanks in mass and in complete isolation from the infantry.

These two diagrams give an impression of the formations adopted by the British Mobile and the German Panzer divisions early on.

It was assumed by the British that their division would not advance into the enemy rear until a hole had been broken in the forward enemy defences by the combined action of infantry and artillery helped by heavy tanks. This was 'Plan 1919' in reverse. Thereafter the Mobile Division would move at speed to as great a depth as possible into the hostile back areas, seeking enemy communication and supply centres and endeavouring to create as much alarm and confusion as possible.

Here, in the van, a screen of light tanks and machine-gun carriers (1) lead the phalanx of Medium tanks (2) by anything up to five miles. They are seeking the enemy points of resistance so that the Mediums may either destroy or by-pass them, leaving it to the following infantry brigade to clear up persistent trouble. The field

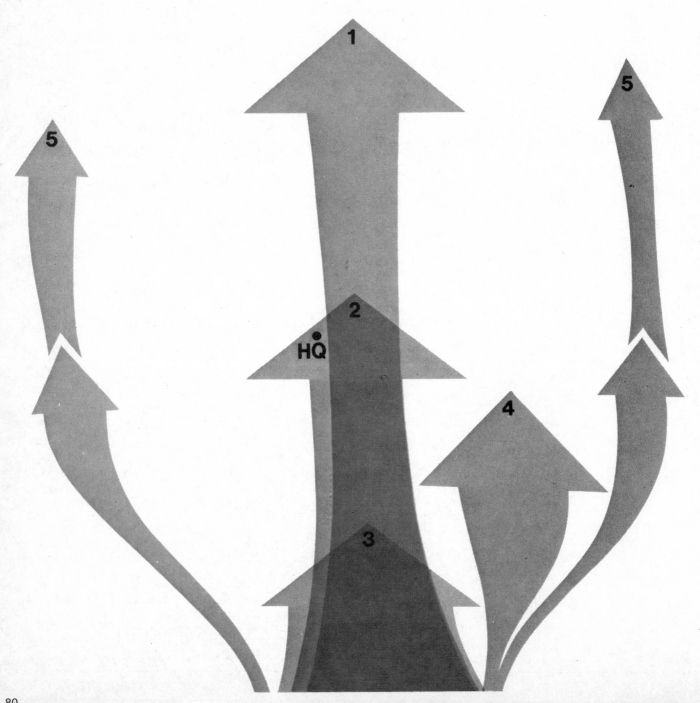

artillery (3) is shown moving with the infantry (4) because their vehicles are better matched to the speed of the infantry's lorries, but if the artillery had been mounted on a tracked chassis, they could equally well have been found close alongside the tanks. Commanders are well to the fore in the advance, receiving information from the armoured cars (5) to the flank and the light tanks ahead; sensing the waxing and waning fortunes of battle and converting their conclusions into plans and orders despatched down the radio link. At any moment they might have to revert from attack to defence and draw enemy tanks on to a defensive position that could be quickly thrown up in tank-proof country, made fast by the infantry's anti-tank guns and supported when necessary by tanks out of reserve.

This German layout (which is almost precisely that actually adopted by Rommel in action on 21st May 1940) shows how the principles adopted by the British in 1934 still held good in 1940.

His reconnaissance unit (6) is probing to the threatened front and flank while the Panzer regiment (7) (equivalent of the tank brigade) is moving far ahead of the rest of the division on a grandiose sweep against a disorganized enemy. Following a mile or two behind are the two rifle infantry regiments (8) in their lorries, their endangered flank protected by a line of anti-tank guns (9). In rear is an arc of towed field artillery (10) firing in support of the leading tanks and of the infantry whenever they bump into trouble against an enemy who has left parties behind in scattered village and copses.

Overhead reconnaissance aircraft circle while a representative of the Luftwaffe is at divisional headquarters ready to call up bombers if heavy resistance has to be blasted aside.

Rommel himself, with his radio vehicles, is close alongside the Panzer regiment, ready to change its route to suit his up-to-date appreciation of an evolving situation, or to dash back and hurry on the lagging infantry by personal example.

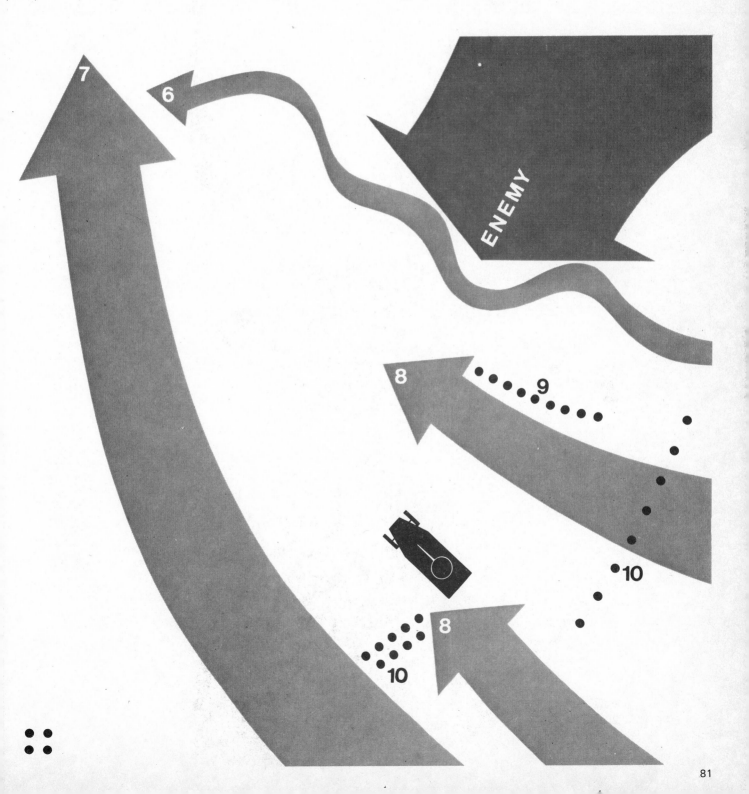

These were the methods that were to revolutionize the art of war and alter the face of Europe.

The all-embracing role of the Panzer division called for a ubiquitous force with a critical balance between speed, firepower, and protection. Combinations of vehicles now became essential since it was not technically possible to build every desirable feature into a single type of machine, and so each vehicle itself represented a compromise between essential features — the very essence of armoured vehicle design. Rejecting a heavily-armoured tank because they hoped to achieve protection from the saturation inherent in mass assault coupled with the shock treatment of fast *strategic* movement impinging upon the enemy back areas, the German General Staff asked for two different tanks — a light and a medium one, each capable of good cross-country performance.

For scouting they took the light PzKpfw-II (148), its 20-mm gun of little use against the armour of most European tanks (other than the very light ones), and its armour insufficient to stop anything other than close range machine-gun fire and splinters.

150

The medium PzKpfw-IV (150) was quite another proposition, although its short 75-mm low velocity gun and relatively thin armour gave it no significant advantage over any other tank of similar vintage. Yet this AFV matched all comers up to 1941 by reason of its *combination* of firepower, protection, and mobility exploited to the full by crews who understood better than any others how to employ these characteristics to best effect. When PzKpfw-IV ran into tough opposition it could stand off, shoot, or out-manoeuvre the opposition, and it could go on doing this over protracted periods because, by 1940, it had acquired sufficient operational use to have given the designers ample opportunities to iron out its principal sources of unreliability. Its 16-wheeled suspension, sprung by elliptic springs, was particularly reliable and never changed throughout the tank's many years on active service.

Having decided on only two types of tank, the Germans, by technical default, went in for a third in 1935. They conceived it, so to speak, out of wedlock between PzKpfw-II and -IV, and compromisingly called it PzKpfw-III (149) (here we show the A Model), intending it to be complementary to the PzKpfw-IV. But whereas relatively thick armour and a big gun made PzKpfw-IV a dominant battlefield factor, the light armour and small 37-mm gun of PzKpfw-III were anachronistic: instead of being able to stand off, it had to come in to close quarters to score a kill, thereby exposing its thin skin to the least powerful enemy anti-tank weapons. But although III A left much to be desired, the initial generous provision of space gave ample room for subsequent development and in due course led to a fighting vehicle almost as well armed, armoured, and powered as PzKpfw-IV. Of particular interest in both the later marks of PzKpfw-II and PzKpfw-III was the introduotion of the simple torsion bar suspension designed by Dr Porsche. This very strong suspension eventually featured on the tanks of many other nations and is celebrated for its strength and compact layout (151). It is simple: the bar is attached to the hull of the tank and flexes with the up and down movements of the wheel.

An essential characteristic in the critical design of a fighting vehicle is its capacity for development to accept thicker armour and mount more powerful weapons. Only by so doing can quality be maintained without total disruption of production lines when repeatedly turning over to brand new models. By 1939 French tanks had passed the point at which they could accept radical modification because they had reached the last possible stage in a line of development which had begun in 1917. Thus the SOMUA S-35 (152) of 1935 looked and behaved rather like the D-1s and 2s. True it had a bit more speed and armour, but the gun remained the short 47-mm and the practice of isolating the commander in his turret bore sad comparison with the German practice of grouping the fighting crew together in one turret. Yet statistics suggested that S-35 was the equal of PzKpfw-III: only battle could demonstrate the manner in which superior German training and doctrine could overcome brute strength.

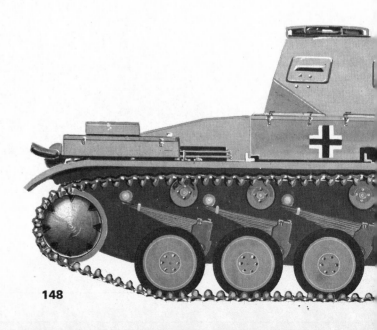

148

	PzKpfw-II D (148)	PzKpfw-III A (149)	PzKpfw-IV A (150)	S-35 (152)
Weight:	10 tons	15 tons	17.3 tons	20 tons
Power Plant:	140 hp	230 hp	250 hp	190 hp
Crew:	3	5	5	3
Armour:	30 mm	14.5 mm	20 mm	55 mm
Speed:	35 mph	20 mph	22 mph	25 mph
Armament:	1 20-mm	1 37-mm	1 75-mm	1 47-mm
	1 mg	3 mg	2 mg	1 mg

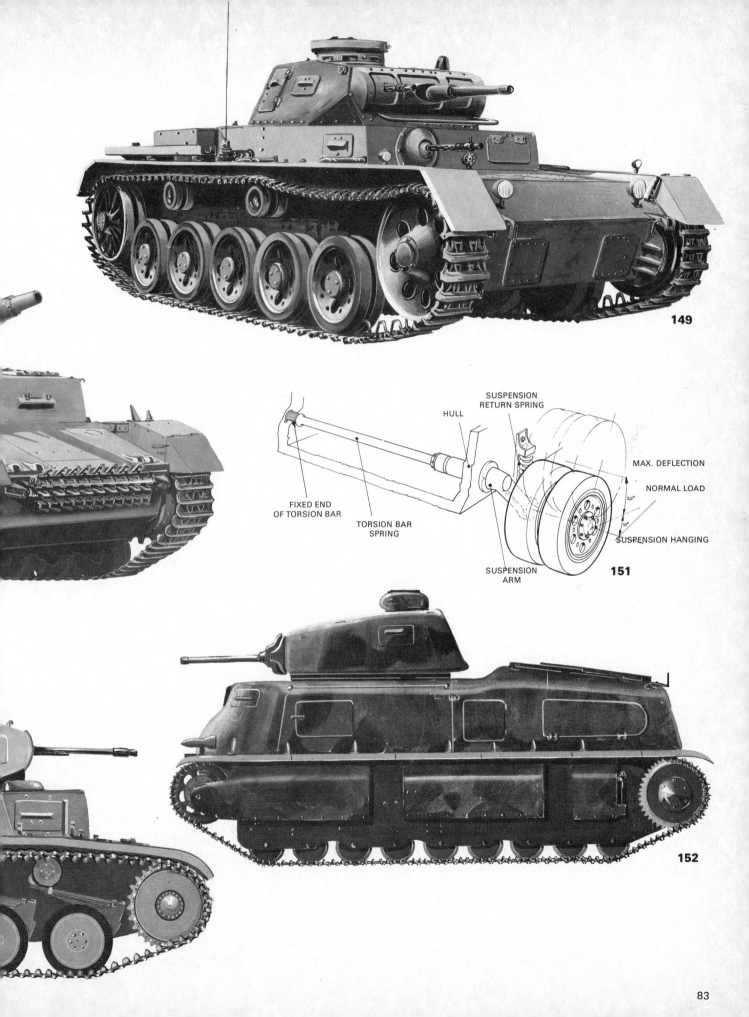

149

SUSPENSION
RETURN SPRING

HULL

FIXED END
OF TORSION BAR

TORSION BAR
SPRING

MAX. DEFLECTION

NORMAL LOAD

20°

10°

SUSPENSION HANGING

SUSPENSION
ARM

151

152

Lighter Combat Vehicles

Up-grading a machine-gun carrier of proven construction to give it the status of a light tank presents few serious difficulties provided nobody expects the outcome to be a main battle tank. In the 1920s the British had urgent need of a cheap fighting vehicle incorporating some of the characteristics of a tank, not to spearhead an armoured force, but principally to help subdue the turbulent frontiers of her Empire. Armoured cars did the job tolerably well, but once a practical trial had proved how tracked vehicles could operate in tropical heat as well as cross even the most broken terrain better than wheeled vehicles, the substitution of tracks for wheels found fewer opponents. This opened up a large market to Vickers, who jumped in to satisfy it with a series of light tanks founded on the early Carden-Loyd models. Here we see Mark I (153) and Mark VI C (154) which were good enough against tribesmen, but whose successors were to have no chance when they met the sophisticated methods and equipment of Panzer divisions in 1940.

A light fighting vehicle cannot possibly survive unless its gun has the power to knock out its most formidable opponent: if it can do that the one quickest on the draw is winner. But British light tanks neither started with, nor could accept at a later date, a gun with the size and power to give superiority over German tanks: in fact they had no greater hitting power than the Crossley (155) and Lanchester (156) armoured cars they were meant to replace as reconnaissance vehicles. Yet such was the confusion in some military minds in the 1930s that an idea got abroad that, just because a vehicle took the name of 'tank', it could respond with the full power invested in the name.

Britain was not alone in this kind of folly. The Belgians and French also had light tanks – the latter in quantity, as we have seen – and the Japanese made one of the most powerful of all the lights, the T-95 (157), and used it, with success at first, against foes who frequently gave way just at mention of the word 'tank'.

The light tank saga seems pathetic in retrospect, but it would be a distortion to suggest that those who called for them entirely failed to appreciate their weaknesses. Those who really understood the vulnerability of light AFVs went to great lengths to get them replaced by thicker-skinned successors or, at least, fitted with more powerful guns; and the evidence of their efforts was plain to see. The mounting by the British of a .5-inch machine-gun in later

153

154

155

marks in lieu of one of the twin .303s in Light VI B was one attempt at up-gunning, extended when the 15-mm Besa machine-gun was mounted in the Mark VI C.

But while minor up-gunning such as this applied insignificant loads upon the vehicle, it overburdened crews, who had to wrestle with heavy ammunition and stiff working parts in a cramped turret made even more confined by the bulk of a larger weapon. It is all the more unhappy to reflect, therefore, that while the British penalized themselves by buying successive types of Vickers Light Tank, other nations went on improving the much better Vickers 6-tonner (which the British had rejected) to give superior fighting value such as that achieved by the Czech firm of Skoda with their 35t (158).

In the midst of all this, confusion arose over the question: 'What is a tank?', when the British War Office invited Guy Motors to produce a 'Wheeled Tank' (159). Yet the reasoning behind the request, besides that of economy, is not difficult to seek, for they asked for a vehicle with almost as good a cross-country performance on *hard* going as any tracked machine, plus the advantage of a fully traversing turret armed to light tank standards. However, the Guy Wheeled Tank made its greatest contribution to British AFV technology by the jointing of armour by welding. This was both a cheaper and stronger method than riveting or bolting: moreover, no longer would rivets pop out when the armour was struck by shot. But, all in all, the Guy was only an armoured car and in this role (under another name) it made its name, later, at war.

	Light Mk I (153)	Light Mk VI C (154)	Crossley (155)	Lanchester (156)
Weight:	4.8 tons	5.2 tons	5 tons	7.5 tons
Power Plant:	58 hp	89 hp	50 hp	45 hp
Crew:	2	3	4	4
Armour:	14 mm	14 mm	8 mm	10 mm
Speed:	30 mph	29 mph	40 mph	45 mph
Armament:	1 mg	2 mg	2 mg	2 mg

	Type 95 (157)	35t (158)	Guy (159)
Weight:	7.4 tons	10.5 tons	5.75 tons
Power Plant:	120 hp	120 hp	61 hp
Crew:	3	4	3
Armour:	12 mm	25 mm	15 mm
Speed:	25 mph	22 mph	35 mph
Armament:	1 37 mm	37 mm	2 mg
	1 mg	2 mg	

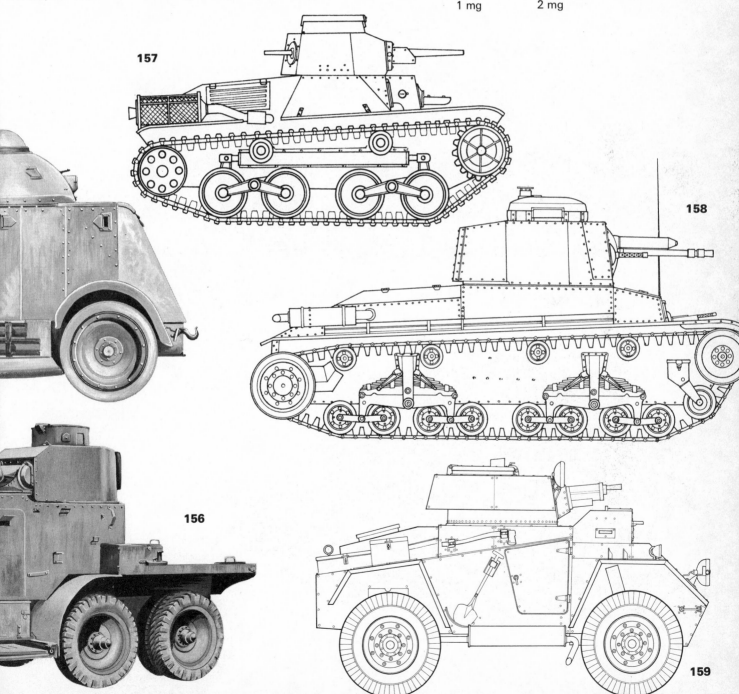

157

158

156

159

Static Defences

Those military thinkers who based their theories on the lessons learnt in trench warfare postulated that the key to safety in future war lay with static fortifications. The French, whose casualties had been highest in trying to overcome siege conditions on the Western Front in the First World War (notoriously among the steel and concrete forts of Verdun), were most attracted to the idea of a wall of forts sealing off their frontiers. So France built the Maginot Line along her common frontier with Germany and sank milliards of francs into a complex immobile system such as we show here. Deep into the earth great galleries were driven in the hope that men and munitions could survive the heaviest possible bombardment and still be able to move in safety to and from the various fire positions that stuck like steel-topped mushrooms out of the ground. The zone was not very wide from the foremost tank-trap to the heaviest artillery in its thickest casemate, but each fort was self-sufficient for a long siege with the chance of inflicting unacceptable

casualties should an enemy choose to attack using tactics similar to those of the non-tank phases of the previous conflict.

The French, who were as blind to the offensive capability of tanks as to the defensive capacity of concrete, convinced themselves (and others) that the tank had not brought total change to land warfare. Yet while it is fair to remember that they began the construction of the Maginot Line on the assumption that it might only impose a temporary delay on an enemy offensive — long enough, in fact, to allow them to complete the mobilization of their reserve armies — and that they expected to use mobile forces in rear of the Line to maintain its integrity, it is also true to say that, in the last analysis, the Maginot Line induced an introvert, brittle, defensive mentality. In any case there were serious defects in the layout of the line. Insufficient attention had been paid to the need for the fire from the various forts to be interlocking: if one happened to be neutralized or screened the others could not always come to

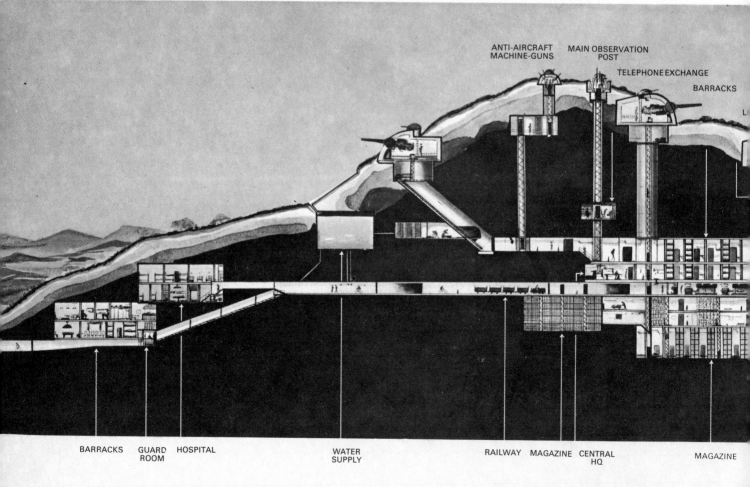

BARRACKS   GUARD HOSPITAL   WATER   RAILWAY MAGAZINE CENTRAL   MAGAZINE
              ROOM   SUPPLY   HQ

Labels on image: ANTI-AIRCRAFT MACHINE-GUNS · MAIN OBSERVATION POST · TELEPHONE EXCHANGE · BARRACKS

its aid and might themselves be weakened on the flanks. Worst of all, the Maginot Line was conceived on the false assumption that the enemy might either destroy himself in a desperate attempt at breaching or make no effort at all. On that assumption the flanks of the line, where they ran along neutral frontiers, were only covered by a thin line of pill-boxes, in places no greater than 200 yards in depth. Thus not only did the Maginot Line's forbidding reputation preclude assault — it actually suggested methods for getting round it. In due course, German Panzer divisions were to move easily round the flank of the main line and then break the pill-box extension in a matter of minutes.

German defensive practice along her frontier with France was different. Her concrete forts — the Siegfried Line — were less sophisticated, cheaper, and easier to build, but sited in much greater depth with carefully arranged fields of interlocking fire. Moreover the battle these were intended to sustain (as they actually had to do

in the winter of 1944–45) was meant to be one in which mobile forces would establish themselves as the core of resistance using the concrete emplacements as a *base*, but not the *essential* element in defence.

The Second World War was to start in 1939 in Poland with an exhibition of mobile warfare by Panzer forces in which concrete fortifications were hardly put to the test. More often than not they were simply ignored and their vast investment of gun-power reduced to idle impotence.

But when armoured forces found themselves in the open against concealed anti-tank guns, they did not always fare so well. The guns in the casemates of the Maginot Line could penetrate any German tank — but so also could those drawn on wheels in the field armies. There was no single tank in service — not even the thickly armoured Char B or Matilda — for which there was not at least one antidote – a hostile gun which could penetrate its skin.

SHELL HOISTS

ESCALATORS

AIR CONDITIONING PLANT   MINE   INFANTRY TRAP   STEEL DOORS   MINE   ANTI-TANK AND MACHINE-GUNS   MINE   MACHINE-GUN   TANK TRAP

Armoured Cars for the Second World War

The fact that armoured cars did not attain the same cross-country performance as tracked vehicles was no reason why they should be totally abolished from the order of battle of armoured forces. The association of wheeled fighting vehicles with thriving truck and automobile industries in itself was a good reason for using them at war since special design overheads could be lowered and greater reliability achieved. Moreover, wheeled vehicles enjoyed a wider radius of action, could be made small and inconspicuous, and, highly important, moved with comparative silence — hence their suitability for reconnaissance, escort duties, and long range raiding which placed them in an indispensable class of their own. However, a wheeled vehicle grows more clumsy to handle as its size increases (and powered gear change and steering were in their infancy in the 1930s), and these problems were increased when attempts to improve cross-country mobility inevitably led to the installation of multi-wheel stations, complex suspensions, and transmissions with consequential sharp rises in manufacturing processes and cost.

Every major automobile firm had its wheeled fighting vehicle project. Probably because quality control, linked with a strict rationalization, took high priority in their initial rearmament, the Germans evolved highly sophisticated designs from the beginning: their SdKfz-232 (166), developed by Bussing NAG, is typical of the family of armoured cars they took to war in 1939. Its bulk suited it best to more open country, hard going, and well-metalled roads. The Japanese Sumida M-2593 (167), however, had few refinements but was big enough to be rewheeled to run on railway tracks which turned out the best way to operate in those Far Eastern countries where roads hardly existed. Tactical doctrine is reflected here, for the Germans envisaged fighting for information and the Japanese were more content to use stealth for its acquisition.

Bearing in mind the desirability of keeping scouting vehicles small, France with her Panhard 178 (168) and Italy with her Fiat Autoblinda 40 (169) followed almost identical rear-engined trends. Standing on the sidelines, the USA stated no avid requirement for an armoured car, despite a plethora of projects by various private concerns of which Marmon-Herrington was pre-eminent: their Mark 2 (170) made in South Africa, with a Ford engine, was developed in several successive generations, with a proliferation of local modifications and a wide variety of different armaments. In the conquest of Italian East Africa in 1941 it played a leading role, employed quite frequently more as a tank than a reconnaissance machine against an enemy who had lost the will to resist.

166

168

171

173

174

The Russians, too, had turned to a Ford chassis, the Bronniford, and by 1941 had armed it with a 45-mm gun (171) and brought it into service in large numbers — factors which failed to preserve it from decimation at the hands of the Germans.

When so many tanks carried their armour at the vertical, it is of interest to observe how armoured car designers of this period sloped the sides and front of their creations. The Dutch DAF of 1938 (172), with its integral hull construction, is a fine specimen — and also incorporated a neat crew arrangement to allow forward and rearward vision by the machine-gunners. Nothing so elaborate is to be discovered on the more conventional Australian Rhino (173) or the Canadian Otter (174), while the Swedish Volvo M-40 (175) conforms to well-established practice also. Yet each makes its contribution and represents the spread of AFV technology throughout the world and the general acceptance by industry of the part they might play in the coming major war.

Provided restrictions on off-road movement were observed and light armour and low gun-power were employed, armoured car troops had a thoroughly useful part to play both in war and in the internal policing of dissident peoples. But their crews had to observe a very strict tactical routine, for success depended upon survival, and survival, when one is outclassed technically, depends upon subtlety and stealth.

	SdKfz-232 (166)	Sumida M-2593 (167)	Panhard 178 (168)	Fiat 40 (169)
Weight:	6 tons	7.5 tons	6.7 tons	7.5 tons
Power Plant:	155 hp	100 hp	105 hp	120 hp
Crew:	4	6	4	4
Armour:	14 mm	13 mm	20 mm	9 mm
Speed:	50 mph	36 mph	50 mph	49 mph
Armament:	1 20-mm 1 mg	6 mg	1 25-mm 1 mg	1 20-mm 1 mg

	Marmon Herrington Mark 2 (170)	Bronniford BA-10 (171)	DAF 1938 (172)
Weight:	6 tons	5.2 tons	5 tons
Power Plant:	95 hp	85 hp	95 hp
Crew:	3	4	5
Armour:	12 mm	15 mm	15 mm
Speed:	40 mph	35 mph	45 mph
Armament:	1.5 inch rifle 1 mg	1 45-mm 1 mg	1 20-mm 3 mg

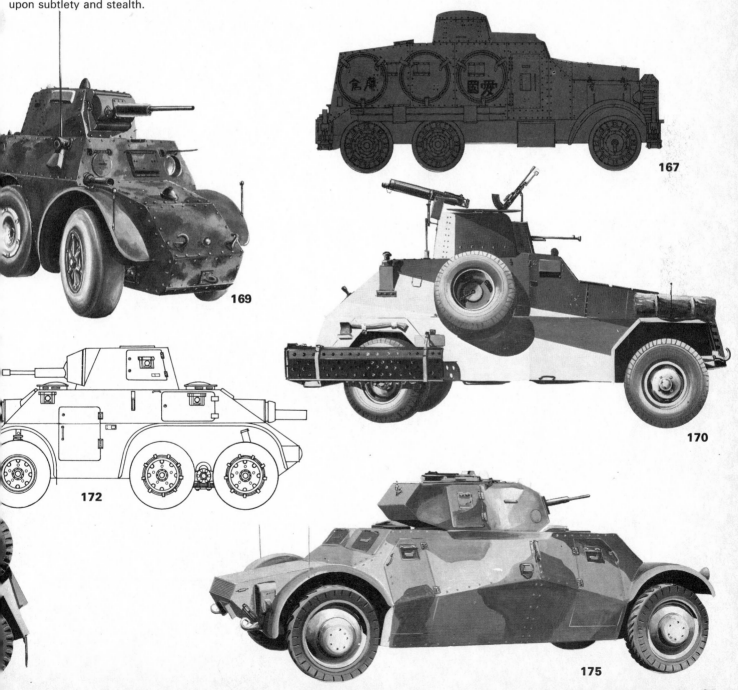

169

167

170

172

175

British Response to German Challenge

176

By 1936 the last veil had dropped from Germany's military preparations, the first three Panzer divisions were taking shape (their components only occasionally exposed to public gaze), and the Rhineland had been remilitarized. Britain could delay rearmament no longer but preferred to give priority to her navy and to air power as independent, economic complements to the much vaunted strength of the French army. By so doing she reduced the funds which, in an earlier generation, might have been spent on the army; above all she starved the army of its most expensive kind of equipment — armoured vehicles. Only a few months before war broke out in 1939 did Britain declare her intention of sending an expeditionary force to fight alongside the French on land: in the meantime British armoured forces had wilted in uncertainty. War Office thought favoured a mass of infantry divisions on the 1918 model, supported by heavily armoured tanks of limited firepower, and relegated an embryonic armoured division to a specialized, secondary category charged with the exploitation of success after conventional forces had breached the enemy line. Naturally this focused higher priority on building a heavy infantry-accompanying tank which would be proof against the current type of enemy anti-tank gun, instead of on the faster cruiser type needed for the exploitation role.

In response to a request by General Sir Hugh Elles, Carden hatched out Matilda I (176), a mockery of the principle of aggression and actually looking as antiquated as the thinking behind its inception. But the underlying principle was cheapness, and thus the British came to be saddled with a tank costing not more than £6,000, armed only with a machine-gun, but with strong armour not less than 65 mm thick. Since low cost and heavy armour dominated, the vehicle had to make do with slow speed, a single machine-gun, and a one-man turret in which the commander became overburdened by his multiplicity of tasks. As a further way of saving cost, the same type of suspension as used on the 6-tonner was adapted and the vehicle driven by a standard Ford V-8 engine. Faced with an enemy tank, 'however, the single .303-inch machine-gun would have been hopelessly inadequate and its substitution by a .5-inch in a few later models did little to help since it took a strong man to operate the gun in such a confined working space. This machine went into battle in 1940 in France and helped achieve one solitary strategic success, but as a fighting vehicle it was an anachronism, the product of a mind — Elles' — which had lost faith in the tanks that had made his name.

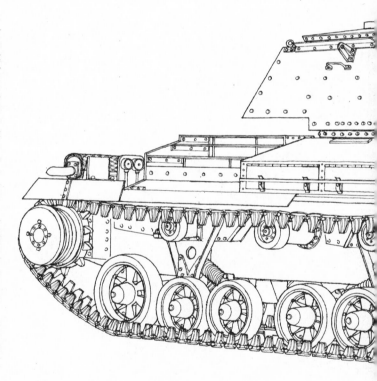

Carden's other valedictory creations, built shortly before his death in an air crash, were A-9 (177) and A-10 (178) — additional compromises in the search for a cruiser replacement for the obsolete Medium and the high-priced A-6 (16-tonner). A-9 epitomizes the evils of financial niggardliness in AFV construction. Her thin, vertical, riveted armour and the light 40-mm (2-pounder) gun (firing only solid shot and no useful high explosive) were not in the least offset by low power and a suspension that restricted speed below maximum. The dustbin machine-gun sub-turrets per-

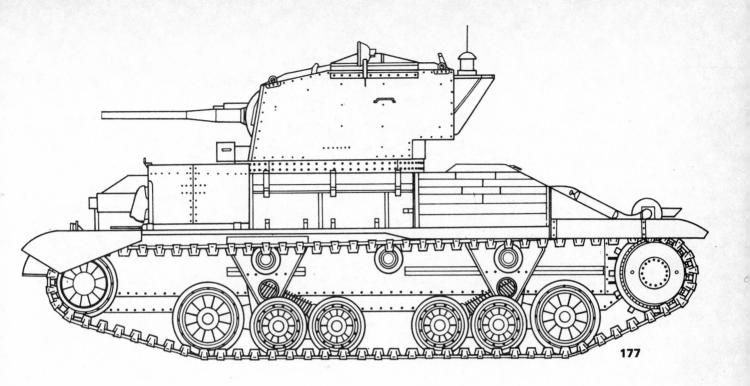

177

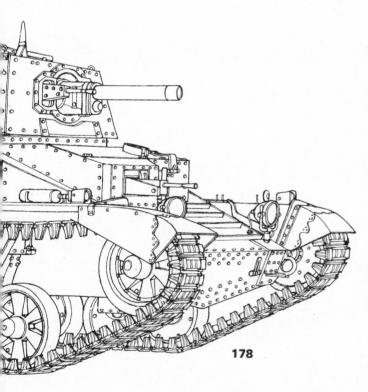

178

considerably better performance, in some respects, than Matilda I; but her armour would not defeat the prospective enemy's anti-tank shot at short range, so she reverted to the role of a slow cruiser to supplement A-9 – a bad compromise. Here she is shown mounting a 94-mm howitzer for use in the so-called Close Support role in lieu of artillery when, as so often happened, the latter could not keep up with cruisers. Only a small proportion of cruisers were made in the Close Support version and became charged with the task of lying behind the leading AFVs to engage urgent targets, such as anti-tank guns, with high explosive and smoke. But their specialized nature told against them since, obviously, it is better to combine all functions in one vehicle if possible. Here the ideal – a dual-purpose gun – had to give way to current technical feasibility.

Neither A-9 nor A-10 turned out much better than Matilda I: all three were interim models and dropped from production the moment something superior could be devised, though not until A-9 and A-10 had fought throughout the campaign in France, the first of the Western Desert battles, and in Greece—where their weak tracks had an unhappy knack of breaking at critical moments. But just as the lineage of Matilda I's suspension can be traced to Vickers 6-tonner, so can that of A-9 with its unique arrangement and Newton and Barnet shock absorbers be recognized as that which later appeared on a much more celebrated British AFV – the Valentine.

Of fundamental importance to Britain's tank-building industry at this time was the breaching of the Vickers monopoly. As will be seen, Lord Nuffield's organization was being steered on to tank work in connection with rearmament so that more production lines could be laid down to ensure large-scale production along with extended know-how if war came. Vickers also spread the production of A-9 and A-10 to different works, A-10 being made on no less than four different assembly lines by different companies – at a commensurate increase in costs of course – but with a proliferation that suited long-term War Office policy.

petuated the taste of those who overrated the importance of machine-gun fire from a tank, while the absence of a high explosive shell enforced reliance on accompanying artillery and a few close-support tanks to supply help on call. Yet A-9 included many innovations, among them the first hydraulic turret traverse system and a small auxiliary engine to power a fan for fighting compartment ventilation and, when dismounted, battery-charging facilities for the radio.

A-10 started life on the drawing-board as an infantry tank with a

	Matilda I (176)	A-9 (177)	A-10 (178)
Weight:	11 tons	12.7 tons	14.5 tons
Power Plant:	70 hp	150 hp	150 hp
Crew:	2	6	5
Armour:	65 mm	14 mm	30 mm
Speed:	8 mph	25 mph	15 mph
Armament:	1 mg	1 40-mm	1 94-mm
		3 mg	2 mg

The Artillery and Tank Contest

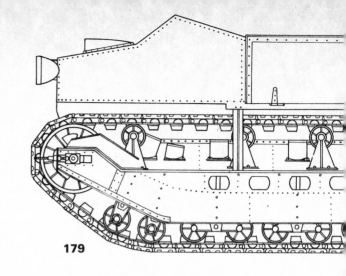

179

From the beginning of the First World War, artillery, lying hidden yet able to dispense its projectiles with indirect and indiscriminate ease upon the cringing infantry, had looked the most likely means of breaking the defensive power of entrenched machine-guns. Quickly the gunners had learnt how to concentrate intense volumes of high explosive, thickened by gas, and to pulverize narrow belts of territory sufficiently long to allow friendly infantry to advance without wholesale fatal consequences to themselves. But thereafter, when the same process had to be repeated prior to the next advance, it became increasingly difficult to do since wheeled artillery (especially if only horse-drawn) could be neither dragged nor supplied with sufficient ammunition through the wilderness of its own creation. In any case, area devastation by high explosive had never ensured the destruction of all opposition: at the last moment the elimination of each machine-gun usually had to be by direct fire or outright capture.

Some infantry and artillerymen boasted how their arm held the key to success (as is the nature of factions, and as was notoriously the case in the French army of 1914), yet neither functioned efficiently without the other. It was not surprising, therefore, that the original tank specifications had fallen somewhere between an infantry or gun carrier while paying due attention to the need for direct action in the assault. The original concept worked quite well until the enemy learnt how it could be countered by shell-fire: henceforward tank losses varied in direct proportion to their use in mass and the volume of artillery support that could be fired in support; infantry then made the best of whatever good fortune the tanks enjoyed. But, by the end of the First World War, the rate of movement had become the pace of armoured combat vehicles which often got too far ahead of artillery to be able to profit from its help. Moreover, the deliberate methods devised for delivery of fire in support of slow-moving infantry had no practical application for armour which required quick concentrations on successive pin-point localities. A tank crew which has been caught in the open by anti-tank guns cannot wait long for rescue by a laboriously calculated programme.

When it became necessary to harness a dozen horses and a score of men to drag individual field guns through the mud, even the hardiest advocate of muscle over petrol power had to concede the need for tractors to tow artillery — a conversion that got slowly under way in the 1920s. Yet the leading protagonists of mechanization had to point out that merely swapping a wheeled machine for a horse still fell short of necessity if the artillery was to be expected to keep up with tracked vehicles, while the more conservative gunners, having absorbed a mass of fresh ideas in four years of war, recoiled somewhat from further complexities. The debate simmered and finally three possible solutions were thrown up.

The first simply substituted a tractor — the Dragon (179) based on the Vickers Medium family — for the horse team, getting it to haul a standard gun. This introduced the gunners to the wheel-cum-track dilemma, asking them if they wanted a tracked or a wheeled tractor. Some highly original, as well as comic, solutions came forth, of which the palm must go to a Cletrac tractor hitched to an 18-pounder field-gun and limber, the whole transported on a long Thorneycroft chassis (180) raising hilarious visions of an old-fashioned fire brigade drafted to the battlefield.

The second course restored worthwhile high-explosive fire support to the tank by mounting a 3.7-inch mortar in the normal Medium tank turret (181), inviting it to carry out the close support role with high explosive and smoke. This went only halfway to resolving the dilemma since it deprived the Close Support tank of an anti-tank armament (see page 93).

The third method was to have a tracked chassis carrying a field-gun on a rotating mounting, able to fire the full programme of artillery support, plus high-angle fire against hostile aircraft — a truly ubiquitous assembly but frightening to the gunner purists of the day. This proposal met the essential requirements for really

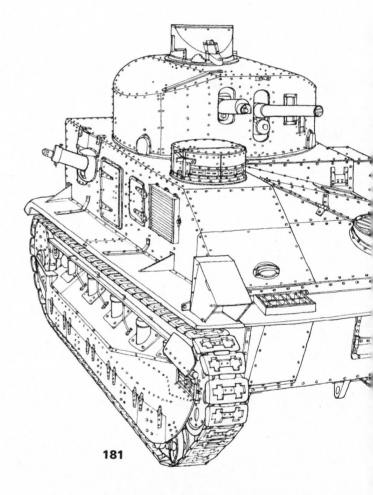

181

mobile artillery capable of fighting with tanks, but progress with development went slowly when many older gunners retracted in mistrust, inhibited by an avowed distaste for petrol engines. Still, by dint of enthusiasm and judicious pressure, the more progressive British gunners kept mechanization on the move and with the 'Birch Gun' (182) went into the forefront of progress. They first mounted an 18-pounder field-gun with high-angle capability on a turntable carried by the Vickers Medium chassis, but later turned to a version where the gun was mounted in a rotating turret that gave the crew full armoured protection, as well as the ability to fire a comprehensive range of artillery support. But this went much too far for influential British gunners of 1930. In essence they shied away from a machine which looked too much like a tank (machines like that, they said, belonged to the Tank Corps), though there are still those who claim that they only gave up the Birch Gun because the Tank Corps did not support them.

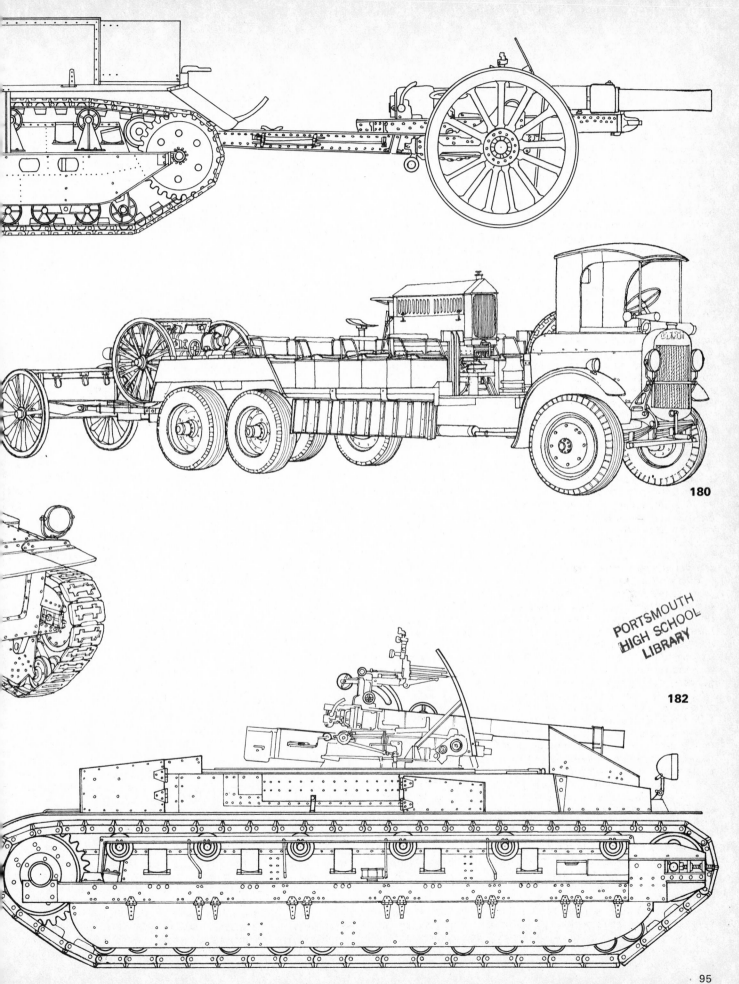

180

182

Other nations meanwhile showed not much greater perception, choosing to regard self-propelled guns simply as weapons to help in a *direct* assault. The cult of the assault gun seemingly infected an interesting French design of the late 1930s, the SAU-40 (183), based on a SOMUA chassis, although, in fact, this was a genuine field artillery piece made in response to an official requirement for self-propelled artillery in the French army. Indeed, for many years a standard way of prolonging the life of an obsolescent battle tank automatically resolved itself by converting them into assault guns since, by eliminating an all-round traverse and mounting the gun with limited traverse in the hull, weapons of a far heavier calibre and greater recoil could be carried. An Italian 47-mm gun in a rotating turret could not have been carried on a light L-6 chassis (184) and the same would have applied when mounting a 40-mm gun on a Carden-Loyd chassis (185), as here.

The Germans equipped their field artillery on similar lines to those of their contemporaries, depending on towed, wheeled guns both in their infantry and Panzer divisions, but with them the self-propelled anti-tank gun found increasing favour and came into prominence when a few PzKpfw-Is became redundant and were armed with the Czech 47-mm gun (186). In the manner of so many fecund ideas, this project started somewhat tentatively, but the French had to enter the same field in sheer desperation and too much haste when the Panzers overran them in 1940: their Laffly chassis with rearward-facing 47-mm gun (187) shows every sign of desperate improvisation.

In essence, therefore, no single nation went to war in 1939 with a fully formed and integrated armoured policy. Each had marched part of the way towards total armoured mechanization — none had got much farther than the halfway stage, while those most directly connected with the genuine, armoured battle formations remained partly in ignorance of their potential. A schism split moderns and traditionalists — a state of affairs that could be largely, but not entirely, resolved in actual combat.

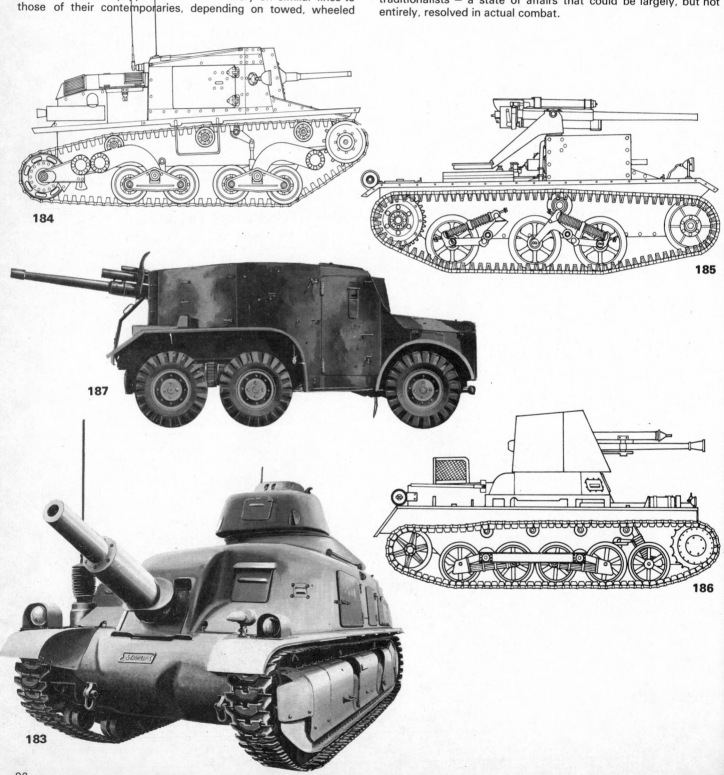

184

185

187

186

183

The USA in the Doldrums

In 1940, the United States of America did not possess a viable army and least of all could she boast an armoured force capable of fighting German Panzers — or any other tank force. Throughout the 1930s, Christie continued to abound in originality while the infantry and cavalry of the US army delayed making up their minds on the sort of armoured vehicles they wanted — being agreed on just one thing, with the Ordnance Department, that Christie was an awkward supplier to deal with. Convinced, however, that they required a light machine bristling with machine-guns to act as a weapon carrier, the infantry came to agreement with the cavalry in 1933 over an Ordnance Department development on Christie lines, called Combat Car T-4 E1 (188). Since the cavalry were looking for a fast vehicle with good cross-country performance, which T-4 E1 (later named Medium Tank T-4) was, both were satisfied.

Though detached from that close consultation which was to characterize Anglo-American AFV development after 1940, the American habit of following research and development with cancellation before production began, bore a remarkable similarity to British practice. Neither seemed prepared to accept that cost could be related to efficiency and that the greater battleworthiness inherent in the more expensive machines might be rewarded. Deluded by the common fallacy that cheapness equates with economy, the Americans followed the world-wide trend and plumped for light tanks.

An outright copy of the Vickers 6-tonner was ruled out in favour of an entirely new engine transmission, suspension, and track arrangement. Disciplined by the tight financial programme, the US Ordnance Department endeavoured to achieve a genuine economy by improving the overall reliability of their AFVs. The new light tank, Combat Car M-1 (189) (later put into production as Light Tank M-1 A1), embodied a radial engine, a simple rugged volute-sprung suspension, and rubber tracks linked by rubber bushed pins while a Cletrac transmission (see page 122) reduced power wastage when steering.

Nevertheless, M-1 remained only a light tank which the infantry persisted in looking upon as a sort of weapon carrier by adding two turrets in the Vickers fashion. This they called M-2 A1 (190) — the last child of infantry domination of armour in America, though the parent of a renowned strain of light tanks to come.

	T-4 E1 (188)	M-1 (189)	Light M-2 A1 (190)
Weight:	12.5 tons	9.7 tons	9.7 tons
Power Plant:	268 hp	250 hp	250 hp
Crew:	4	4	4
Armour:	15 mm	15 mm	25 mm
Speed:	35 mph	50 mph	45 mph
Armament:	2 mg	3 mg	3 mg

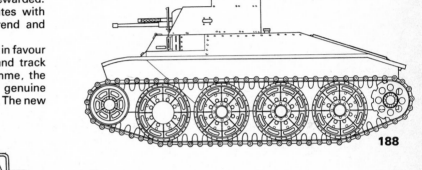

188

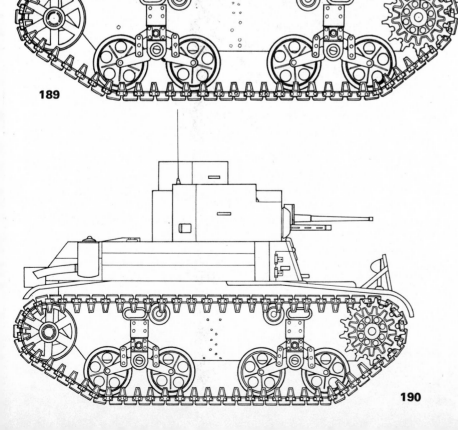

189

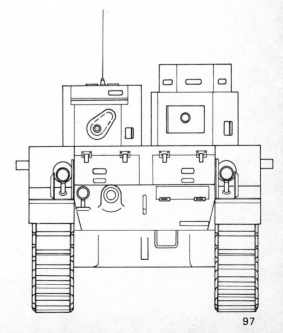

190

A New Breed of Heavies

In the middle 1930s, the Russians started to put various armoured vehicles into mass production. By 1941 they had 21,000 AFVs ready for war – four times that of the Germans. This upsurge in numbers also matched increases in protection, hitting power, and therefore weight, as shown by the T-35 (191) which, for all its similarity to the Vickers Independent and the 16-tonner, weighed nearly three times that of the latter and carried more than twice the gun-power. SMK (192) – a 58-ton monster – went even further to exemplify the views of those who believed in domination by land battleships, but this mobile fortress, fortunately, never reached production and, if it had, probably would have suffered the same fate suffered by T-35 at the hands of the smaller, more versatile German AFVs and artillery in 1941.

Nevertheless, components from T-35 and SMK could readily be adapted to later machines – and the turrets, guns, and, perhaps most important, the suspension of SMK (suitably down-scaled) were later mated to give birth to the KV series. (See page 99.)

The British also built a heavy tank within the limitation of an amended General Staff policy which said in effect, 'If tanks are to survive at infantry pace while supporting men on foot, they must resist the fire of current anti-tank guns, and yet retain the ability to destroy hostile men and weapons, *including enemy tanks.*' When

Matilda II's (193) design was sealed in 1938 it could do all that except fire a high-explosive shell and did it in battle in 1940 and again in 1941 – a few even performing on the Russian front. But in due course more powerful enemy anti-tank guns defeated its armour just when the 40-mm could no longer penetrate thickened enemy armour. Worse still, the small cast turret and hull (which taxed the capacity of English steel foundries to the full) were incapable of being up-armoured to improve protection or of an increase in size to carry a bigger gun. So Matilda, having won an enviable but ephemeral reputation as Queen of the Battlefield, was to fail the test of longevity which was passed so convincingly by the later Russian designs.

	T-35 (191)	**SMK** (192)	**Matilda II** (193)
Weight:	45 tons	58 tons	26 tons
Power Plant:	500 hp	500 hp	2 x 87 hp (diesel)
Crew:	10	7	4
Armour:	30 mm	60 mm	80 mm
Speed:	18 mph	15 mph	15 mph
Armament:	1 76-mm	1 76-mm	1 40-mm
	2 45-mm	1 45-mm	1 mg
	5 mg	3 mg	

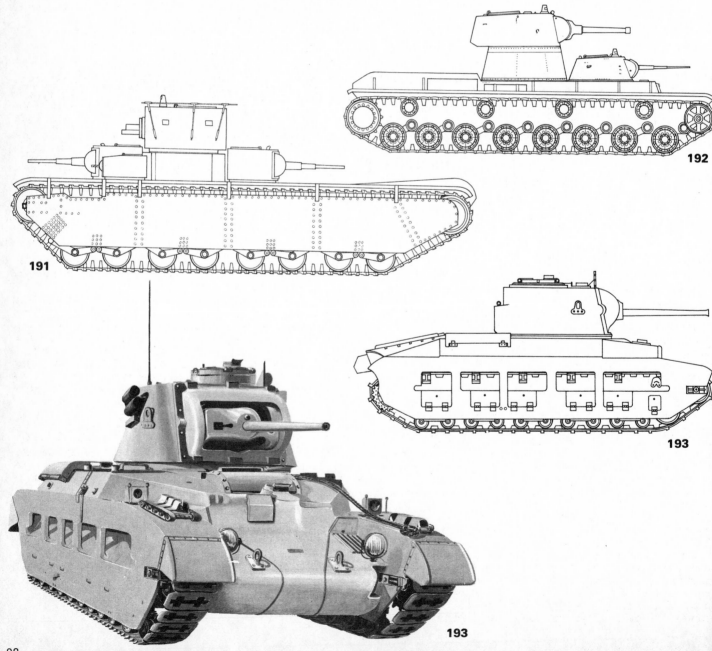

191

192

193

193

195

194

Common sense reasserted itself among Russian tank designers in 1938 – largely because their desire for quantity had overstretched Russian manufacturing capacity. Tank-building almost invariably taxes industry to the limit and, in those earlier days in particular, called for unusual metallurgical processes that are common knowledge today. But tank design is always close to the frontiers of knowledge since only rarely are comparable types of vehicle needed in civilian practice. Faced with the unavoidable choice of having more smaller AFVs or fewer large ones, the Russians opted for the former, continuing with the production of BTs and certain light vehicles, rejecting monsters and super heavies but beginning instead on a rationalized heavy tank – KV-I (194).

KV-I was just about the first wholly Russian-conceived tank design to enter full production. Its partially sloped, thick armour, its 76-mm gun, diesel engine, and wide tracks, all underlined the national commitment to a balanced mixture of strong protection with weighty hitting power carried with maximum regard for mobility to compete with the wide atmospheric range and uncertain terrain of the motherland. If two severe, practical tests of an armoured fighting vehicle are ordeal by battle and a subsequent prolongation of life in service, KV-I was a success – and like the earlier BTs it bore many successors, several of which continue in front line service to this day.

Clinging resolutely to their vision that war in 1939 would simply take up where it had left off in 1918 and contradicting their specification for Matilda, the British General Staff pointed to the ponderous existence of the Maginot Line and its less pretentious opposite number, the Siegfried Line, as evidence that continental armies still really believed the same. That being so, armoured

vehicles might still have need to cross wide ditches and broken ground as before and for that reason they restated the original 1915 requirements for a tank.

First, and almost unique among the contenders, was TOG-I (195), the letters standing for 'The Old Gang' to notify all concerned that the sponsors were none other than those who had made the first tanks – and history – in the First World War; namely Stern, Swinton, Tritton, Wilson, Ricardo, and the firm of Fosters. In fact, there is reason to suspect that the specification was written by the sponsors and sold, lock, stock, and barrel, to an unwitting General Staff. Anyway, the parentage of TOG-I can be in no doubt: every line of its silhouette is that of a bygone period, the footling turret armament, the short 75-mm gun (the same as on the French Char B) relegating this monster to symbolism. As a sitting 80-ton target TOG would have had few equals, but, fortunately, the Germans exposed its fallacy (just as work started on the prototype). Even so experiments and trials were extended late into 1943, always in the belief, it seems, that trench warfare must start once again.

	KV-I (194)	**TOG-I** (195)
Weight:	46 tons	80 tons
Power Plant:	550 hp	600 hp
Crew:	5	8
Armour:	106 mm	68 mm
Speed:	25 mph	7 mph
Armament:	1 76-mm	1 75-mm
	3 mg	1 40-mm
		4 mg

Armoured Skins

It will have been noticed how the armouring of fighting vehicles changed with increased battle experience in the First World War and how the demands for greater protection raised weight to such dimensions that the metallurgists and designers had to find more efficient methods of forming and hanging armour on the vehicle.

The quality of plate has to be high with a minimum of impurities to save it from failing when struck. High-quality armour is often most difficult to work, however, and this can lead to many almost insurmountable production difficulties and insupportable costs. Thus, while the whole business of tank design devolved upon one compromise after another, that of armour selection and design caused most compromises at all stages.

For instance, the industrial boiler plate used on early armoured vehicles was easily obtainable and simple to attach to existing vehicles by means of bolts (196). Unfortunately boiler plate was made of low-grade steel and let through bullets, while the bolts sheered off all too readily under a few sharp blows.

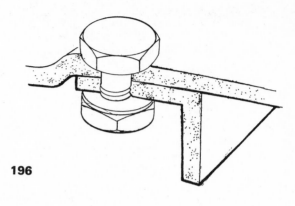

196

The thin armour plate carried by the first tanks could not be welded because electrical welding was not to be had. In consequence the plate had to be drilled and then hardened – a tricky job that often led to cracking. The plates were then riveted together and attached to a frame (197). But gaps inevitably occurred and when these were struck by missiles the molten metal (splash) given off would be flung about the inside of the tank to the peril of the crew.

As experience grew it became possible, largely, to eliminate 'splash' by improved jointing, but the problems of hardening armour became much more involved. Each combination of heating, rolling, forging, or quenching introduced peculiarities of its own. Vickers' cemented-armour, up to 20-mm thickness, for instance, was made by a carburizing process giving a Brinell hardness number of 600 while the core remained at 400, but this plate was difficult to make, liable to distortion, and thus called for additional processes which introduced unwanted stresses into the material.

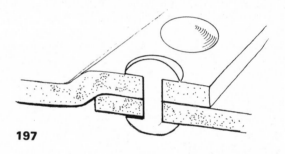

197

Homogeneous 'hard' armour – so called because of its uniform hardness – could not be machined but was used with difficulty in tanks such as A-9 and A-10. Homogeneous 'soft', however, which could be machined and cast, greatly simplified construction since cast parts could be used in awkward corners to eliminate the need for difficult manufacturing processes such as bending or riveting. Small castings, of course, were usually well within normal industrial capacity, but when it came to casting complete turrets or large sections of the hull, such as for Matilda II, special foundries had to be prepared and became a major factor when selecting design criteria and laying down production.

Largely because civilian firms had no great use for heavy electric welding (198) before the Second World War, this method of jointing was slow to come into use, although research had shown ways in which it could be done. Only by degrees were British firms persuaded to adopt this superior method and to their reluctance (prompted by the expense of new investment as much as ingrained conservatism) can be attributed the persistent complaints about inferior British armour during the war. On the other hand all German tanks, post-1934, were welded and gained strength in relation to their riveted and bolted opponents. Despite the technological problems involved in connection with uneven cooling, cracking, and other difficulties, welding incorporated great strength and at the same time eased and simplified production to the instant advantage of increased numbers and reduced cost.

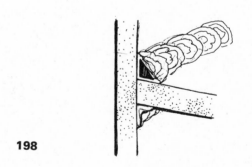

198

BMC

Churchill

More adaptable to the real battlefield because of its thicker armour and smaller silhouette, the Churchill Mark I (199) (built by Vauxhall Motors) nevertheless perpetuated, in 1940, the anachronism of the light high-velocity gun in the small turret supplemented by a Close Support weapon carried between the tracks. In her case, however, the choice of the 40-mm gun was enforced by events, for a larger 57-mm gun (the 6-pounder) was well advanced in design and could have been fitted quite soon, had not the Germans destroyed the bulk of British army equipment at Dunkirk. Priority simply had to be given to the manufacture of those weapons actually in production rather than expend time, effort, and factory retooling on items that could not be made available even in so short a time as a year. Amid the shortages of 1940 almost anything was better than nothing.

Churchill Mark I brought into service the Merritt-Brown regenerative steering which had demonstrated its possibilities when tried in A-6 a decade earlier. Not only did this system save much of the power lost when steering, it also enabled the driver to vary his turning circle in relation to the gear engaged — the lower the gear, the tighter the turning radius until, when in neutral, the tank could actually be pivoted on its axis. The close mesh of this gearbox-designers' masterpiece made it necessary for an oil pump to be integrated to ensure adequate circulation of lubricating oil to the shaft bearings. On pages 122 and 123 the outline working of this type of gearbox is explained.

Apart from its gearbox, the Churchill tank incorporated several interesting innovations. Steering and clutch control were actuated by hydraulics which helped reduce driver fatigue. The 22 bogie wheels sprung by nests of concentric springs gave a rather rugged ride but had the great virtue that they could be shot off in quantity and still leave enough over to support the tank. This was a roomy tank with scope for development, as will later be seen. When fitted with the small 40-mm gun it could carry no less than 150 rounds of this ammunition plus fifty-eight of the 76-mm. In its Mark III version with a 57-mm gun it first saw action with Canadian crews in the landing at Dieppe in 1942 and from El Alamein until the end of the war was in almost constant battle on one front or another.

Churchill Mark I

Weight:	38.5 tons
Power Plant:	350 hp
Crew:	5
Armour:	102 mm
Speed:	15 mph
Armament:	1 76-mm
	1 40-mm
	1 mg

1 Driver's steering tiller
2 76-mm Howitzer
3 40-mm gun
4 Gunner's telescope
5 Trigger grip
6 Radio
7 Bedford 12 cylinder 350 hp engine
8 Auxiliary fuel tank
9 Final drive
10 Commander's pedestal
11 Gunner's seat
12 Hand traverse
13 Delco auxiliary generator
14 Power traverse
15 Compass

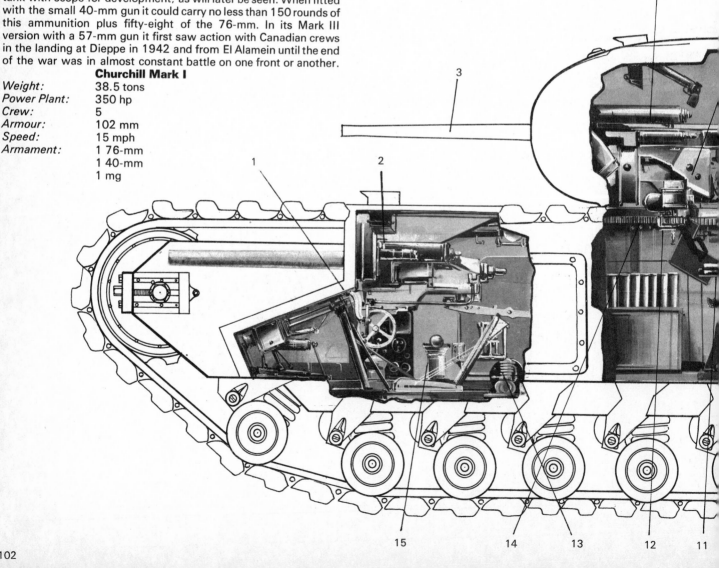

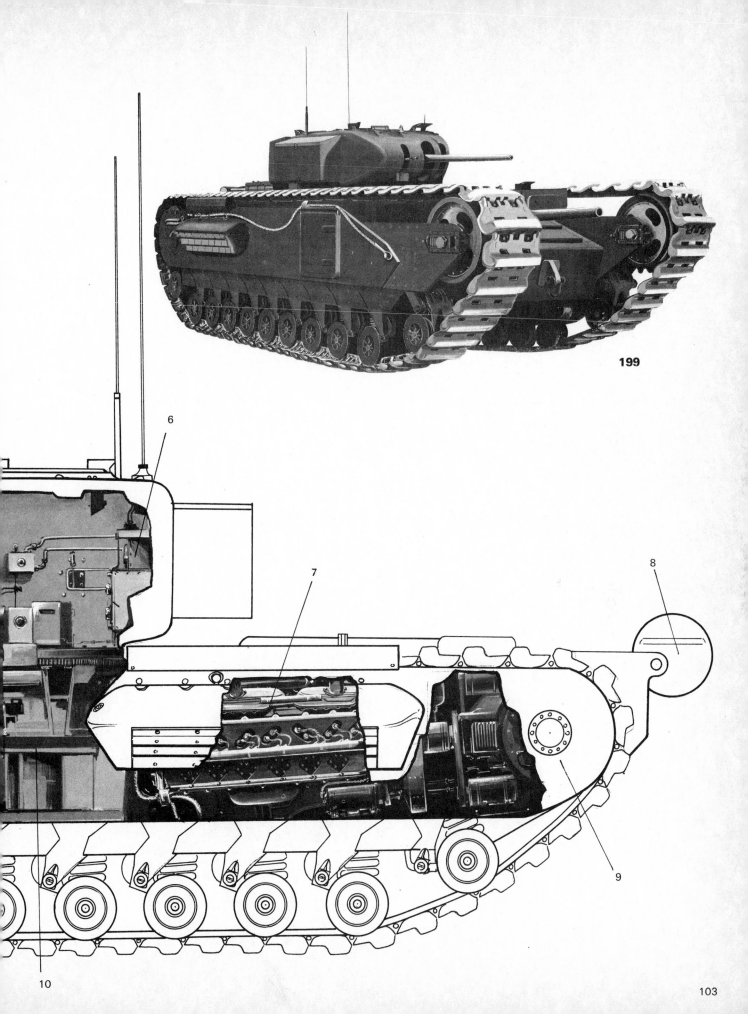

199

6

7

8

9

10

Cruisers

Britain's Cruiser A-13 (200) appeared as the direct result of the purchase of a Christie hull and suspension by Morris Motors, at the instigation of the War Office, and as another means to break the Vickers tank monopoly. Morris Motors then carried out a complete redesign to strengthen the original machine and make it battle-worthy. The speed had to be reduced since, good as the Christie suspension was, it could not sufficiently cushion the crew against injury at speeds of over 30 mph across country — a physical limitation that applies to this day.

In France, in 1940, A-13 came into combat with the 38t (201) — a cross between Vickers and Christie parentage. Taken over by the Germans when they seized Czechoslovakia in 1939, the Czechs had improved on the 35t (see page 85) by substituting a Christie-type suspension (with Swedish derivatives) for the old Vickers type, thereby enhancing the agility of an already sound vehicle. A comparison of A-13 and 38t is interesting — as the data shows — for in hitting power, speed, cross-country ability, and armoured protection there was little to choose, though 38t came out 5 tons lighter without quite the same reserve of power afforded by the modified Nuffield Liberty aero engine in the A-13. However, although 38t enjoyed greater reliability than A-13, it had almost reached the peak of potential as a battle tank, whereas A-13's cruiser successors could be strengthened considerably. But, as will be seen, the Germans later found fresh good uses for the 38t.

Japan and Italy never matched the pitch of technological evolution achieved by Russia, Germany, Britain, and the USA — the Japanese because their maritime theatre of war did not encourage uninhibited tank battles, the Italians because their hearts and minds were not in the struggle. Shortly before the outbreak of war in Europe, however, Japan did introduce a new tank which owed much to her own designers — the Medium Type 97 (202) called Chi-Ha that came into service in 1942. This tank — an elongated version of Type 95 — had a useful potential and was later developed to carry a variety of armaments including, in one version, a 150-mm gun and, in another, a 300-mm mortar.

Vickers' inspiration dominated the Italian M-11/39 (203) which owed nothing to the British firm for the manner in which the main armament with limited traverse was positioned. Built just in time for the war as an infantry assault tank, M-11 amply demonstrated the penalties of premature rearmament. While other nations scrapped the original Vickers 6-ton suspension and most were turning to welded instead of riveted armour, the Italians left their tank production tied to an industry that could not change its methods without bringing large-scale disruption.

The level to which an industrial nation might elevate its knowledge of tank technology rapidly was best demonstrated by Sweden — admittedly with German connivance — when in 1934 the little experimental Landswerk 60 (204) put in its appearance. Strictly neutral as she remained, Sweden nevertheless took a keen technological role in the struggle and enriched her own industry at the same time.

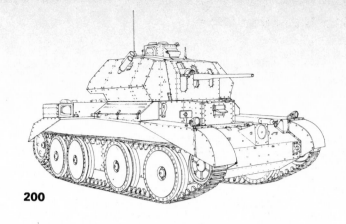

200

201

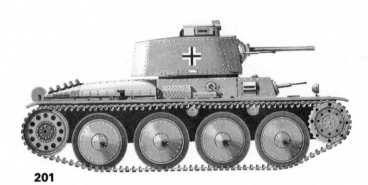

202

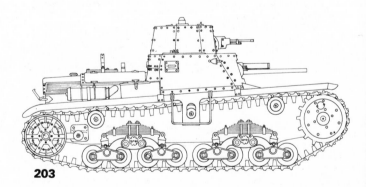

203

	A-13 (200)	**38t** (201)	**Type 97** (202)
Weight:	14.8 tons	9.7 tons	15 tons
Power Plant:	340 hp	125 hp	170 hp
Crew:	4	4	4
Armour:	14 mm	25 mm	25 mm
Speed:	30 mph	21 mph	20 mph
Armament:	1 40-mm	1 37-mm	1 57-mm
	1 mg	2 mg	2 mg

	M-11/39 (203)	**Landswerk 60** (204)
Weight:	11 tons	6.8 tons
Power Plant:	105 hp	160 hp
Crew:	3	3
Armour:	29 mm	13 mm
Speed:	20 mph	30 mph
Armament:	1 37-mm	1 20-mm
	2 mg	1 mg

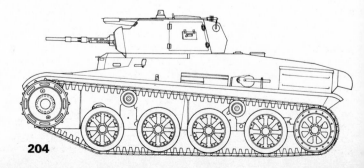

204

The Valentine Story

Almost every successful armoured fighting vehicle design demonstrated its versatility by proving capable of being put to a great many more roles than were envisaged in the primary design, and few tanks found so many conversions or fought on a greater variety of fronts in different armies than Valentine (205).

She was proposed by Vickers to the War Office just before St Valentine's Day in 1938 with a view to producing a heavily armoured tank with some of the characteristics of the A-9 and A-10 (see pages 92 and 93) cruisers, but with far greater reliability. Wherever possible Vickers used parts that were well tried and easy to manufacture. Manganese steel tracks had a life of 2,500 miles, the suspension was the most successful part of A-9, the AEC engine was that used in the London double-decker buses, and the gun was the standard 40-mm, then in quantity production. The armour was bolted and riveted together but not set in a frame as had been common Vickers practice up to then. Even so the War Office took its time taking a decision and did not sign a contract for over a year — just on the eve of war — though asking for first delivery in less than a year. This Vickers achieved without building a proto-

Nevertheless, though Valentine was described as an 'infantry' tank and most frequently employed in this role, it was included in some armoured divisions as a cruiser when, after the severe losses at Dunkirk, British industry could not produce enough tanks of any sort to satisfy demand. Hence the ease with which Valentine could be built was a distinct advantage in 1940 and 1941 when almost any tank to the British was better than none at all. And the same applied when the Germans invaded Russia in 1941 and the latter were in dire need of tank replacements. Valentines were those that Britain sent in greatest number and some of them the Russians rearmed with their own guns.

Valentine's début in action, however, came in the Western Desert in 1941 where it performed with credit until it came up against German anti-tank guns with a calibre of 50 mm and upwards. At this time the introduction of a three-man turret (206), still armed only with a 40-mm gun, corrected the more obvious difficulty of crew control, but when the larger and more powerful 57-mm (and, later still, 75-mm) gun (207) was substituted extra space had to be found by reducing the crew to its original number

205

type — and got away with the risk by a thoroughly sound piece of competitive mechanized engineering.

From a crewman's point of view Valentine in its pure tank form provided contrasts in good and bad features. The driver's compartment was cramped and difficult to enter or leave; the steering levers demanded a fair amount of effort to apply and changing gear on the five-speed gearbox, while providing the driver with a sense of personal satisfaction, demanded skill and frequency of operation. This was all rather fatiguing. The turret was even more cramped than the driver's compartment and, in the early two-man version, posed awkward problems to the commander who had to command, operate the radio, and load the gun. Since vision was extremely limited when closed down, this tank suffered from several fundamental tactical disadvantages.

But Valentine was reliable, whether powered with the AEC petrol or diesel engine or the General Motors diesel; the tracks gave next to no trouble and the suspension stood up well when at maximum speed on rough country — though a top speed of 15 mph was hardly compatible with claims to employment in the cruiser role.

and, at the same time, making do with less ammunition.

Along with progressive changes in armament, crew layout, and engine there also came a fundamental alteration of the method of construction brought about by the need to make the chassis waterproof for wading. Welding took the place of rivets and bolts along the lower hull seams, and in due course entirely replaced the original jointing throughout the hull.

By the end of 1943 Valentine in its original form, and even when given the 57-mm gun, was passing into obsolescence as more powerful cruisers and the Churchill came into service against German tanks of infinitely greater power. However, uses still had to be found for the hundreds of chassis that remained and for a production line which it would be uneconomic to close down. Quite a number found their way into the service of foreign armies — several going to the French army in North Africa for use in the latter stages of the Tunisian campaign. Marks VI and VII (both 40-mm armed two-man types) were built in Canada. A great many more were used to instruct new crews in the art of driving, but the bulk were turned over to special but subsidiary tasks.

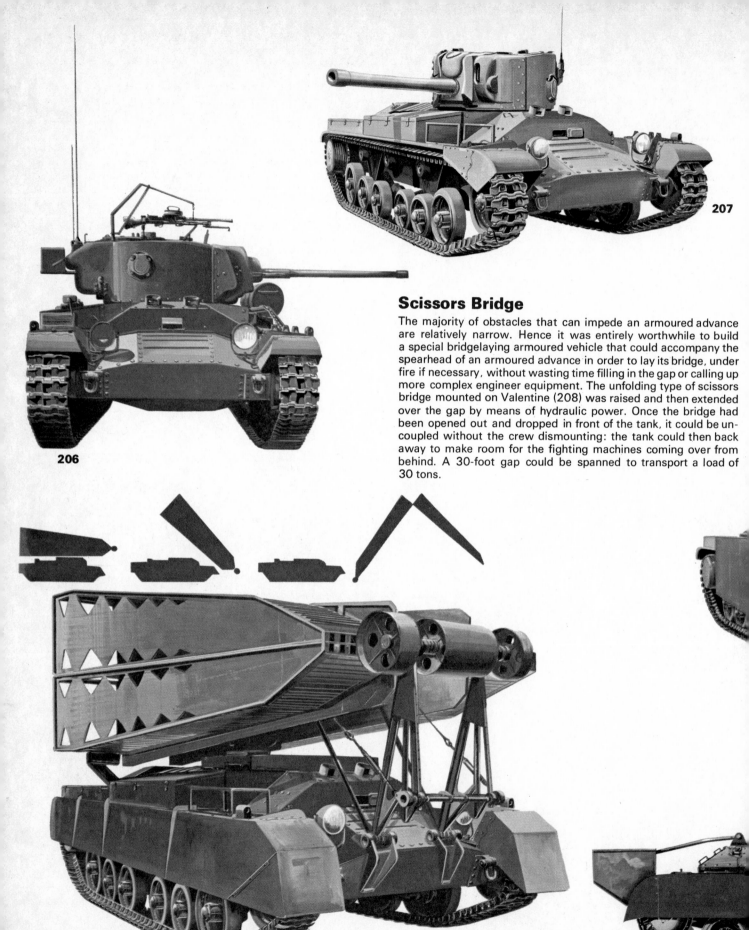

Scissors Bridge

The majority of obstacles that can impede an armoured advance are relatively narrow. Hence it was entirely worthwhile to build a special bridgelaying armoured vehicle that could accompany the spearhead of an armoured advance in order to lay its bridge, under fire if necessary, without wasting time filling in the gap or calling up more complex engineer equipment. The unfolding type of scissors bridge mounted on Valentine (208) was raised and then extended over the gap by means of hydraulic power. Once the bridge had been opened out and dropped in front of the tank, it could be uncoupled without the crew dismounting: the tank could then back away to make room for the fighting machines coming over from behind. A 30-foot gap could be spanned to transport a load of 30 tons.

206

207

208

Self-propelled guns

In line with the earliest practice from the First World War, various attempts were made to mount artillery on tanks — the Valentine providing the chassis for the first British SP field-gun since the abortive Birch Gun (see page 95).

Called Bishop (209), this vehicle, mounting a 25-pounder gun-howitzer, gave the gun crew protection from all types of fire except from overhead, but suffered from restrictions in traverse and elevation that discouraged further production when the superior American 'Priest' SP with a 105-mm gun became available.

Even less successful was the SP version carrying a 57-mm gun (210) with restricted traverse, particularly since the same gun could be mounted on Valentine in a fully rotating turret. But a complete realignment of layout to mount the much bigger 76.2-mm gun (17-pounder) which could not possibly be housed in a fully rotating turret on Valentine, saw a great deal of service in the latter part of the war and then found its way into several different foreign armies. This is Archer (211) with the gun pointing backwards over

the engine decks and provided only with limited traverse either side of centre. This powerful gun was vital to the British from 1943, since it came into service at a time when the heavy armour of German tanks was almost proof against the 57-mm gun and when only a very few Allied tanks had yet been given the 76.2-mm gun. It had a muzzle velocity of 2,900 feet per second and, at one critical period, was the only Allied gun with a good chance of killing Germany's toughest tanks.

Of the other specialized Valentine adaptations, only the mine-clearing version saw active service. An attachment called Scorpion (212) was fitted to the tank (less its fighting turret) and driven by two Ford V-8 engines. By means of a flexible drive the drum on the end of the girder was rotated so that the bobs on the end of the chains struck the ground and detonated the mines. More effective flail tanks were produced later in the war (see page 141) and the principle of mine clearance by flailing remains viable and necessary to this day.

The flame-throwing Valentine (213) never got beyond experimental purposes though it showed what could be done by the sophisticated systems produced in Britain during the war.

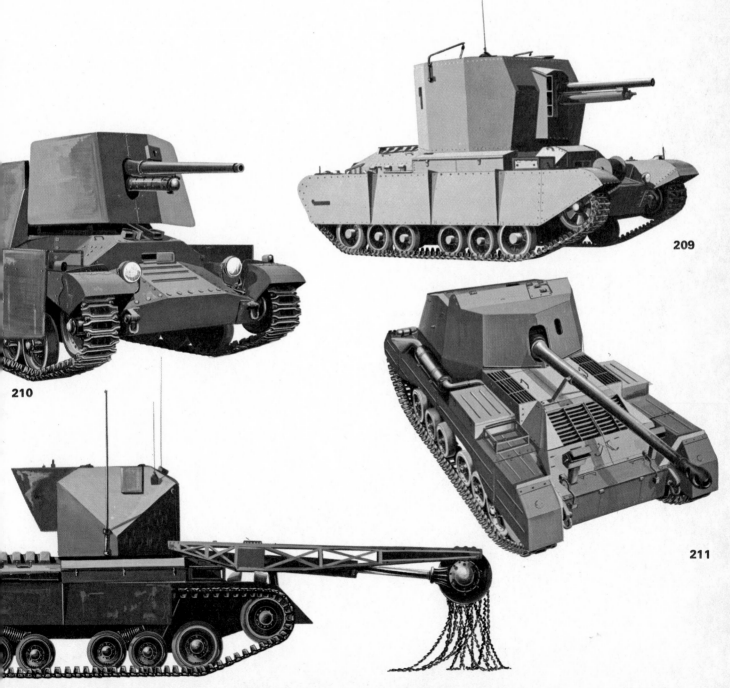

210

209

211

212

However, the swimming Valentine, even though it would have been quite inadequate, nearly found itself consigned to the assault on the Normandy beaches because an opinion was held in the War Office that it would be sufficient for beach landing against concrete defences if nothing else. Duplex Drive (DD) Valentine (214) was the invention of Mr Nicholas Straussler and consisted of a collapsible canvas screen attached and sealed to the hull of the tank. When erect the screen displaced the tank's volume in the water and enabled it to float. The propeller was driven by Duplex Drive from the engine. Due to the height of the screen the gun could not be fired when waterborne but only when coming ashore after the screen had been collapsed. The Normandy assault was eventually carried out by Sherman DD (see page 139) while Valentine DD was fortunately relegated to training purposes.

Finally there are two unique adaptations of Valentine — the jumping version and Valiant.

The Jumper (215) was simply a test vehicle made to examine the feasibility of rockets lifting an armoured vehicle across a 50-yard gap. It was not a success and usually threw the tank upside-down — but as a spectacle it took some beating.

Valiant (216) was a more serious proposition to up-gun and up-armour the Valentine into a heavy assault vehicle. Mark I, built in 1943 as an experiment with a diesel engine, and Mark II with a Rolls-Royce Meteorite were too late to be taken seriously when much more powerful tanks were already taking their place in battle.

From Valentine I to Valiant we witness the locust years as British tank design lagged from its peak in 1939 to its nadir in the post-Dunkirk period when immediate production was given priority over farsighted research and development. In tank design the gathering of experience has to be continual or time lost can hardly ever be made up.

	Mark I (205)	Mark III (206)	Mark VIII (207)	Archer (211)	Valiant (216)
Weight:	16 tons	16 tons	17 tons	18 tons	27 tons
Power Plant:	131 hp	131 hp	131 hp	131 hp	210 hp
Crew:	3	4	3	4	4
Armour:	65 mm	65 mm	65 mm	65 mm	114 mm
Armament:	1 40-mm 1 mg	1 40-mm 1 mg	1 57-mm 1 mg	1 76.2-mm	1 75-mm 1 mg

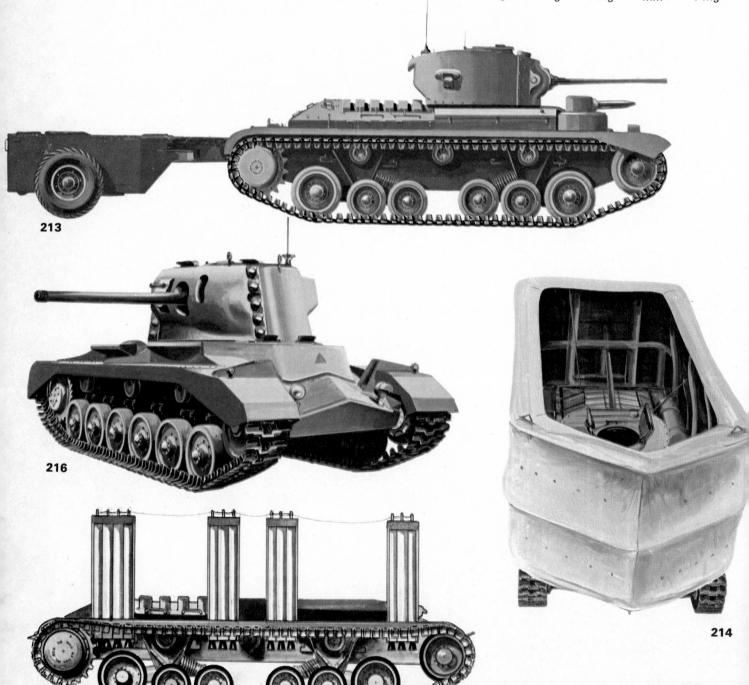

213

216

215

214

Desert Warriors

Three tanks which clashed in the Western Desert throughout 1941 and 1942 were the British Crusader I (217), the American Stuart I (218) (crewed by the British), and the Italian M-13/40 (219). Each represented entirely different design concepts, for while Crusader was third in the British line of succession to the Christie cruiser, the Stuart was the American successor to Combat Car M-1 (page 97) which had come into being after the Americans had rejected Christie, and M-13/40 was only a major improvement on the ill-founded M-11/39 (see page 104). Yet in armament and armour there was little to choose between them, though the Italian vehicle was a good bit slower than either of its opponents.

Undoubtedly Crusader suffered the greatest disadvantage of them all because it was unreliable, having been forced through production and brought into action before all its defects had been detected and ironed out. In her first engagement, against the Germans in Operation 'Battleaxe' in June 1941, more fell into enemy hands through mechanical failure than by battle damage. Wildly fluctuating tank strengths did not so much indicate hits from the enemy as sterling work by crews and fitters in repairing machines which had broken down from trivial failures in minor components.

Both Stuart and M-13/40 came into action following a long period of development. Their failings stemmed from inadequate protection and hitting power in the face of sterner opponents. In the case of the Stuart it was found that high speed and elusiveness were no substitute for thicker armour when action had to be pressed home, while the relative value of the Italian tank with its low cross-country speed of 7 mph caused by low power-to-weight ratio, left it far inferior to its opponents. Scores of these machines fell into British hands at the Battle of Beda Fomm in February 1941 and while some were shipped to help the Greek army fighting the Italians in Albania, others were put into British service to fight Rommel's Afrika Korps at a moment of dire British shortage when the Germans first entered the desert. This was a measure of British tank bankruptcy at the time.

Some people believe that a graceful machine must be a good one. By that standard, Crusader should have been one of the best tanks of all time for she both looked and sounded the epitome of pace and power, and when at speed, with dust pouring out behind her, gave a marvellous impression. Yet the ugly Stuart was quite as effective and in the light tank role remained in service through many marks until long after the war.

	Crusader I (217)	Stuart I or M3 (218)	M-13/40 (219)
Weight:	18.5 tons	12 tons	14 tons
Power Plant:	131 hp	250 hp	125 hp
Crew:	5	4	4
Armour:	40 mm	38 mm	40 mm
Speed:	27 mph	37 mph	20 mph (only 7 mph cross-country)
Armament:	1 40-mm 2 mg	1 37-mm 2 mg	1 47-mm 3 mg

217

218

219

Power Plants

The first of many subsequent engines for armoured fighting vehicles were of commercial design and had to operate in extremes for which they were not originally designed. There was the difficulty of finding space for the engine within the tank hull, especially since the early models did little to conserve either volume or weight: it took the invention of aircraft and armoured vehicles to bring engine size and weight to a premium. Other compromises had to be reached by reducing demands from the ideal to build practical power plants which would give maximum power with the least possible fuel consumption; operate in extremes of temperature, dust, and altitude; keep going when cocked at any angle even though the widest possible ranges of revving were called for — from flat out to tick-over (such as an aircraft engine, for instance, rarely has to do); run for protracted periods without detailed repairs and be thoroughly accessible when repairs had to be carried out; be easy to start, and not vulnerable to an excessive fire risk.

Although not high on the designer's list of priorities, tactical factors must have something to do with the choice of a tank's engine. Bulky silencers have to be fitted since it is sometimes desirable to run engines when stationary, in hiding, in order to recharge radio batteries, but these take up extra space. Quite often special auxiliary engines are mounted to carry out this task, but they must still be carefully silenced. Exhaust smoke is a well-known 'give-away' of hiding places, either because an engine is worn out and burning excessive lubricating oil, or because it is a diesel and subject to heavy smoking when starting up or under hard acceleration. A stationary tank is much more difficult to spot than a moving one, but even when on the move may be harder to spot providing its engine is not smoking.

Cooling systems take up great space. The easy flow of air through a frontal radiator as in a normal motor vehicle is impossible in a tank where it has to be force-fed by means of fans

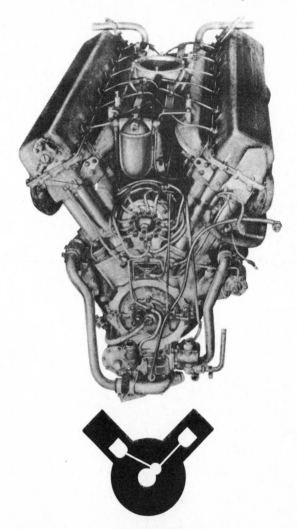

In Line – The Ricardo 150-hp 6-cylinder of 1917 This engine — the first ever specially designed to power a tank—came about as the result of Mr H. R. Ricardo being asked to design a simple power plant that would not use aluminium or high-tensile steel. In other words, it was to be in the same 'throw-away' style as that of all the early tanks. It turned out a highly efficient water-cooled engine of great simplicity but considerable bulk, because the need to restrict volume in the early Mark V tank in which it was first fitted, was minimal. In fact, the Ricardo 150 was a highly accessible engine: given plenty of room to walk round it, the crew could carry out running adjustments and, if necessary, most repairs without taking the engine out of the tank. At first this engine was designed to start by compressed air, but it first went into service needing four men to crank it and only later acquired an electric starter.

Vee – Russian V2 12-cylinder diesel 500-hp. This highly reliable water-cooled motor was developed from a diesel aircraft engine and fitted experimentally to one of the early BT tanks of Christie extraction in 1934 – several years after the first tank diesel of all was put into the British A-6. It was used in both the T-34 and KV-I tanks and was highly reliable, being particularly suitable for running in the extremes of Russian winter and summer. Starting was by compressed air forced into the cylinders – in much the same way as Ricardo had desired with his 150-hp engine.

over radiators tucked away between armour, engine, and other bulky components. Moreover in extremes of climate there is either a severe risk of freezing up in the Arctic or of using too much water in the desert where water supply becomes a major administrative headache. Anti-freeze and sealed systems solve these problems, but they are all additional complications inflicted on designers and crews. It follows that air-cooled systems offered many attractions and several fine examples have been employed in various tanks.

Up to the 1930s tank engines had run on petrol with spark ignition. However, once multi-carburettor systems came into use, complications in adjustment arose and there was always the fire hazard normally associated with petrol. (It should be noted however, that more fires were caused by ammunition than petrol as the result of hostile action in the Second World War, and that the nature of fuel supply was decided as national policy on the basis of availability.) Until light-weight diesels were produced, the petrol engine reigned supreme, but the robustness of the compression ignition diesel engine offered so many attractions that industry thought it worth while carrying out research in the 1920s and 1930s both for use in commercial vehicles and in aircraft. Eventually, as the result of determined effort and expenditure on research and development, some extremely sound designs were produced in all the leading manufacturing countries.

For convenience of design in order to suit specific characteristics, designers have selected a variety of configurations, though it should be remembered that, quite often, they merely picked on an existing engine because it was marginally suitable for adaptation to tank use. The first tank engine of all – the Daimler 105-hp – was adapted because it had shown reliability as a tractor engine and was immediately available from existing production in sufficient numbers. Here we illustrate four of the most common engine layouts – cylinders in line, in a vee, radial, and opposed.

Radial – Wright Whirlwind 9-cylinder 340-hp. This air-cooled engine was adapted from aircraft and first used in the US Medium M2 A1 and subsequently in the Grant, Lee, Ram, and Sherman tanks. Although reliable and with good power-to-weight ratio, as was to be expected from an aeroplane engine, it posed problems of installation since its diameter forced up the height of the engine compartment and thence of the tank itself. Nevertheless it was readily accessible and could be taken out and replaced with speed and ease. A few diesel radials were also produced.

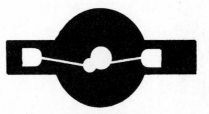

Opposed – Bedford Twin Six 350-hp. Designed for the Churchill tank, this engine aimed primarily at achieving compactness and accessibility – it satisfied the former requirement but certainly not the latter. Somewhat sluggish and with a poor power-to-weight ratio it reflected its commercial antecedents and, like so many British tanks at the beginning of the Second World War, was rushed into service with many uncured defects. The hydraulic tappets, which were meant to run without adjustment, broke; the flexible drive to the petrol pump, that could only be reached from under the engine, snapped; and the four carburettors, worked by hydraulic linkage from the throttle, easily got out of adjustment. In due course these faults, along with others in the Churchill, were rectified, but the tank's reputation had slipped – to the disgust of the man after whom it was named.

Tanks in Shadow

Some tanks were made for a preconceived purpose after the most profound combined thought by soldiers and designers, and these more often than not were a success providing sufficient time could be given to trials and development. Other tanks came into existence prematurely either because operational emergencies had to be satisfied or because designers and soldiers had moved out of accord: the four tanks shown on this page all suffered from one or more defects for these reasons.

Covenanter (220) for all its good looks gave no better combat value than the Crusader, and had the additional disadvantage of being over-complicated in layout. For instance, the radiator was at the front and the engine at the rear, the interconnecting pipes doing a good incidental job heating the fighting compartment, but introducing unwanted complexities. For a while this tank equipped British Home Defence divisions and was then relegated to training work. It was built by the London, Midland, and Scottish Railway works and never went to war.

The US M3 A1 (General Lee) (221) happened to be one of America's medium tanks under development in 1940 when their urgent need to rearm arose. For want of something better this badly arranged tank had to go into production and in June 1942 a modified version (see page 124) played an important part with the British army at the Battle of Gazala where its 75-mm gun proved effective. Nevertheless, mounting the main armament low in a sponson forced the tank to expose its bulk in order to engage the enemy, and placed it at a disadvantage to German PzKpfw-IIIs with their equally powerful turreted gun.

The German PzKpfw-III J (222) also took part in its first desert action at Gazala though it had already fought on the Russian front. The long 50-mm gun was easily accommodated for the reason given on page 82. It was a match for the short 75 in the Lee, because while the American gun threw a 14.4-lb shot at 1,850 feet per second, the German achieved 2,700 feet per second with a 4.5-lb shot. But PzKpfw-III was being rapidly superseded by superior marks of the PzKpfw-IV, and by V and VI, and was to cease production late in 1942.

The Ram (223) tank was a hybrid built in Canada in response to strong nationalist spirit using both British and American parts. When up-gunned with a 57-mm gun replacing the original 40-mm gun, it arrived too late for use in battle, but when converted into a field-gun carriage or as an armoured personnel carrier, with the turret removed, it saw action in the latter stages of the war.

	Covenanter (220)	General Lee (221)	PzKpfw-III J (222)	Ram I (223)
Weight:	18 tons	30 tons	22 tons	28 tons
Power Plant:	280 hp	350 hp	300 hp	400 hp
Crew:	4	6	5	5
Armour:	40 mm	88 mm	77 mm	76 mm
Speed:	30 mph	25 mph	25 mph	25 mph
Armament:	1 40-mm	1 75-mm	1 50-mm	1 40-mm
	1 mg	1 37-mm	2 mg	2 mg
		3 mg		

220

221

222

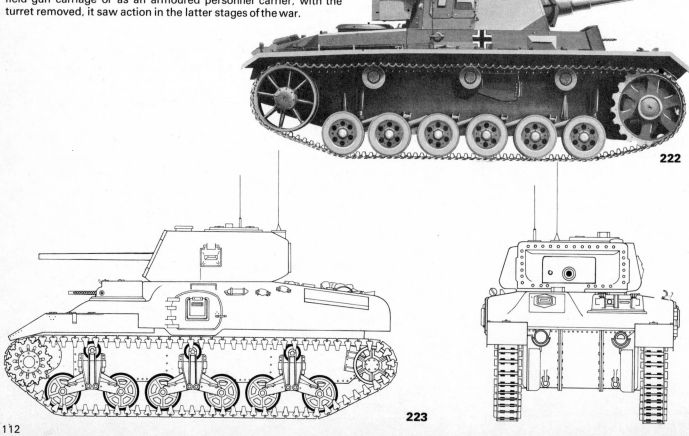

223

Tanks in Limelight

Beyond a shadow of doubt the most startling fighting vehicle revelation of the Second World War was the Russian T-34/76 (224) when first it came into action against the German invasion in summer 1941. The German PzKpfw-IIIs and IVs, which up to then had carried all before them, had been allowed to stay in production with hardly a serious attempt to up-armour or up-gun, even though plans were ready to do so if necessary. Suddenly the German crews found themselves confronted by a tank with a gun that could knock them out at ranges in excess of those at which their guns could respond. T-34, in fact, combined a beautiful balance between hitting power and self-protection, long range, speed, and reliability and with its broad tracks and low ground bearing pressure (10 lb per sq inch) could keep going on some types of soft ground when the German tanks became bogged. Only because of the initial ineptitude of the Russian commanders and crews were these excellent tanks robbed of the full fruits of their technical superiority.

T-34 was in direct line of succession from the Christies, its reliability coming about through a mass of experience and industrial information gleaned by the Chief Designer, Mikhail Koshkin, when he worked on the early BTs. The V12 engine has already been described on page 110. The tank was built in a number of factories throughout Russia, beginning in June 1940, and it is said that about 40,000 of all models were eventually built, but like all figures for Russian production this figure is best taken with a pinch of salt.

What was much more important at the time was the fillip given by T-34 to the gun and armour race. Considerably shaken, the Germans at first demanded that their industry should make a straight copy of the Russian tank—a council of despair which ignored the time industry would take to develop all the necessary manufacturing processes even had they full access to all the secret

Russian know-how with armour, tracks, and engines. In any case, the Germans had a perfectly good tank in their PzKpfw-IV which, though it had none of the skilfully sloped exterior of T-34, could readily be given thicker armour and a gun that was equal to the Russian 76-mm. So while the Germans speeded up development of two new, fundamentally advanced tanks that would not only be a match for T-34 but also against its logical up-gunned successor, they gave PzKpfw-IV the ability to take on T-34/76 on equal terms. The first up-rated model, of several to come, was F2; the final mark of all, J, shown here (225). By the time this tank came into production in 1944, the war had turned against Germany, her armies were everywhere in retreat, her armour outnumbered, and her tank factories under persistent aerial bombardment. Serious shortages of materials, the constant needs to improvize and disperse production and the consequent difficulty of maintaining quality and delivery to the front became apparent in various mechanical failures (aided by sabotage from foreign workers) and a declining standard of maintenance by the tank crews.

Nevertheless PzKpfw-IV remained a battleworthy weapon to the end of the war in tank fighting which came to take place at ever longer range and with a greater emphasis on accurate tank gunnery than before. The revolution was quick to come and historically inevitable. The immediate cause was the excellence of T-34.

	T-34/76 B (224)	PzKpfw-IV J (225)
Weight:	28 tons	25 tons
Power Plant:	500 hp	300 hp
Crew:	4	5
Armour:	60 mm	80 mm
Speed:	32 mph	24 mph
Armament:	1 76-mm	1 75-mm
	2 mg	2 mg

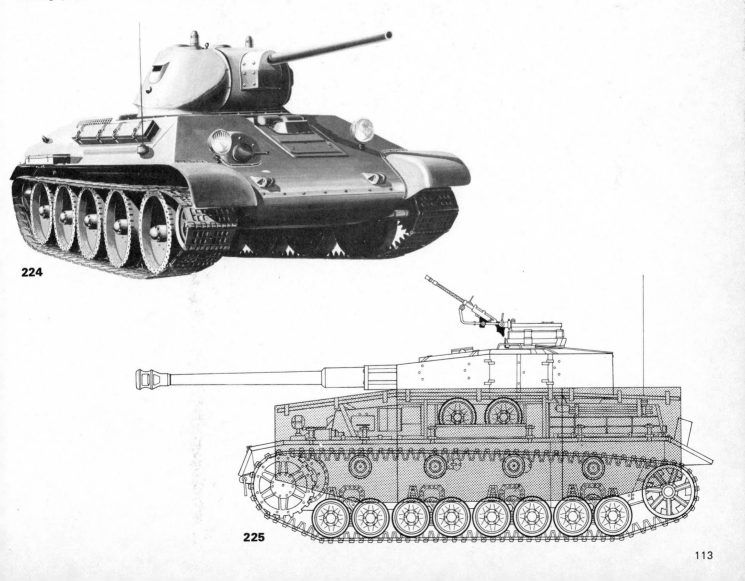

224

225

Armoured Trains

Sheer bulk, as we have seen, is no criterion of fighting power and usually because it sacrifices mobility. Armoured trains have been no exception to this rule though they have been given parts to play in a great many wars throughout the past century. Quite naturally they had to be improvizations, their armour acquired from local resources and their guns supplied from whatever happened to be available. But so long as armies depended upon railways for the movement of goods in bulk and the railways ran through country vulnerable to enemy raiders, there was a need for armoured trains as escorts and for the armouring of rolling stock to give protection to passengers and cargo.

Battles between trains have been rare, though there was an instance of this in the US Civil War involving a train not dissimilar to this one (226). The ambushing of trains was much more common, one of the most celebrated incidents occurring early in the Boer War (227) when Mr Churchill was taken prisoner. In the Second World War the British built armoured trains to patrol railways laid along the coast where it was threatened by invasion (228) and both the Germans (229) and Russians (230) used them along the lengthy tracks running across the steppes and through the thick forests. In Russia, ambush and derailment were the perpetual hazards in a war on communications fought in isolation from the armoured drives at the front, but absolutely vital to the fighting soldiers who depended on supplies brought by rail.

229

228

227

226

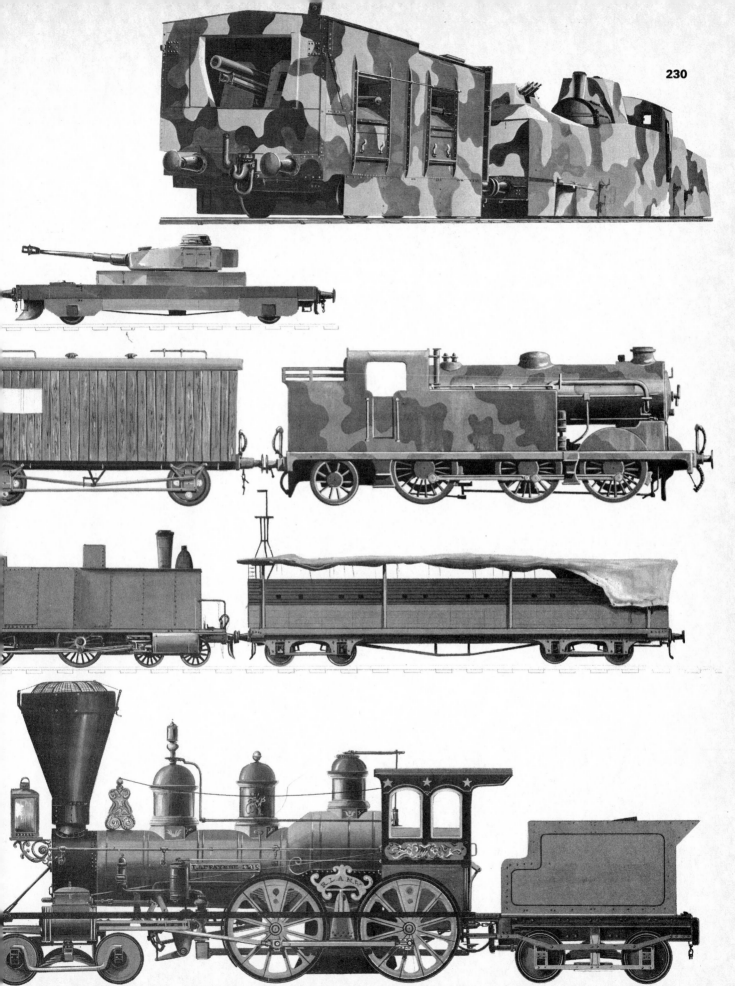

Bigger anti-tank guns

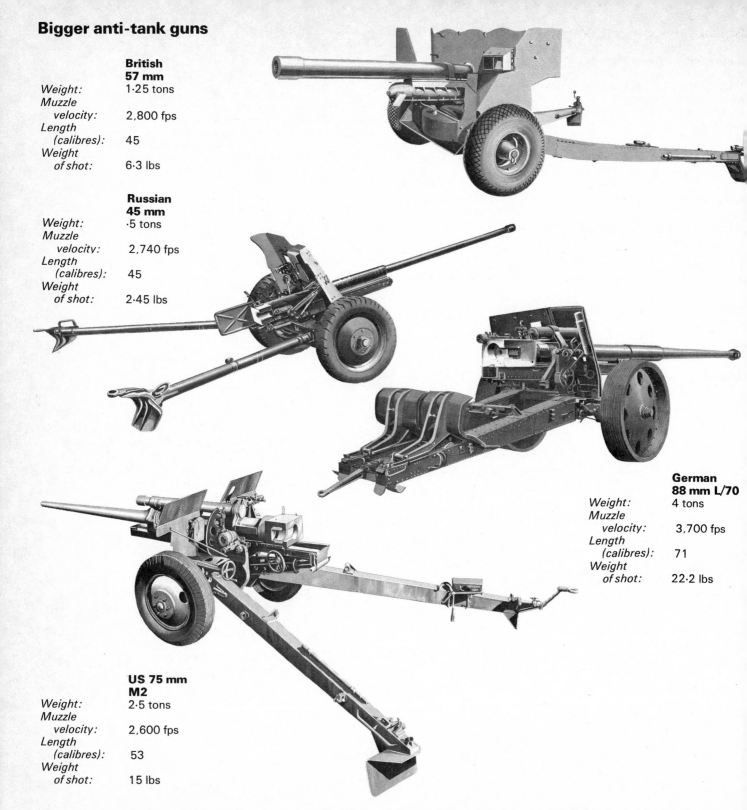

British 57 mm

Weight:	1·25 tons
Muzzle velocity:	2,800 fps
Length (calibres):	45
Weight of shot:	6·3 lbs

Russian 45 mm

Weight:	·5 tons
Muzzle velocity:	2,740 fps
Length (calibres):	45
Weight of shot:	2·45 lbs

German 88 mm L/70

Weight:	4 tons
Muzzle velocity:	3,700 fps
Length (calibres):	71
Weight of shot:	22·2 lbs

US 75 mm M2

Weight:	2·5 tons
Muzzle velocity:	2,600 fps
Length (calibres):	53
Weight of shot:	15 lbs

The consensus of military opinion before the war suggested that field anti-tank guns were a tank's worst enemy even though high explosive shells might deliver crippling blows if they hit or if their debris removed vital unarmoured parts such as bits off the suspension. Tank enthusiasts tempered this judgement by saying that the anti-tank gun carried by the tank into a tank versus tank engagement would be most effective. It took several battles and heavy losses to show that a combination of all types of weapon working in close co-operation produced the optimum damage. For instance, tanks that moved without the help of artillery or infantry fell prey most easily to anti-tank guns which had only the enemy tanks to concentrate on, while anti-tank guns that were harassed by teams of tanks and infantry often shot badly or were given no chance to shoot at all. For the tactics employed see pages 134 and 135. A screen of well emplaced anti-tank guns was much to

be feared because the guns, being mounted on low carriages were easy to hide and, in any case, usually took up positions behind a fold in the ground (in enfilade) to shoot tanks in the side when the gun was not visible to the enemy to the front.

Here are four different types of gun with performances that were characteristic of their day. Usually a gun first appeared on a field mount, then as a self-propelled gun based on some obsolete tank chassis and finally in the turret of a full blown battle tank – but this was by no means the rule. Of vital importance was the increase in weight and bulk that went with each step upwards in calibre and power until we find the German 88 transgressing every rule of size and mobility. Indeed, field-guns in these dimensions were as much their own enemy as anybody else's, for they needed bigger tractors, were hard to emplace, difficult to conceal, and almost impossible to extract once pinned down by fire.

Bigger self-propelled guns

As the war progressed and gun designers on both sides strained their ingenuity to make weapons which would pierce any known thickness and arrangement of armour, the pieces they produced nearly always became too big to be mounted in a conventional tank turret. But by doing away with the turret and mounting the gun within a hull or special superstructure, and thereby restricting traverse, sufficient space was provided for the gun's recoil and for loading – at a price in tactical flexibility, since clearly a tank whose gun could not traverse was vulnerable to the flank because it would have to turn bodily to engage targets in that quarter.

The Churchill chassis (231) mounting a 76-mm anti-aircraft gun was a British venture in this field that was made obsolete before completion, but the 105-mm howitzer mounted by the Germans on an ex-French H-35 hull (232) saw service as self-propelled artillery in Panzer divisions, while the German Sturmgeschutz III (233) (based on PzKpfw-III), though introduced primarily as an assault gun to work in close co-operation with infantry, could equally well engage in support of and against armour in the anti-tank role. A

great many of the latter came into service from 1941 onwards.

The Italian Semovente (234) mounting a 75-mm gun on the 13/40 chassis was their equivalent of the Sturmgeschutz III – and indeed the largest gun that the Italians managed to get into service on an armoured vehicle of their own production. Self-propelled guns appeared in even greater quantities as the war progressed. They were easier to make than tanks, used up old chassis that would otherwise have gone to waste and packed a punch such as many tanks could not equal, but because of their tactical limitations they had to stay under cover when opening fire or in the second wave of an attack. Fundamentally they were defensive and not offensive weapons like the tank.

	105-mm on H-35 (232)	Sturmgeschutz III (233)	Semovente 75-mm (234)
Weight:	12 tons	21 tons	14 tons
Power Plant:	75 hp	300 hp	125 hp
Crew:	4	4	4
Armour:	34 mm	50 mm	25 mm
Speed:	15 mph	22 mph	20 mph

231

232

234

233

Tiger

Once Germany had got her main tank production programme under way before the war, her soldiers and designers turned to consider the next generation of fighting vehicles. They felt there might be a need for a heavy machine with immensely thick armour and a very big gun, but their forecasting was tentative and development consequently slow. The shock administered by T-34 in 1941 changed all that. Development was undertaken in indecent haste and forced Tiger I (235) — full of weaknesses — into its first action on the Russian Front in September 1942.

In both gunpower and armour protection Tiger put the Germans ahead of the Russians and far in advance of the British who first met and were overawed by this giant in Tunisia late in 1942. All too frequently, however, she broke down and her great bulk made her difficult to manoeuvre — earning her the German nickname 'Furniture Van', and condemning her to use in mainly defensive operations.

So, though Tiger could outshoot almost any Allied tank, she suffered in the succession of withdrawals which characterized all German operations from 1943 onwards when, too often, she was outflanked, and isolated.

In almost every way, however, she was unique and incorporated several interesting features. The use of a torsion bar suspension with overlapping bogie wheels is noteworthy, while the ability to wade to a depth of 13 feet with the help of a schnorkel tube attached to the engine added appreciably to her mobility. The Maybach V-12 was a vee combination of two 6-cylinder engines and went through various vicissitudes, cast iron having to be substituted for the original light alloy, and the attempt to develop 700 hp at 3,000 revs having to be derated to 2,500 revs in order to improve reliability. The cough of this engine starting up in the distance was something all Allied soldiers remembered with respect.

	Tiger I E
Weight:	56 tons
Power Plant:	590 hp
Speed:	25 mph
Armour (maximum):	100 mm
Crew:	5
Armament:	1 x 88-mm gun
	2 mg

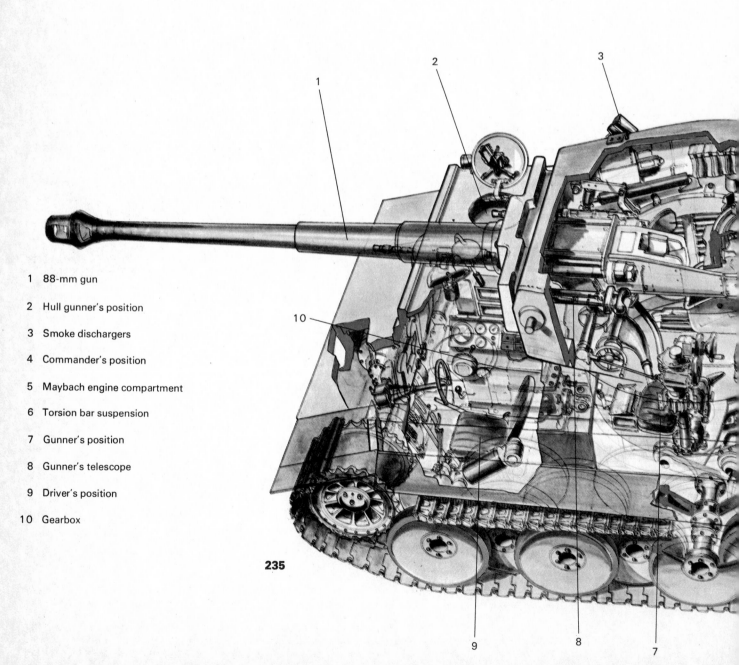

1 88-mm gun

2 Hull gunner's position

3 Smoke dischargers

4 Commander's position

5 Maybach engine compartment

6 Torsion bar suspension

7 Gunner's position

8 Gunner's telescope

9 Driver's position

10 Gearbox

235

236

Armour Versus Shot

On page 100 we showed the various methods of jointing armour and explained how this could affect the quality and protection given to a fighting vehicle. Throughout this book readers will have noticed the many different arrangements adopted by designers, ranging from the vertical bolted plates to be found on the early machines, to riveted plates and thence castings of increasing size allied to welded plate. High-quality steel was clearly of vital importance in getting rid of metallic weaknesses that would cause the armour to fail under stress or attack. The manufacture of high-grade armour plate is dependent upon the skill both of the metallurgist and of the foundrymen who, between them, arrive at the critical mixing of alloys at the right temperatures and see that all subsequent treatments, such as hardening and tempering, are carried out at what is judged to be the ideal moment. Finally, of course, it is essential that all the necessary additional materials such as chrome, molybdenum, and nickel are available. The latter, for instance, came into short supply in Great Britain during the Second World War when the other Services, including the Air Force, were also increasing their demands for it. In fact the nickel content in armour was dropped by four-fifths without dire results, though quality control had to be improved to eliminate failures.

Generally speaking the use of homogeneous armour (see page 100) was more effective than any other – provided the enemy persisted in using armour-piercing shot that was capped (see page 126). On the other hand, armour which was face-hardened offered better protection against uncapped shot since it caused the shot to break up. The British used homogeneous armour and shot without a piercing cap but the Germans made extensive use of face-hardened armour. However the British continued to use homogeneous armour and in 1942 started to use capped shot against the German armour. This technical game of cat and mouse went on interminably.

Naturally the angle at which shot struck armour had a lot to do with whether or not it went through, was broken up, or deflected. For a long time, largely to facilitate riveting, armour was hung vertically, but the advent of cast and welded plate made sloped armour easier to fit. The Dutch DAF armoured car (see page 91) provided a good early example of sloped armour, but quite the finest of all was the Russian T-34 in which every plate that could be sloped without inhibiting room for the crew, mechanical functions, or unduly increasing the width or height of the tank, was sloped. By sloping armour at 50 degrees to the angle of attack, protection can be doubled without increasing the actual thickness or weight of the plate carried. This dividend to a designer needs no further emphasis.

For many years some designers favoured spaced armour (236) – that is plates arranged in two skins with an air space in between. This allowed them to work with thinner plates and also took advantage of the air space as a factor of protection to help in the break-up of the shot or to detonate a shell before it reached the second layer of plate. The bigger the gap the better, and therefore the thin side plates on the German PzKpfw-IV J (see page 113) were useful – more so, in fact, than the narrow spaced turret armour on Crusader shown on the next page – but the wider hull spacing that contained the shock absorbers was of much greater value. Spaced armour is also supposed to dissipate the effect of hollow-charge or HEAT projectiles (see page 127) (and on occasion does so) but a hollow-charge shell gives its best effects at certain critical distances from the armour and it is therefore possible for the outer layer of spaced plate actually to conspire to enhance attack on the inner one.

Although aluminium armour was not to come into use until after the Second World War, it was among a number of new materials that were kept constantly under consideration when attempts were being made to maintain an acceptable level of protection and at the same time save weight – but, of course, reductions in weight usually incurred increases in bulk, and aluminium was no exception to this rule.

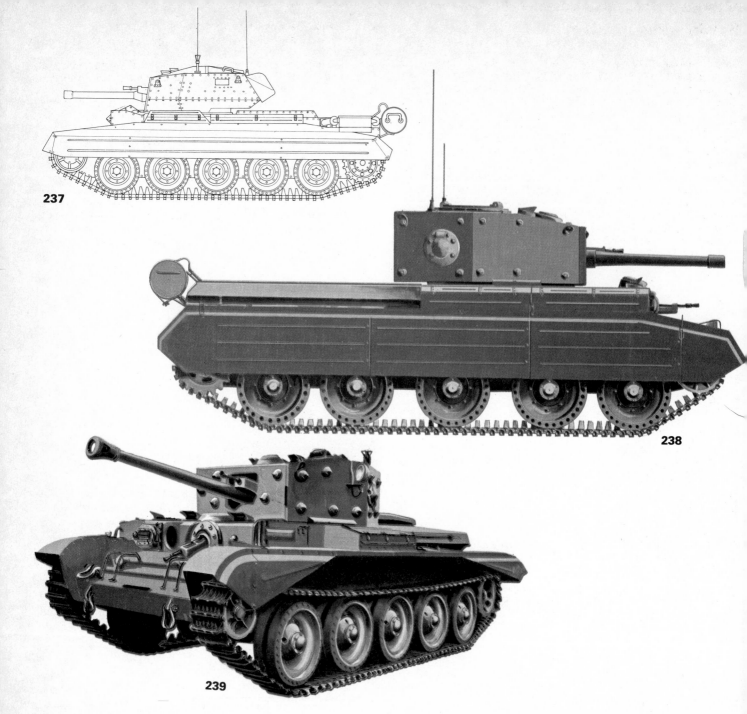

237

238

239

The British Eclipse

Britain's tanks fell sadly into decline after 1940. The last of the Christie cruisers which had been planned before the war – Crusader – had gone into action with the 40-mm gun and been found mechanically unsound as well as under-gunned. At the sacrifice of the loader and the front gunner, enough room was made in Crusader III (237) to fit the 57-mm gun and carry a worth-while amount of the bulkier ammunition. But Crusader III's spaced armour could not defeat German shot and her speed was no guarantee of safety, first, because it is tactically impossible to move all the time and, second, because with the gun control and sighting devices of that time it was almost mandatory to halt to fire and have a chance of hitting the target.

Since Crusader had such difficulty in mounting the 57-mm gun it should have been clear that any successor based on her dimensions would have the same trouble. Yet, from the compelling desire to field large numbers, the British had to go on making the best of existing production lines when constructing their next generation of tank – Cavalier (238). From the start this tank was a

mechanical failure and condemned to be inferior to what the Russians had made and the Germans were bound to emulate. Cavalier never got into service, but its successor, Cromwell (239) did – over two years late. Apart from a good record for reliability it then found itself hopelessly outclassed by the next generation of German tanks and barely a match for the latest PzKpfw-IV.

Yet Cromwell IV with its 75-mm gun was an improvement over Cavalier with the 57-mm, since the former could fire an effective high-explosive shell, in addition to shot, whereas the latter could fire only shot. Cromwell stayed in service for several years and was adapted to other purposes. In 1942 it would have been a winner: in 1944 it only showed the depths to which British tank production had sunk.

	Crusader III (237)	**Cavalier** (238)	**Cromwell** (239)
Weight:	20 tons	27 tons	28 tons
Power Plant:	345 hp	395 hp	600 hp
Crew:	3	5	5
Armour:	52 mm	76 mm	76 mm
Speed:	27 mph	25 mph	38 mph
Armament:	1 57-mm	1 57-mm	1 75-mm
	1 mg	2 mg	2 mg

Seating arrangements

Before the war tank design had settled into certain well-established configurations that were to remain until the end, then well into the peace, and finally the Cold War. But after action had been joined designers at last had the opportunity to ask questions of men with up-to-date experience of battle and modern tactics. They no longer had to depend on theoreticians. High among the requirements of veteran crews was a desire for a rationalized arrangement within the fighting vehicle to make the maximum use of the optimum number of men. The smaller the crew the better, some said, since this meant more tanks could be manned or fewer men trained and put to risk. But too small a crew (as in the one- or two-man turret) could reduce fighting capacity below the danger point and impair the ability of the crew to service the tank after action. Moreover, tank crews were always in need of sleep and often had to do so in their vehicles as well as to provide guards at night and cook their own meals: therefore a spare man such as the somewhat under-employed co-driver or front gunner could be a boon.

The actual positioning of the crew was decided by available space. But as guns and ammunition got bigger along with sloped armour, space came to be at a premium. Quite often the location of so small a unit as the wireless set could be critical: if put in the hull (as was most usual in German, French, and Russian tanks) the operator had to be there too: if in the turret the operator had either to be the gunner or the commander, but in three-man turrets he was nearly always the loader. The more components there were in the turret that drew power or carried voice signals to and from the hull, the greater was the complexity of a box called the base junction that rotated along with the turret at its centre and, by contra-rotating slip-rings, established the essential contacts. When there was no electronic intercommunication between crew members and signals passed by kick, hand signs, voice tubes, and tugs on bits of string, the base junction could be very simple or need not exist at all.

We show the five basic crew arrangements in use during the Second World War.

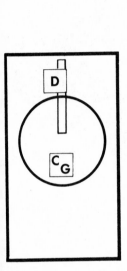

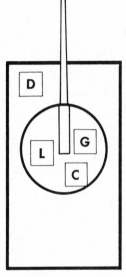

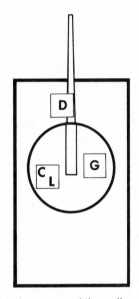

Two-man: Driver and commander who also operated the radio, loaded and fired the gun.

Three-man: Driver; gunner who fired the gun and may have operated the radio; commander who loaded the gun and may have operated the radio.

Four-man: As for five but less the co-driver and with a generally less adequate division of labour.

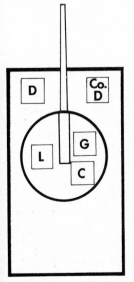

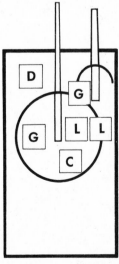

Five-man: Driver; co-driver who was just that, fired the bow gun, and made the tea; gunner who fired the main armament; radio operator who was also loader and sometimes used as second in command; commander who really could get on with his job unimpeded.

Six-man: As in the General Grant. Driver; sponson gunner who fired the 75-mm gun; sponson loader; upper turret gunner who fired the 37-mm; upper turret loader who loaded the 37 and operated the radio; commander.

Transmissions

In the original Mother tank, no less than four people combined to steer and change the gears. Basically, all they did was shift from lower to higher gears and, to steer, broke the drive and applied a brake to one track (240) and in this way sent a good 50 per cent of power to waste through the track that had been put out of operation. Later, in Mark V, it became possible for just one man to do the work of four, but the process of disengaging the drive and applying the brake (241) was still employed. Nevertheless everything possible was done from the earliest days to retain the power lost by steering – the bowed tracks of de Mole and Johnson were precursors of a system that later found widespread use in the Bren-gun Carrier and the Tetrarch tank, while in the Whippet each track was clumsily driven by a separate engine enabling power to be constantly applied to each side.

As much work went into steering and gearbox development during the mid-war years as into engines, suspensions, and tracks. In principle the designers tried to do away with outright braking (enormous effort was already lost through the friction between the engine and the final drive and between the tracks and the ground) by transferring power from one track to another, and gradually this led them to incorporate the steering mechanism, the differential, and the gearbox all in one unit. These systems were called 'regenerative'.

Controlled differentials (242), first introduced in 1916 by the US Cleveland Tractor Company and called 'Cletrac', were extensively used in American tanks including the Grant and Sherman (see pages 124 and 129). When the steering brake was applied to one side, power was transferred mainly (though not entirely) through subsidiary pinions to the other. Thus there was no actual track braking. However, since the gearbox had nothing to do with the transaction, the ratios applied were always the same, and so the turning circle was always the same – a disadvantage when sharp turns were needed.

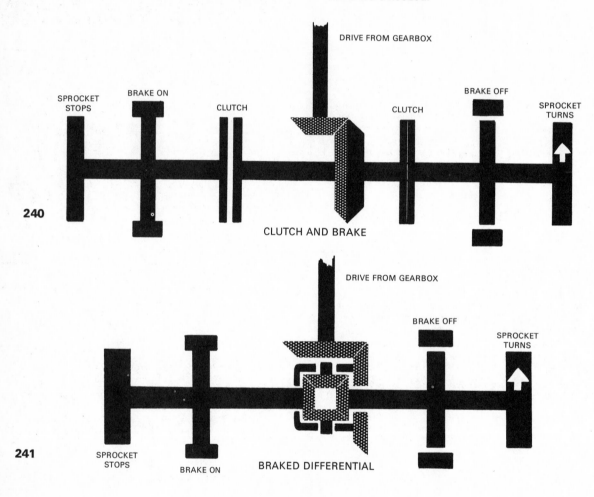

240   CLUTCH AND BRAKE

241   BRAKED DIFFERENTIAL

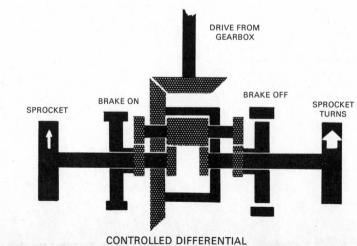

242   CONTROLLED DIFFERENTIAL

Quite the most important advance in gearbox and steering design came when Wilson **(right)** used the Vickers A-6 (see page 74) as the vehicle for a double system in which two separate gearboxes co-ordinated by an interlock acted in unison on the tracks to give steering in ratio to the gear that happened to be engaged. But later he designed a single box which, though never put in a tank, revolutionized transmissions by employing a gearbox linked to the steering system by epicyclic gears which enabled the tank driver to make three different radii of turn for each gear engaged. In a more simplified form, Dr Merritt later converted a German Maybach gearbox into the one that was first used in the Churchill tank (and subsequently many other tanks to the present day) and called Merritt-Brown (see page 102).

Right: The Merritt-Brown box (243) in various states of operation.

First we see the course taken by power from the clutch to the final drive when third gear is engaged and the tank is being driven straight ahead. The power input is applied to the pinions on the primary shaft and thereby to all the constantly engaged pinions rotating freely on the layshaft. But because third gear happens to be engaged to the layshaft by a 'dog' which slid into position when the driver selected third gear, power follows a balanced path through both steering epicyclics to the right- and left-hand tracks.

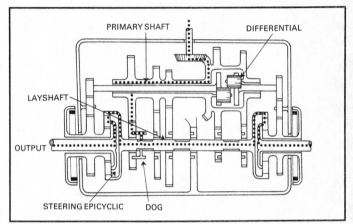

243

Now, if the right-hand brakedrum is held by applying the left-hand steering tiller, the right-hand differential shaft is also held and this causes power to be transferred to the left-hand shaft at redoubled speed. In consequence the sun-wheel of the left-hand steering epicyclic is speeded up and this, in the nature of epicyclics, slows down the left-hand track and speeds up the right-hand track. Thus, by applying the left-hand brake the right-hand track is accelerated and the left-hand one slowed down so that the tank is made to steer to the left.

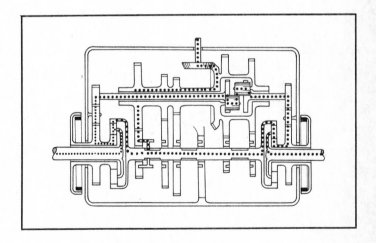

If, however, the gearbox is in neutral with none of the sliding dogs engaged to the layshaft pinions, application of the right-hand steering brake stops the right-hand sun-wheel. This then transfers power in equal proportions through the differential shafts to enable half to reach the right track and the other half the left. Thus one track moves forward and the other backwards and the tank tries to pivot about its centre. In practice, different ground resistances forbid a perfect rotation about the axis, but the effect is there just the same.

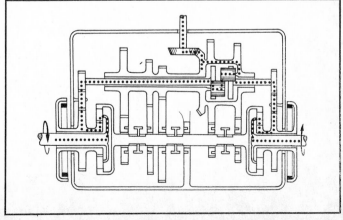

American Combat Vehicles Grow up

American-built tanks began to arrive in the African and European theatres of war just as the race between guns and armour got into a higher gear. The first medium US tank to go into action was the M3 A5, or Grant (244) as the British called it. It was reliable and its armour and 75-mm gun were a match for the German PzKpfw-IVs, but its ungainly layout led to tactical disadvantages because the tank had to expose so much of its bulk before opening fire. This came about not because the Americans were satisfied with the idea, but because, in 1941, their industry was incapable of producing the castings and some other components which would enable them to build a tank that could house the 75 mm gun in a turret.

The Americans were not slow to appreciate the importance of increasing guns and armour, if necessary, at the expense of speed. Their M6 A2 (245), introduced in 1942, gave clear indications of this line of thought, but a weight of 54 tons was considered too much for transhipment by sea, and so production was not begun. In like manner the T-14 (246) which was founded on existing tank parts to a British requirement for an assault tank, got no further

than prototype in 1944, and was dropped once it was realized the tactical need for this sort of machine had passed.

In quite another category were the US M-10 Tank Destroyers (247). Like T-14 they were founded on basic parts from normal tank construction, but they sacrificed armour (they had no overhead cover and only thin sides) in order to concentrate thicker armour in front and mount the most powerful gun available. Thus the Americans first equipped it with their 76-mm gun and then the 90-mm, while the British fitted their own 76.2-mm which was more powerful than the American 76-mm. The American version is shown here.

	M3 A5 Grant (244)	M6 A2 (245)	T-14 (246)	M-10 (247)
Weight:	29 tons	54 tons	42 tons	30 tons
Power Plant:	400 hp	740 hp	520 hp	500 hp
Crew:	6	6	5	5
Armour:	57 mm	127 mm	133 mm	59 mm
Speed:	25 mph	27 mph	22 mph	26 mph
Armament:	1 75-mm	1 76-mm	1 76-mm	1 76-mm
	1 37-mm	1 37-mm	2 mg	1 mg
	4 mg	3 mg		

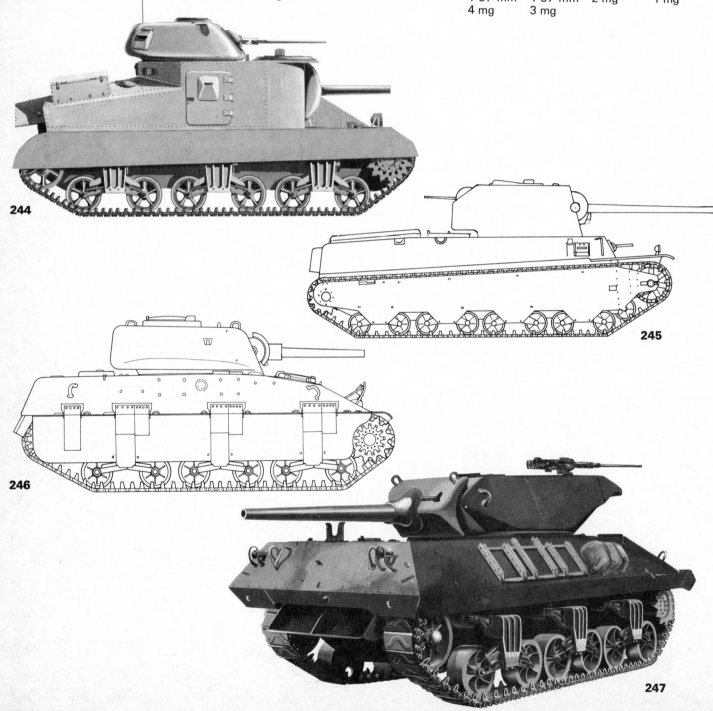

244

245

246

247

Shot and Shell

In discussing the composition and selection of armour on page 119, we touched on a few of the many different kinds of projectile that were invented to improve the penetrative qualities of anti-armour weapons. The first really effective anti-tank weapon was high-explosive fired by low velocity artillery, but this lost its penetrative power against thicker armour. From then on either high velocity shot fired from guns of steadily increasing calibre had to be used or some improved form of high explosive shell with armour-piercing characteristics.

At first, simple armour-piercing shot – AP (248) – made of solid alloy steel, like armour itself, was sufficient to deal with most types of armour, but was found to break up when it struck specially face-hardened plate. To overcome this a cap was fitted to the shot and called Armour Piercing Capped – APC (249) [later versions having a further ballistic cap added to improve streamlining and called APCBC (250)], but by the time this had come into service tanks were carrying such thick armour plate that, regardless of compositions, much bigger and more powerful guns were needed to effect penetration.

Methods simply had to be found to increase the velocity of shot without causing a further increase in the size of the gun, and the first general solution arrived at was 'squeezing'. Either the barrel could be tapered and the shot forced through until it emerged at the other end like the cork out of a champagne bottle, or the shot itself could be squeezed within itself without the need to modify the gun barrel and, incidentally, the need to restrict the gun to firing only one type of armour-piercing ammunition, to the exclusion of other natures such as high explosive and smoke. Or, alternatively, means could be found to exert greater pressure against a small projectile within the limits of a normal barrel.

The Germans made a tapered barrel that squeezed a tungsten-cored shot from 28 to 20 mm and reached a muzzle velocity of 4,600 feet per second (251), but in the act of designing bigger weapons of the same kind found themselves short of tungsten and had to discontinue. The British simply fixed a squeeze device called the Littlejohn Adaptor (252) to the end of a 40-mm barrel so that the original speed of the shot was accelerated from 2,650 to 4,000 feet per second.

It was tactically preferable to use an unmodified gun barrel and for this reason the Germans produced Armour Piercing Composite Rigid – APCR (253) – ammunition wherein a hard core surrounded

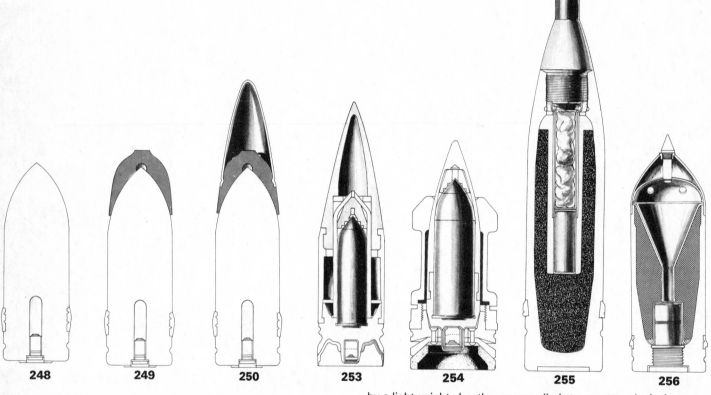

248   **249**   **250**   **253**   **254**   **255**   **256**

251

by a lightweight sheath was propelled at a greater velocity because of its lower weight to surface area. The APCR shot fired from the German L/60 50-mm gun as fitted to later PzKpfw-IIIs accelerated up to 3,930 feet per second.

The British caused extra acceleration to take place in the barrel of the gun by casing the hard armour-piercing core in a jacket (or sabot) made of plastic or some relatively light material. This was called APDS (254) Armour Piercing Discarding Sabot, and simply made it possible for a relatively greater charge to be applied to the base of a smaller and lighter shot thus giving it higher speed. Once the shot and sabot had left the end of the barrel, the sabot would fall off – to the additional peril of anybody who happened to be standing in front or to a flank.

Finally we show an ordinary HE shell (255) in order to compare it with the hollow charge or High Explosive Anti-Tank shell – HEAT (256). HEAT penetrates armour by bursting on the outside and directing a jet of gas and molten metal at 27,000 feet per second through the armour. Unrotated (when used as the war-head on a rocket, for instance) it can penetrate between 200 and 400 mm of armour regardless of the range at which it is fired, but this performance falls off sharply when spun from a rifled gun. Moreover, HEAT can be erratic in its performance depending on the way it happens to strike the target.

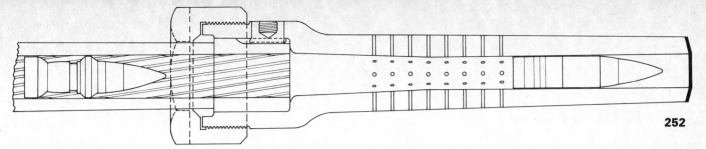

252

The essential difference to a gunner firing high-velocity AP or low-velocity HEAT ammunition is that between the flat trajectory of the former and the high one of the latter. To kill a tank, a direct hit in a vital spot has to be obtained — near misses only go to frighten the enemy crew and give them time to take cover or to riposte. Our diagrams **(below)** show how the flat trajectory of a high velocity gun is roughly matched to the gunner's line of sight at the beginning of flight. Therefore there is little need for the gunner to judge range if his sight is accurately adjusted in line with the bore of the gun: in theory he should score a hit first time. But with a high trajectory the gunner has to make an accurate assessment of range

in addition to line and so his chances of a hit, even at the shorter ranges, are much reduced. This is the basis of the tank gunner's problem. From the middle of the Second World War onwards the problem became vital so that, in status, the gunner rose from being the most under-privileged member of the crew in peacetime to the doyen next to the commander — and when one miss looked like being the last miss against an enemy who shot the straighter, he was their darling.

On page 125 we showed a picture of a burning tank that had been the victim of good shooting. Here we show the kind of holes made by shot (257) and HEAT (258).

High velocity

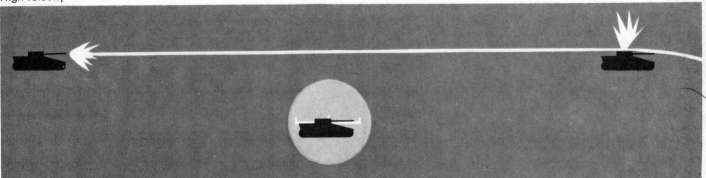

Low velocity

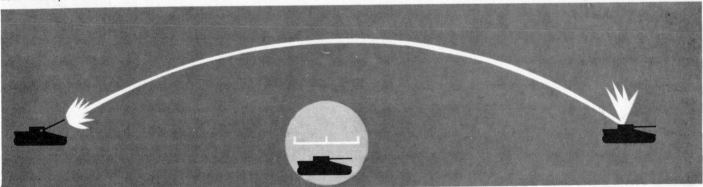

257

258

The struggle for tank superiority

A new phase in armoured warfare opened with the Battle of Kursk in early July 1943. Armoured tactics in the German, Russian, British, and American camps had settled into a more or less standardized pattern. Both sides had a sufficiency of tanks (though Allied production was always greater than that of the Germans) and were making consistent use of Battle Groups comprising infantry and artillery in armoured vehicles to work alongside the tanks both in defence and attack. Combat vehicles worked in massed formations, but, with the longer range of the latest guns, could stand off to engage targets, forcing anti-tank guns to take even more care to conceal themselves from being shelled at long range. The role of the light tank in the armoured mêlée was over, though they could be found on the fringes of battle scouting for information and, perhaps, foraging out in raids upon less well-protected lorries and headquarters – an effective tactic since armoured formations were more than ever dependent on their supply lines now that fewer of the larger rounds of ammunition could be carried in the tanks.

Self-propelled guns – above all the tank destroyers or Jagdpanzers as the Germans called them – tended to lie back in support of the medium and heavy tanks when they broke into the enemy defences to become embroiled in a slogging match with enemy medium tanks. Generally speaking, however, when tanks ran their heads against a forewarned and prepared enemy (as the Germans did against the Russians at Kursk) they suffered intolerable losses; but when they got loose among shaken defences their presence could be decisive and quite overwhelming against infantry in the open.

Here we see the two prime German and Russian contenders in 1943 – respectively Panther D (259) and T-34/85 (260). The latter was a perfectly logical step forward from T-34/76 (see page 113), its thicker armour and more powerful gun achieving the sort of improvement the Germans had expected when they evaluated its predecessor. Their Panther D was its match, despite frightful teething troubles due to the enormous rush that put it into production. In fact there had been a scheme for a new German medium dating from 1939, but it had to be drastically recast in 1941; thus a virtually original design came into production late in 1942. From this haste came a plethora of faults, not all of which could be rectified before the tank's first major action. Transmissions were unreliable, gunnery optics were inadequate (and this reduced hitting power), and there was a nasty 'shell trap' under the mantlet which made the tank vulnerable to high explosive and small arms. Of the first 300 constructed, every one of the few that survived Kursk had to be returned to the factories for rebuilding. Nevertheless, Panther

	Panther D (259)	T-34/85 (260)	Elephant (261)	Sherman V (262)
Weight:	43 tons	32 tons	68 tons	33 tons
Power Plant:	650 hp	500 hp	600 hp	425 hp
Crew:	5	5	5	5
Armour:	120 mm	75 mm	185 mm	81 mm
Speed:	27 mph	31 mph	22 mph	25 mph
Armament:	1 75-mm	1 85-mm	1 88-mm	1 75-mm
	1 mg	2 mg	1 mg	2 mg

259

261

260

was a fine tank – superior to T-34 in all its versions and much preferable to its German running partner, Tiger I (see page 118), by reason of its superior speed and manoeuvrability. Panther's tragedy, from the German point of view, was that she could never be made in sufficient quantities to meet a desperate situation. Even though the German Production Minister, Albert Speer, managed to increase output to almost miraculous quantities, only 5,508 Panthers were built compared with many times that number of T-34s alone.

The bombing of her factories, the dilution of skilled labour and the failing supply of critical materials all hindered the German effort, too much of which, in any case, was spent on less advantageous equipment. The Porsche 'Elephant' or 'Ferdinand' (which had been an unsuccessful competitor for the Tiger design) (261) is an example of wasted effort, for the ninety models upon which much labour was expended turned out hopeless failures. In strength lay weakness for their immensely thick armour allowed them to do what other assault guns could not – that is, lead the attack in immunity. But once cut off in the enemy rear and with only a limited traverse weapon and one machine-gun as protection, they were at a hopeless disadvantage and hunted down like vermin.

To match Panther, the Allies had Sherman (262) which, in 1943, was armed only with a short 75-mm gun firing shot at 2,030 feet per second as compared with the 3,068 feet per second attained by Panther's long 75-mm. Sherman was the Americans' standard main battle tank choice – they actually deferred making a more powerful vehicle in order not to disrupt production and lower numbers of Sherman. The British took Sherman by default because their own industry had failed to make anything as good in time. No fewer than 49,000 Shermans were made during the war – so there were plenty to go round and there was scope for innumerable modifications. Indeed, as late as 1967, the most recently modified Shermans were being used by the Israelis against some old T-34s in the Egyptian Army, a few PzKpfw-IVs in the Syrian Army as well as the most modern Russian and British tanks in use with the Egyptians and Jordanians. Sherman incorporated many lessons learnt by the British up to 1942 and had one or two innovations of its own. The multi-bank Chrysler engine shown here is unique, comprising five six-cylinder commercial engines assembled round a central crankshaft – giving thirty cylinders in all. Both petrol and diesel engines powered various marks of Sherman, some made by General Motors, some by Ford, and others by Wright. Another innovation was the gun stabilizer that tried, without much success, to allow the gunner to maintain the same elevation on the gun while on the move without relaying: the result (since the device could not keep pace with the pitching of the tank) was bizarre, with shots flying all over the place, but not without effect if a bullet spray was required.

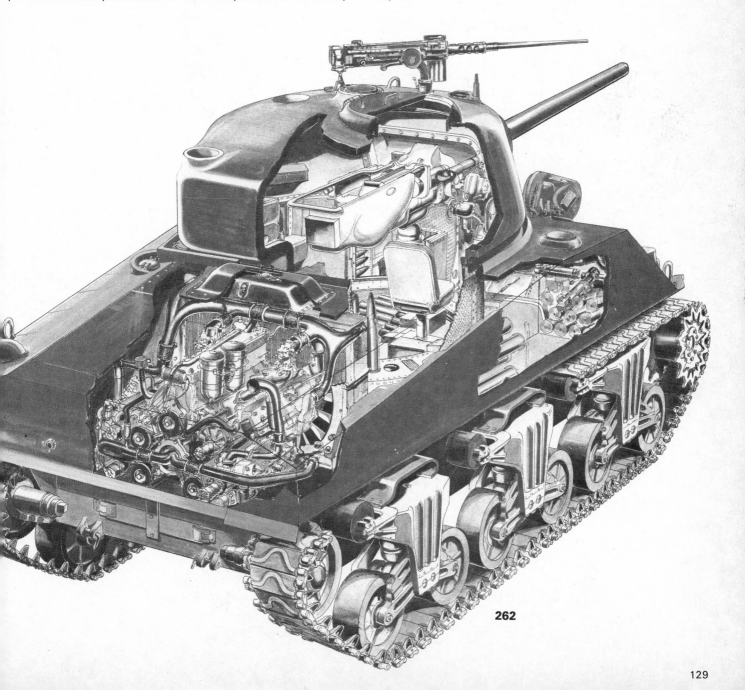

262

In the same period the Russians still persevered with light tanks — their T-60 (263) is one example of a dying breed—in the same way as the Allies continued to use Stuart light tanks to reconnoitre. But the Russians had less use for light tanks than the Allies and preferred to develop medium and cruiser types. Thus KV-85 (264), which appeared in 1943, was an interesting attempt to merge the sound KV chassis with a modified T-34/85 turret — a venture which led to the next and more significant Stalin series of heavy tanks.

British attempts to up-gun were less fortunate. Since Cromwell could not mount a turret that would carry a gun larger than the 75-mm, and the much more powerful 76.2-mm was desperately needed in service by 1944 to match Panther and Tiger when the British army invaded Normandy, a lengthened version of Cromwell, with an extra bogie wheel and the gun mounted in a grossly enlarged turret, was improvized and called Challenger (265). It belied its name.

It was inevitable that a nation's tanks became the reflection of the creative genius and practical application of its industry and that this would be adjusted by the degree of priority accorded to strategic demand. Thus Russia, who stood or fell on the strength of her army in a war fought by armour, simply had no alternative but to apply many of her best brains and resources to tanks both in the factory and the field. Their latest heavy tank of 1944, the successor to KV-1 and KV-85, was a remarkably powerful machine — Josef Stalin or JS-2 (266).

The Italians, on the other hand, were left behind in the arms race, having started too early and been forced to put much effort into naval and air production to the detriment of her tank force. Her next generation medium tank showed improvements but not sufficient to put it into a dominant category, and in the event, P-40 (267) did not enter service before Italy fell out of the war in 1943.

Nor did the Japanese, also consumed by the need for naval construction, give an overwhelmingly high priority to tank construction as the war progressed. Mostly they concentrated on up-scaling existing designs — Chi-Nu (268) with its 75-mm gun being a good example of a modified Type 97.

Likewise the Australians, although they produced an original design with their Sentinel (269) and later planned to give it a 76.2-mm gun, had neither reason nor facilities to expend much tank effort on a maritime war, backed by vast American resources in territory that was mainly covered by jungle.

And the Canadians, proud that they had produced Ram in the first place (see page 112) could not do much with it even when they armed it with a 57-mm gun (270). Only nations with continental strategies had cause to make powerful tanks in worthwhile numbers.

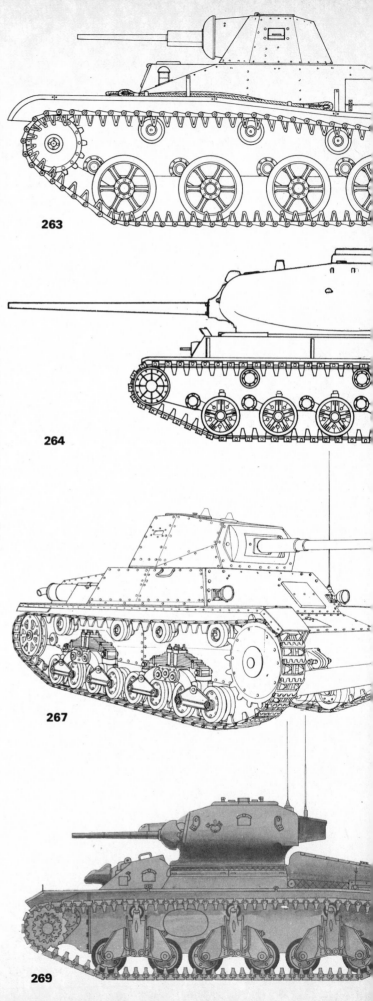

263

264

267

269

	T-60 (263)	KV-85 (264)	Challenger (265)	JS-2 (266)
Weight:	6 tons	46 tons	32 tons	46 tons
Power Plant:	85 hp	550 hp	600 hp	550 hp
Crew:	2	5	4	4
Armour:	20 mm	110 mm	102 mm	160 mm
Speed:	28 mph	26 mph	32 mph	26 mph
Armament:	1 20-mm	1 85-mm	1 76.2-mm	1 122-mm
	1 mg	3 mg	1 mg	4 mg

	P-40 (267)	Chi-Nu (268)	Sentinel (269)	Ram II (270)
Weight:	26 tons	19 tons	26 tons	30 tons
Power Plant:	275 hp	240 hp	397 hp	400 hp
Crew:	4	5	4	5
Armour:	60 mm	50 mm	75 mm	76 mm
Speed:	23 mph	25 mph	20 mph	25 mph
Armament:	1 75-mm	1 75-mm	1 40-mm	1 57-mm
	1 mg	1 mg	2 mg	2 mg

265

266

268

270

It is ironic that the Germans, who had sedulously resisted demands for heavy tanks in the 1930s, were the first to be converted in the 1940s to a great effort to build the biggest of all, though it is important to remember that their giants came about at the behest of technologists, such as Porsche backed by Hitler's sense of grandiose, rather than at the will of front line soldiers who generally speaking wanted nothing much different from the Panther.

Certainly, heavily armed and armoured fighting vehicles could assert a fearful influence upon the enemy, but equally their transportation created logistical factors that could not be ignored. The Americans had dropped the concept of a heavy tank on the grounds of difficulty in shipping them to overseas theatres: indeed every time the weight of tanks rose, greater engineering effort had to be placed at their disposal.

Attempts to protect tanks with an immense thickness of frontal, side, back, and top armour raised weight to fantastic levels – as can be seen from the German Maus (271). Though its armour was generally proof against shot, it could still be penetrated by hollow charge missiles and, if all else failed, the vehicle could be by-passed and left in sultry occupation of the small acreage within its vision. In any case, since only a few giants could be made, saturation of the front by them could not be contemplated, for large-scale production of these monsters was quite beyond German manufacturing capacity in relation to her other requirements at any time – and ludicrous when defeat stared her in the face.

A far more practical future was assured for the Jagdpanther (272) which came into service in 1944, using the Panther hull carrying the long L/71 88-mm gun with a restricted traverse. The Germans recognized the special nature of these very formidable tank destroyers by grouping them in special units under army control – only allocating them to sectors on the front where they were specially needed and avoiding tying them down as an integral part of Panzer divisions.

On the other side of the hill Jagdpanther would find itself pitted against Sherman Firefly (273) – the British adaptation of a standard Sherman with a British 76.2-mm gun fitted into the turret after modifications had been made to the turret mantlet and bustle to enable the gun to be mounted in place. But the larger ammunition required meant that extra space had to be found – so the front gunner had to go. At the time of the Normandy landings Firefly was the only Anglo-American tank capable of dealing effectively with any of the German Panther or Tiger breed – and even then there were not enough available to equip more than 25 per cent of British armoured regiments – a state of affairs that came about because, in 1942, the British Ministry of Supply had resisted the conversion on the grounds that it was impossible and only given way in 1943 when they were out-manoeuvred in committee by a few desperate soldiers in the War Office.

No matter what difficulties the Germans and Russians may have suffered over priorities and shortage of materials, they were at least clear in their minds that domination of the battlefield depended upon maintaining a fleet of armoured vehicles whose guns could penetrate enemy tanks out to about 1,500 yards range, and whose armour could withstand hits from existing guns at 1,000 yards in the frontal arc – where analysis showed most hostile shots seemed to fall. If, as with the superb Tiger II (274), weight got a little out of hand, at least the error was just on the right side. The sloping of armour, the arrangement of crew positions, the accessibility of parts, the excellence of the optics to match the L/71 88-mm gun made Tiger II one of the most powerful tanks of the war. It came into service in 1944 and only 484 were built. Each was a formidable opponent, worthy of the names 'Royal' or 'King Tiger'.

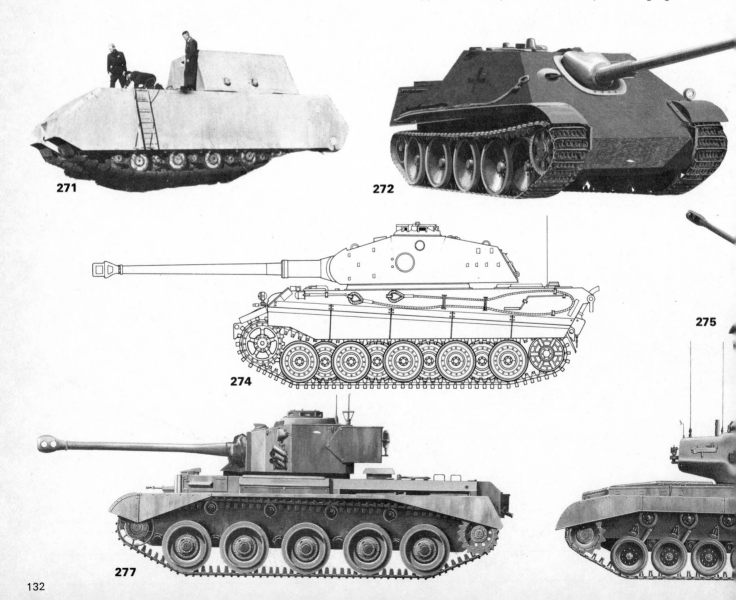

271

272

275

274

277

The Russian JS-3 (275), named after Josef Stalin, also came into production in 1944, though not many were in action up to the end. By its sloped armour and domed turret its designers engineered almost complete protection, while the 122-mm gun gave a good performance. But they too overdid compromise, for though this tank was the bogey of western armies for many years, it later became apparent that the well sloped armour, leading to a low silhouette, reduced the amount of ammunition carried, severely restricted crew space, and lowered the rate of fire and endurance to a relatively poor level.

Just towards the end of the war both the Americans and the British brought out tanks that put them back in the armour race again. The US Pershing (276) was fundamentally an improved version of the T-20 tank they could have had in service in 1943 if they had decided not to concentrate on Sherman. The British Comet (277) came into service on the heels of Cromwell just as quickly as possible to retrieve a disastrous situation — but unlike many another project of despair turned out a great success in its shortlived battlefield career between March and May 1945. Here was a machine that exploited the known reliability of Cromwell, with a sloped turret and the improved version of the British 76.2-mm gun — the so-called 77.

Only very late, and then without conviction, did the British enter the field of heavy tank and heavy tank-destroyer development. TOG (see page 99) had hung on throughout the war waiting for a return to the heavy tank cult, with its backers trying hard to persuade the War Office to buy it armed with a 76.2-mm gun.

But in the end the only real giant of their own that the British took anything like seriously in the Second World War was Tortoise (278) — of which only five prototypes were made. She was easily the heaviest fighting vehicle they ever made — a real monster with

a 94-mm anti-aircraft gun as main armament and plenty of room for the crew. Nevertheless she was out of date before setting track to ground, for though she was conceived in 1942, it was 1946 before she ran — the same kind of treatment that the US giant — T-28 (279) — received after its birth in 1943. All one can say of these monsters is that presumably they had to be attempted if only to show that they were as ridiculous as the equally over-weighted armoured knights of old.

	Maus I (271)	Jagd-panther (272)	Firefly (273)	Tiger II (274)	JS-3 (275)
Weight:	188 tons	46 tons	33 tons	68 tons	46 tons
Power Plant:	1375 hp	600 hp	425 hp	700 hp	550 hp
Crew:	6	5	4	5	4
Armour:	240 mm	80 mm	81 mm	185 mm	200 mm
Speed:	12 mph	28 mph	25 mph	24 mph	25 mph
Armament:	1 128-mm 1 75-mm 2 mg	1 88-mm 1 mg	1 76.2-mm 1 mg	1 88-mm 2 mg	1 122-mm 2 mg

	Pershing (276)	Comet (277)	Tortoise (278)	T-28 (279)
Weight:	42 tons	33 tons	78 tons	75 tons
Power Plant:	500 hp	600 hp	600 hp	350 hp
Crew:	5	5	7	—
Armour:	110 mm	101 mm	225 mm	205 mm
Speed:	30 mph	29 mph	12 mph	10 mph
Armament:	1 90-mm 2 mg	1 77-mm 2 mg	1 94-mm 2 mg	1 105-mm 3 mg

273

279

276

278

Tanks in battle

Although the basic ideas behind Fuller's 'Plan 1919' had undergone modification by the time armoured formations went to war in earnest in 1939, the underlying employment of armour remained as he had forecast. It was still used to breach the front, drive deep to flank and rear and attempt to disrupt the enemy's will to fight. In putting these principles into action, tanks and armoured personnel carriers in conjunction with artillery and aircraft still employed the same tactical gambits in 1945 as had been worked out between the wars.

Armouring a vehicle gave its crew a chance of survival when moving in full view of the enemy. Nevertheless, as anti-tank weapons increased in power and number, it became imperative that no movement should take place in the open unless the enemy was also engaged by fire. In this diagram (280) we show the successive positions taken up by tanks prior to and during an advance.

First the commander positions himself so that he alone can see ahead — this is Turret Down (a). Next he advances slightly to Hull Down (b) so that the gun can be brought to bear. It can be seen that in order to fire down the slope it must be possible to depress the gun quite considerably (281) if the tank is not to come too far forward and expose its entire hull: hence turret roofs have to be a little higher than might be expected in order to allow the breech of the gun to be raised inside the turret — another compromise decision which had to be taken by the designer when trying to reduce silhouette.

Having decided that the coast is clear or that the fire of artillery or other tanks can take care of whatever opposition discloses itself, the tank troop commander may order his troop to advance. In this diagram (**below**) we see the troop advancing two tanks up (c) with two lying back (d) in support. Meanwhile smoke has been fired in order to screen one flank and when the leading pair get to the cover of the next bound they will be joined by those waiting in rear.

280

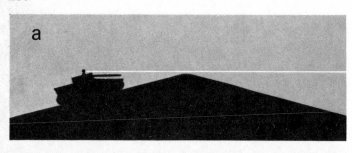

281

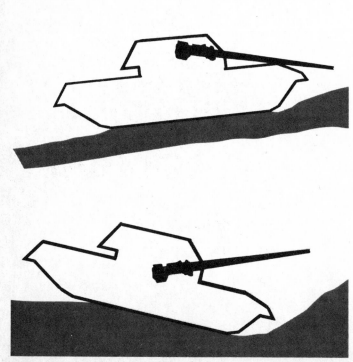

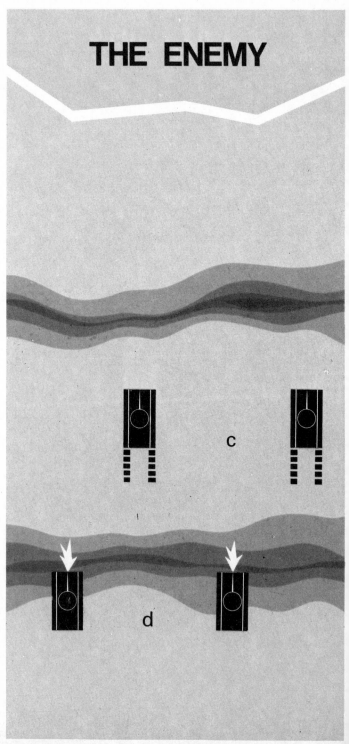

THE ENEMY

Likewise a squadron of tanks might advance troop by troop or it might even advance all at once if another squadron were in support or if very heavy artillery fire could be fired on to the objective or known enemy positions.

More often than not, infantry would accompany the tanks — either in armoured carriers or on their feet. Here (**below**) we show a deliberate assault in which the infantry of a combat team have de-bussed from their carriers in cover (e) and are going forward on foot to an objective which is held by enemy anti-tank and machine-gunners. The tanks try to knock out the enemy guns with high-explosive and machine-gun fire while some of their number lie back in case enemy tanks put in an appearance and have to be engaged with shot. Wherever possible the infantry endeavour to rush in on the enemy guns, seeking to co-ordinate their movements with the tanks by means of a prearranged plan or by a scheme devised on the spot by wireless conversation — though during the Second World War infantry radios were notoriously unreliable. The guiding principles of infantry tank co-operation stemmed from the idea of each making best use of its special characteristics and advancing by the routes most suited to feet or tracks. This made co-operation more difficult, but it was often better than having infantry stay close to the tanks and thus the indirect recipients of every sort of enemy fire that was invariably thrown at tanks when-ever they appeared.

The role of tanks in defence has, by their very nature, to be mobile and offensive. To stand still is to invite destruction, so most usually they would be positioned (**below**) just to the rear of the threatened ground and either moved into a concealed fire position (f) when the enemy came into view, or sent round to a flank (g) in order to catch the enemy from an unexpected direction.

Surprise, which had been the essence of the Battle of Cambrai, continued to govern successful tank tactics as it had governed strategy and tactics the world over. No amount of armour or superior gunpower makes up for sterile and unimaginative tactics in the long run, though there might be occasions when by sheer impudence they will retrieve what looks like a hopeless situation.

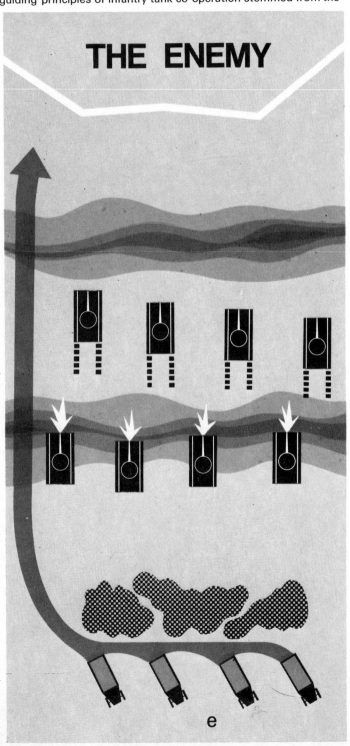

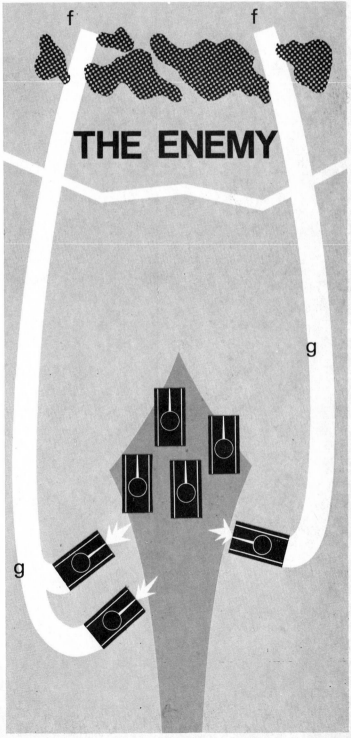

Light vehicles in the shade

Armoured cars, like light tanks, with their inherently thin armour and low gunpower allied to reduced mobility off the roads, fell into disrepute during the war. Only the British used them to any great extent and this came about mainly because armoured cars seemed to satisfy the traditions of cavalry regiments, were easy to improvise when armoured vehicles were in desperately short supply in 1940, and because the Western Desert was particularly suited to wheeled vehicles. Even so the main role of armoured cars could be scouting alone and, occasionally, in the special conditions of open warfare, raiding. Those armoured cars which were given heavier armament received it at the loss of still more mobility and solely to enable them to give support to their lighter brethren.

The British Humber IV (282) armoured car was in direct line of succession to the Guy Wheeled Tank (see page 37) but had acquired a 37-mm gun to give it a better chance against enemy armour in emergencies.

Marmon Herrington VI (283), which never went into production, was quite a different proposition to the Mark II shown on page 91, and resembles much more the German SdKfz-232.

Daimler II (284) was also an original design and probably the most successful armoured car devised by the British. It saw service from 1941 until the early 1960s, was reliable and, with its powered steering and preselector gearbox, quite easy to drive.

The US Greyhound (285) also came into early service with their army even though not greatly favoured as a fighting or scouting vehicle. Very fast and exceptionally quiet (an essential prerequisite for a scouting vehicle) it may be found in service to this day in various parts of the world where armoured cars are the work-horses of hard-pressed police forces fighting guerrilla bands.

Beaverette (286) was merely one of a number of different improvisations that came into being in Britain during 1940. Fortunately their dubious combat value was never put seriously to the test.

Staghound I (287) was another US armoured car with powered steering, an automatic gearbox, and a stabilizer on the 37-mm gun. Like many armoured cars it received numerous modifications to its armament as time went by: the Mark III took a Crusader tank turret with a 75-mm gun to fit it to the close support role.

In the same way the Germans adapted SdKfz-232 to carry a 50-mm gun and called it Puma (288) or SdKfz-234/2.

Finally it was left to the British to produce a special close support armoured car – the vast AEC III with its 75-mm gun (289) – a most clumsy vehicle that had a low cross-country performance and great potential for blocking the roadway.

282

286

	Humber IV (282)	Marmon Herrington VI (283)	Daimler II (284)	Greyhound (285)
Weight:	6.5 tons	10 tons	7.5 tons	7.5 tons
Power Plant:	90 hp	95 hp	95 hp	110 hp
Crew:	3	4	3	4
Armour:	14 mm	12 mm	14 mm	25 mm
Speed:	45 mph	40 mph	50 mph	55 mph
Armament:	1 37-mm 1 mg	1 40-mm 2 mg	1 40-mm 1 mg	1 37-mm 1 mg

	Beaverette (286)	Staghound I (287)	Puma (288)	AEC III (289)
Weight:	2.1 tons	13 tons	8 tons	12 tons
Power Plant:	14 hp	176 hp	155 hp	165 hp
Crew:	3	4	4	3
Armour:	10 mm	32 mm	15 mm	25 mm
Speed:	40 mph	50 mph	50 mph	40 mph
Armament:	1 mg	1 37-mm 2 mg	1 50-mm 1 mg	1 75-mm 1 mg

288

284

283

287

289

285

The Battlefield of 1944

In June 1944 the Anglo-American armies which had fought on the periphery of Hitler's Fortress Europe until the spring of 1944, mostly in the Mediterranean theatre of war, braced themselves to stage a major invasion of France across the Normandy beaches. The Germans had erected intricate fortifications at every likely landing place. Moreover, these fortifications were only the outer crust of a defensive zone which reached in depth to the very frontiers of Germany itself, founded upon two principles. First, the invaders were to be held in close combat on the beaches where the maximum toll could be taken before the effects of the sea voyage had worn off: second, any lodgement was to be destroyed as quickly as possible by rapidly mounted and fiercely executed counterattacks carried out by armoured forces already deployed within striking distance of the threatened area. In practice this made the Germans spread their infantry formations within only a few miles of the coast, while ten Panzer divisions — at various strengths — lay hidden in concentration areas, in some cases as close as ten miles from the coast, in others as much as sixty miles inland.

The problems facing the Allies were those of advancing across a heavily defended beach and then to thrust strong, mobile forces inland to seize positions of sufficient strength to defeat the German Panzer divisions before they could intervene on the beaches. But the very nature of the beach defences was such that a conventional assault by infantry after a preliminary bombardment by aircraft and naval gunfire stood only the remotest chance of success. So special armoured vehicles were given the task of gapping the beach defences before joining with infantry, artillery, and tanks in the subjugation of the inland defences.

Here is a diagram showing the beaches protected by mine-fields and barriers and swept by the fire of machine-guns and artillery from trenches and concrete pill-boxes. Inland are anti-tank ditches and more trench systems, often grouped round villages, woods, and high ground. Each kind of obstacle called for special tactics by teams of specialist vehicles, in addition to the destruction or neutralization caused by bombing and naval and field gunfire.

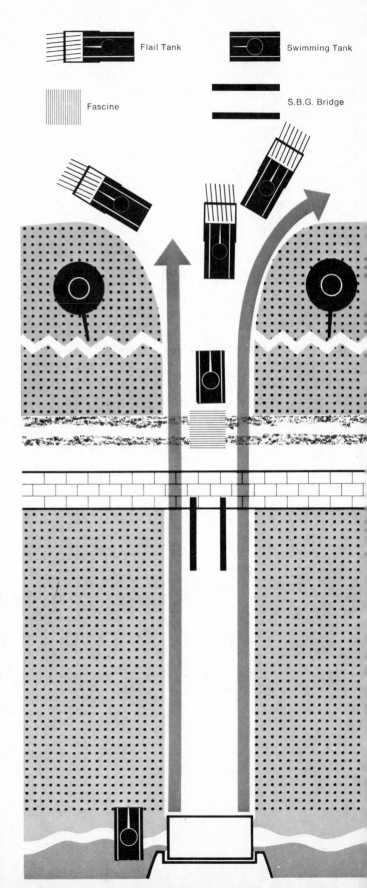

Flail Tank

Swimming Tank

Fascine

S.B.G. Bridge

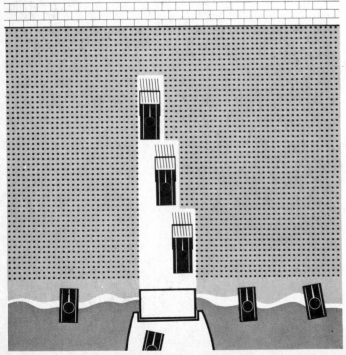

Swimmers

The primary task had to be the subjugation of the German guns. Some of these might be demolished by the initial bombardment, but, from past bitter experience, it was accepted that those which escaped could still, on their own, wreck an assault landing. A tank was needed to wade ashore in the forefront of the invasion at the water's edge, to aim direct fire through the slits in the enemy pill-boxes before other troops reached the shore. Swimming tanks, like most specialist vehicles in 1944, had been made before. In 1931 the Russians had copied a Vickers Carden-Loyd light tank into their Light Amphibious Tank T-37 (290) but no swimming tank such as the DD (see page 108) invented by Mr Straussler had been seen before.

Because DD, unlike T-37, relied on a collapsible screen and not a bulky pontoon, it took up hardly any more room in a landing craft than an ordinary tank, and this made it possible to transport more

tanks in each Landing Craft Tank IV (LCT) — the principal carrier of armoured vehicles in the assault.

Here is Sherman DD (291) which led the Normandy landings. On grounding at the water's edge, the front of the screen would be dropped to permit the gun to engage the enemy, but the rear would be kept erect so that following seas could not swamp the engine by breaking over the tank's back.

Much more bulky than DD, but effective in its way, was the US LVT 4, since it could be used as a personnel and weapons carrier or converted to mount a turret as in the A-4 shown here (292). LVTs first went into operation in the Pacific, taking part in General Mac-Arthur's reconquest of those islands which had fallen to the Japanese in 1942. On several occasions the Japanese, too, had used amphibious tanks, the most usual version being this T-95 (293) floating in pontoons.

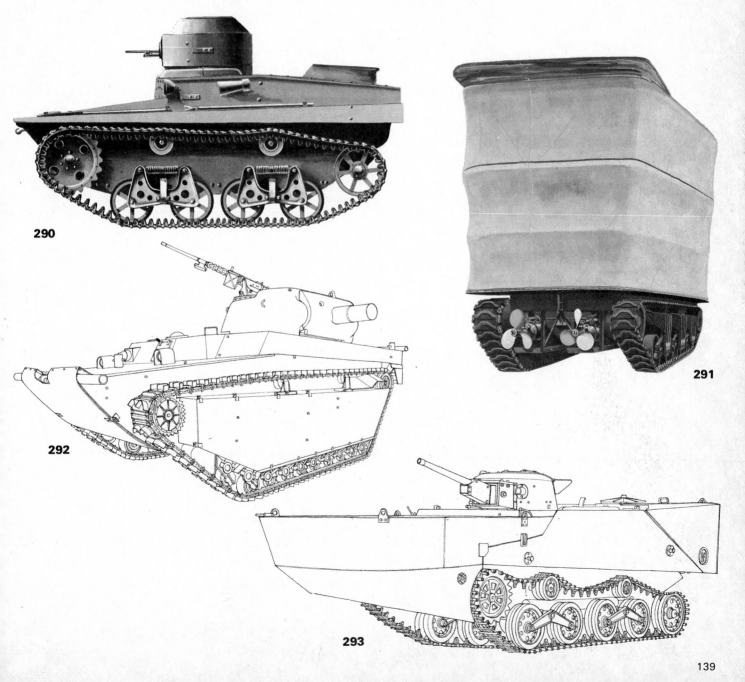

290

291

292

293

Waders and Assailants

Another way of getting an armoured vehicle through a water barrier was to make it wade. It was quite easy to waterproof vehicles so that they could enter the water up to their air inlets, but since most major water obstacles were deeper than that, deep wading techniques had to be evolved. The British were first in this field when they attached a breathing tube to an A-9 tank (294) in 1939 and drove the tank successfully underwater — but there they let the idea rest when more important matters needed urgent attention.

Next to try were the Germans who attached a flexible hose to a buoy that floated on the surface and allowed air to be drawn into a submerged PzKpfw-III (295) which was totally sealed. There were not many fatalities, it seems. This device was first intended for use in the invasion of Britain but, when that did not take place, the specially trained crews (and the training of underwater crews poses many physiological and psychological problems) carried out an unopposed crossing of the River Bug on the first day of the Russian Campaign in 1941 and later were used under the Dnieper.

Faced with the difficulty of finding bridges strong enough for their Tiger Is (296), the Germans fitted breathing (or schnorkel) tubes to all versions of this tank, though it seems not to have been used very much in practice. But since those days, in an effort to solve the problem of crossing water obstacles, nearly all the world's most modern tanks have been designed to accept this facility — with practical advantages that have yet to be demonstrated in action.

Even more detrimental to movement in the second half of the war were dense minefields. Clearance by hand took too long and often led to heavy casualties if the minefield was covered by fire. Hence armour had to be called in, and though several mechanical devices had already been turned down in England, the sheer desperation of the situation in the Western Desert made the British convert a few Matilda tanks to flail the ground ahead with chains carried on a rotating drum. This was Baron Flail, whose immediate successor was the Scorpion flail attachment, that could be mounted on a Sherman or Valentine tank (see page 107) in addition to Matilda. Here we see an unarmed Baron (297) in which the flail was powered by a Ford V8 engine.

Much more powerful and, better still, fully armed for battle when not flailing was the Sherman Crab (298) whose drum was driven from the main tank engine. A maximum speed of only $1\frac{1}{2}$ mph could be reached while flailing and the thick cloud of dust or mud thrown up usually obscured the crew's vision (all sorts of station-keeping devices were tried out, but, in the last resort, practice alone overcame this problem), while the main armament was prevented from engaging the enemy. In consequence, flails were highly vulnerable to enemy action when beating their way through a minefield, and it became mandatory for other gun tanks to escort them at this moment — a task for DDs on the beaches, for instance.

Other far less effective mine clearance devices, all of which stemmed from the past, were Ploughs (299) and Rollers (300). Though much simpler in construction than flails, they were respectively in the habit either of failing to push the mine fully to one side, or else the weight of the roller would not always be enough to detonate a well-buried mine. Of the pair, Plough may have been worthwhile on soft ground where the flail would bog down. There were ripostes to all these devices, of course — a delayed fuse was particularly effective if it could be timed to set the mine off under the flail. Even so, flails continue to have their uses to this day, and the mere fact of their existence makes minelaying more complex.

294

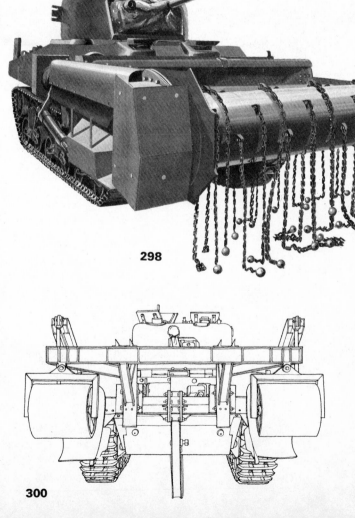

298

300

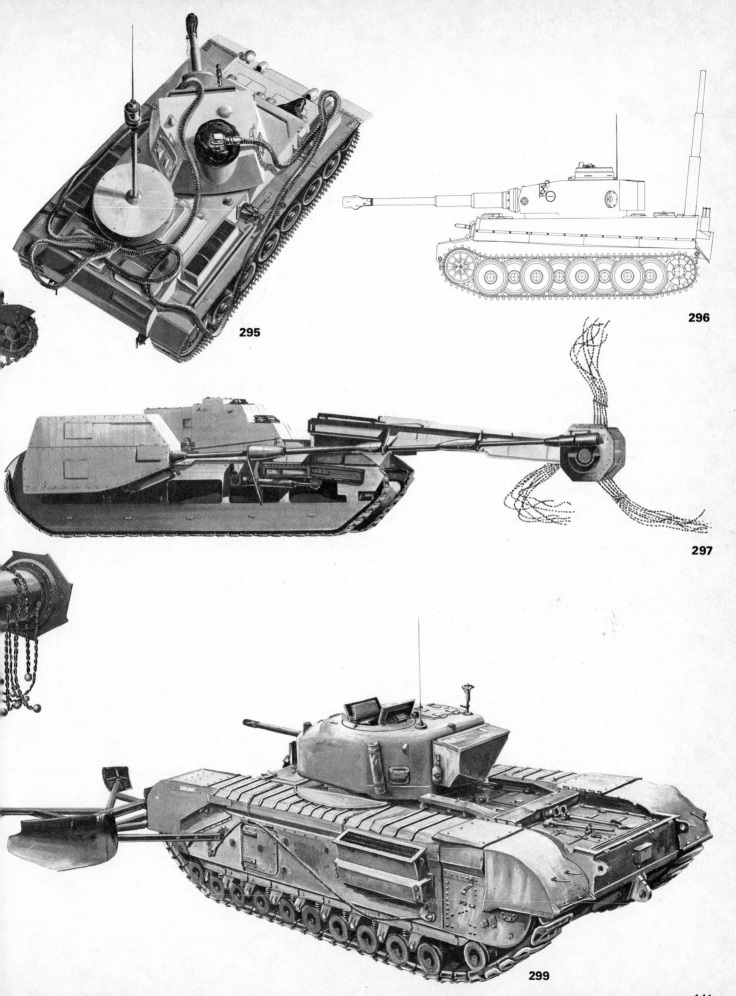

295

296

297

299

Apart from water and minefield obstacles, natural and man-made barriers such as, respectively, sea-shore tidal defences or deep ditches could impede vehicles and cause delay while breaches were made or the ditches filled in. At Cambrai fascines had been used to fill in the Hindenburg Trench; for Middelkirke, in 1917, detachable ramps had been devised and in later years tanks had been made to carry bridges. Specially for the Normandy landings variations on these themes were developed and grouped in the 79th Armoured Division under the British tank pioneer, Major-General Sir Percy Hobart.

The basis of the obstacle-crossing vehicle was an Armoured Vehicle Royal Engineer (AVRE) which sprang from the mind of a Canadian called Denovan. Taking the gun out of a normal Churchill IV tank, he substituted a mortar, called a Petard, which threw a 25-lb charge in a Flying Dustbin a distance of 120 yards — a rugged, general-purpose demolition bomb when used to destroy pill-boxes, beach obstacles, promenades, houses, and almost any structure not strong enough to resist its relatively small charge of explosive. In addition the AVRE carried other types of charge that could be placed by dismounted crewmen working in the shelter of the vehicle's side.

For the quick crossing of gaps the AVRE crew could suspend a detachable 'Small Box Girder' Bridge (SBG) (301) in front of the horns of its tracks, steer its awkward load into position, fire a small charge to release the tackle, and let the bridge drop swiftly into place.

The 'Fascine' (302) mounted on the front of the AVRE, could be rolled over walls to soften the tank's landing on the far side, or into the deep anti-tank ditches. In several of the British sectors, AVREs had to cross sea-walls with an SBG Bridge and then an anti-tank ditch filled by a fascine laid from another AVRE after it had crossed the bridge. And since it was not at all unusual for still more mines

301

303

to be found on the other side of the ditch, Crabs might then be called across the bridge and the fascine before commencing to flail again (see page 138).

It can be seen that the employment of these complex breaching operations – the modern equivalent of ancient siege methods – demanded a carefully worked-out drill with the most intimate teamwork. The crews of the specialized armour were taught to fight their own way through to the open country beyond, their mere presence helping to distract enemy attention from the infantry who, in return, played their part in capturing German anti-tank weapons that threatened the DDs, AVREs, Crabs, and ordinary gun tanks.

Another aid to gap crossing was the 'Ark' (303) – in this instance a Churchill hull surmounted by ramps that could be dropped at either end, after the vehicle had been driven bodily into the gap or stream, allowing other vehicles to drive over.

Praying Mantis (304), however, was something unique – an attempt to give special armoured assistance to infantry in villages and close country by enabling a machine-gun to be raised above walls, pointed into upper floor windows or over high hedges to aim at the enemy without in any way exposing the gunner to view. Mounted on a carrier chassis, it did not enter service: some devices can be so specialized as to be more trouble than they are worth.

Of far greater assistance to infantry were flame-throwing tanks of which this 'Adder' (305), mounted on the Sherman chassis, is an example. When burning napalm (jellied petroleum) is shot into a confined space, such as a pill-box, its effects are suffocating since the flame exhausts all the oxygen present. In the open, flame-throwers do not suffocate to the same extent but can cause serious casualties if the enemy stands firm. But the flame-thrower principally attacks morale, for men fear fire most of all; the numbers who have surrendered unharmed to the suggestion of flame far exceed those who have been burned for being brave.

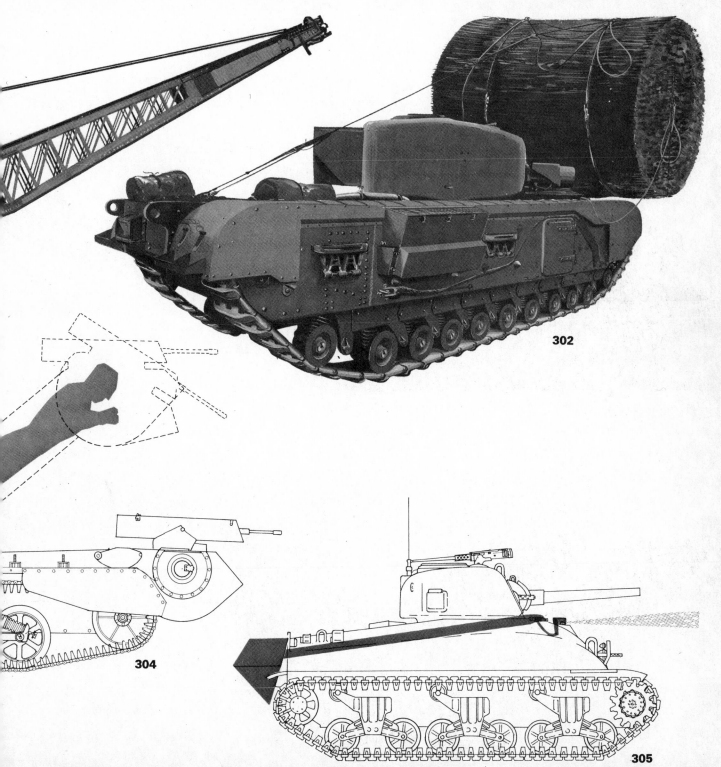

302

304

305

The most devastating and dramatic of all the flame-throwers was the British Crocodile attachment on the Mark VII Churchill tank (306). For a start, the Churchill VII carried 152 mm of armour hung differently to that on the earlier Mark IV. Indeed on the first models it was discovered that the glacis plate was insecure and might drop across the driver's legs following only a light blow — a defect that caused crash modifications to be embodied on the battlefield.

Mark VII also boasted the first British cupola equipped with an array of periscopes giving all round vision, even when closed down. This innovation — common enough already on German tanks — conferred vital benefits on the Crocodile crews who had to work at close range to enemy positions, for the flame-thrower could only project its hot shot up to 120 yards, and usually did not open fire until about 80 yards. 400 gallons of napalm were carried in a 6-ton, armoured trailer towed behind the tank; the link bar, connecting tank and trailer, performed the additional task of transporting the pressurized fuel through a series of flexible joints and pipes that led to the flame gun (307) in the hull gunner's position. Impetus was applied by nitrogen gas from five cylinders (also carried in the trailer) at an initial pressure of 3,000 lb per square inch, reduced to a working pressure of 280 lb. The flame fuel would be shot from the gun at 4 gallons per second, in a solid 'rod' ignited by a spark and petrol vapour system. This 'rod' could be aimed with tolerable accuracy, even though subsequent shots might be difficult to observe because of obscuration by smoke and fire; but a good gunner, aided by simple corrections from his commander, could actually 'post' a 'rod' through a pill-box slit at near extreme range.

It was a recognized fact that when Crocodiles were used in action, the infantry working with them suffered far reduced casualties. But if flame-throwers were not present or normal gun tanks could not pay full attention to their infantry's tormentors, the infantry had to take care of themselves. The original purpose of a tank was to carry infantry through shell and machine-gun fire, and as the threat to infantry became greater, the need for armoured personnel carriers increased. Bren-gun carriers were conceived as armoured vehicles for infantry (see pages 66–67), but were just not available in sufficient quantity to put every man behind armour. Likewise the French and Germans made armoured personnel carriers and issued them as fast as possible to their armies — but inevitable when industry was straining to make tanks to a higher priority, carriers were among the last vehicles to be made.

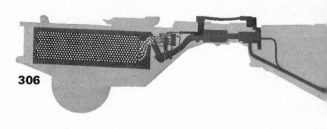

306

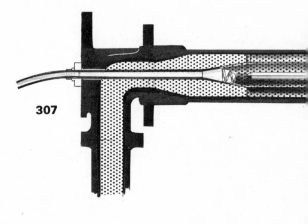

307

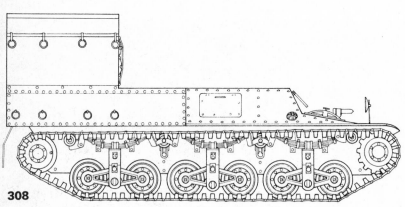

308

309

However, in 1940 the French had their Chenillette Lorraine APC (308) – devised to carry the infantry belonging to their armoured formations and also for use as a tracked supply vehicle. The infantry compartment in the rear carried very few men and was unarmoured on top – nevertheless this vehicle was well in keeping with the armoured idea and showed where the drift of French thought might have gone had not the Germans defeated them so conclusively. As it was, Lorraine went down with defeat though, on at least one occasion, it played its part in rescuing British infantry cut off behind the German lines. Thereafter the Germans gratefully accepted all the Lorraine hulls they could lay their hands on and converted them into a useful fleet of armoured self-propelled guns.

Unlike the French, the Germans put their armoured infantry (later known as Panzer Grenadiers) in armoured half-tracks such as the SdKfz-251 series (309). Something like 18,000 of these 3-ton vehicles must have been manufactured during the Second World War. By giving infantry the ability to keep close to the centre of battle without being unduly exposed to fire, they facilitated co-operation between tanks and infantry and helped maintain the momentum which is so essential in an armoured advance. They also did service as weapon and supply carriers, as well as command vehicles, and were in constant demand in a wide variety of supplementary roles. Here we show the basic infantry carrier.

Of the same school was the US M-3 half-track (310) with a lineage which may be traced back to Combat Car T-2 (see page 77) and service which has ranged from its introduction in 1941 to the present day when it can be found still doing yeomen service in many an army, including the recently victorious Israeli one. Like so many other half-tracked armoured carriers, this one found diverse employment and in the British army, for instance, was a great success when used to carry the fitters who repaired broken-down tanks.

Having foregone building a proper infantry carrier of their own in the Second World War, the British made use of the US M-3 and also took the turrets off a number of Canadian Rams and adapted obsolete artillery carriers to the purpose. Known as Kangaroos (311), these fully tracked machines had the advantage of working alongside tanks whose cross-country performance tallied quite closely with their own – and this was important, for it is often necessary for infantry to follow hard on the heels of the tanks and even, at times, to precede them on to the objective.

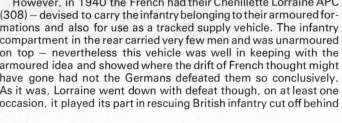

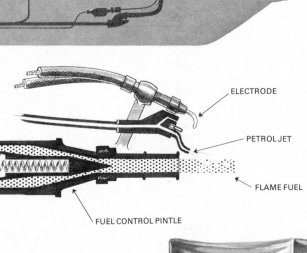

ELECTRODE

PETROL JET

FLAME FUEL

FUEL CONTROL PINTLE

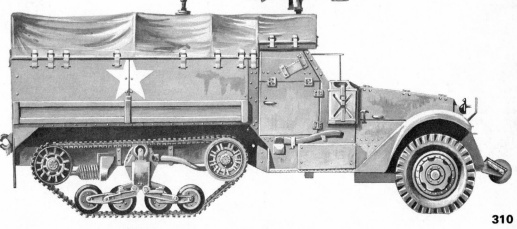

310

311

Post-War Trends

At last, when Britain reorganized her tank industry towards the end of the war, she put a stop to numerous half-baked projects based on the Cromwell design. In 1944 work began on a project called A-41 and by early 1945 the first batch of an entirely new type of medium tank was being rushed into service before the war ended. This was Centurion I whose successors, to this day, bestride the battlefields like giants, though the five sent to Germany to try to catch the last whiffs of the Second World War were, symbolically, just too late.

Centurion I mounted the 76.2-mm gun plus a 20-mm machine-gun and weighed 47 tons. The double skinned hull that once housed the suspension in the old cruisers was superseded by a single plate and an external suspension system, and — a great moment in British tank design — the glacis plate was sloped at last.

But Mark I was nothing like as efficient as Mark III (312), shown here in cutaway, for this machine, first seen in 1948, contained a wealth of wartime experience supplemented by a study of German records, and took advantage of the latest technology in gun making and electronics. Indeed, although the armour was better designed than on any previous British tank and the cross-country perform-ance good, it was the gunnery equipment that took pride of place. Not only was the new 84-mm gun, with its muzzle velocity of 4,800 feet per second, extremely accurate, the weapon itself was stabi-lized both in elevation and azimuth by means of gyroscopic equip-ment. That is, it maintained the angle and bearing set by the gunner, regardless of the manoeuvring of the tank. This did not mean that the gun tracked the target but it did provide a very steady platform and assisted accurate fire when on the move, if necessary.

At the end of the First World War the pundits had foretold the eclipse of the tank and to a lesser degree did the same at the end of the Second by pointing out how the increasing killing power of cheap anti-tank weapons would sweep armour from the battlefield unless tanks took on a subsidiary role to infantry and artillery. The pundits also emphasized the success of more exotic types of com-bat, such as airborne landings, and suggested that increased pro-tection would have to be found in night fighting. But airborne landings and night operations, some thought, might be beyond the capability of tanks.

Those who plumped for the decisive qualities of airborne forces had as difficult a row to hoe as the early tank pioneers, and could not quote the same number of decisive victories in their favour. Armour had helped the airborne to a certain extent — the British Tetrarch (313) and the US Locust (314) both played minor roles when air-landed into battle, but their light weight, armour and gun-power told against them and, invariably, no airborne landing that was meant to stay in place felt safe until it had been joined overland by main battle tanks.

313

	Centurion III (312)	Tetrarch (313)	Locust (314)
Weight:	50 tons	7 tons	8 tons
Power Plant:	635 hp	165 hp	162 hp
Crew:	4	3	3
Armour:	152 mm	16 mm	20 mm
Speed:	22 mph	37 mph	40 mph
Armament:	1 84-mm	1 40-mm	1 37-mm
	1 mg	1 mg	1 mg

312

314

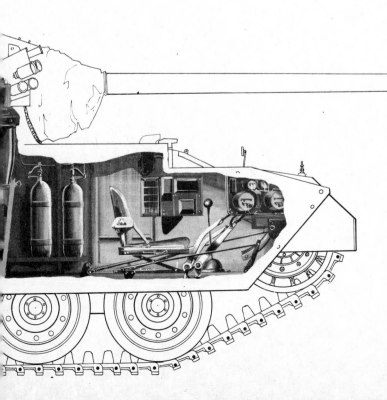

The new threat

On pages 119 and 127 we mentioned the ease with which hollow charge or HEAT rounds could penetrate very thick armour, and showed how much more efficient these warheads were if fitted to an unspun missile. We also pointed out on page 116 how clumsy the enlarged field, anti-tank guns were becoming as the Second World War began to draw to a close. Infantry did not necessarily appreciate guarding a large gun whose bulk and discharge gave away their positions, even though it gave them the best protection against the much feared tank attack. They wanted a large number of cheap, hand-held anti-tank weapons that could easily be concealed and fired without self-advertisement by an enormous flash. Light weapons with the HEAT warhead provided an answer in part, though they lacked the range and extreme accuracy of the conventional high-velocity guns, and by 1944 nearly every infantryman in the American, German, and British armies had some weapon of this sort at his disposal.

Both the Germans and Americans, quite independently, went for rocket types of similar configuration—the former for several kinds, of which Panzerschreck (315) was the largest, the latter for the 50-mm Bazooka (316). The British adopted the spring loaded Projector Infantry Anti-Tank (PIAT) (317) – a rather Heath Robinson looking device that gave no flash but had one or two disconcerting habits, of which the inability to fire pointing below the horizontal (because the bomb slid out of the projector) could be embarrassing.

With very little chance of scoring a hit at much beyond 100 yards, the infantryman who tried his hand against a hostile tank with one of these weapons had his fair share of courage, particularly bearing in mind that tanks were nearly always escorted by other tanks or friendly infantry who were on the lookout for bazooka men. Moreover, even after a penetration of armour had been achieved, there was no guarantee the tank would be destroyed: on more than one occasion tank crews merely closed hatches which had been blown open by the explosion and went on fighting – having incidentally dispelled the rumour that the blast from the internal explosion was in itself lethal.

Nevertheless, infantrymen with these weapons were difficult to spot and their tactical effects profound since the threat alone induced apprehension and caution in the tank crews who were loud in demanding additional, time-consuming protection from infantry – all causing a slowing down in armoured operations which, experience showed, thrived best on speed.

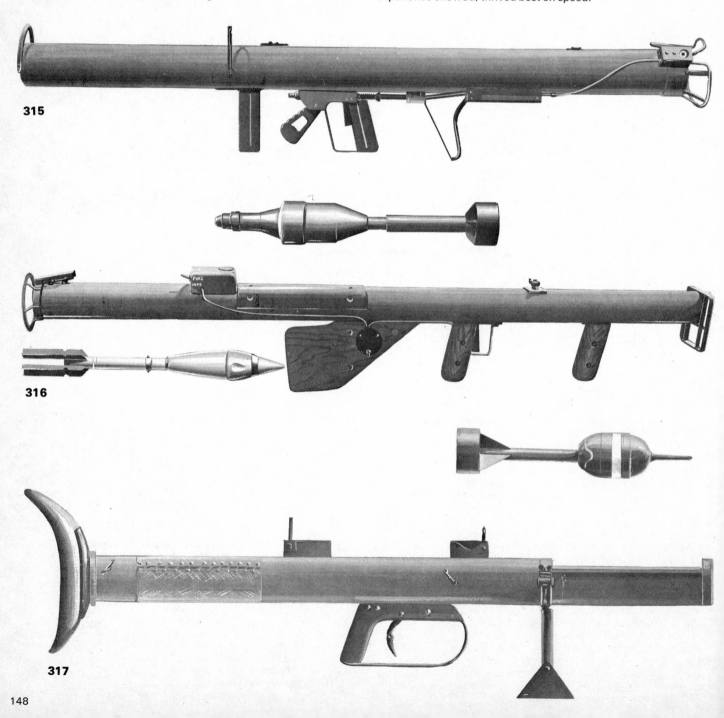

315

316

317

Night and Airborne Warfare

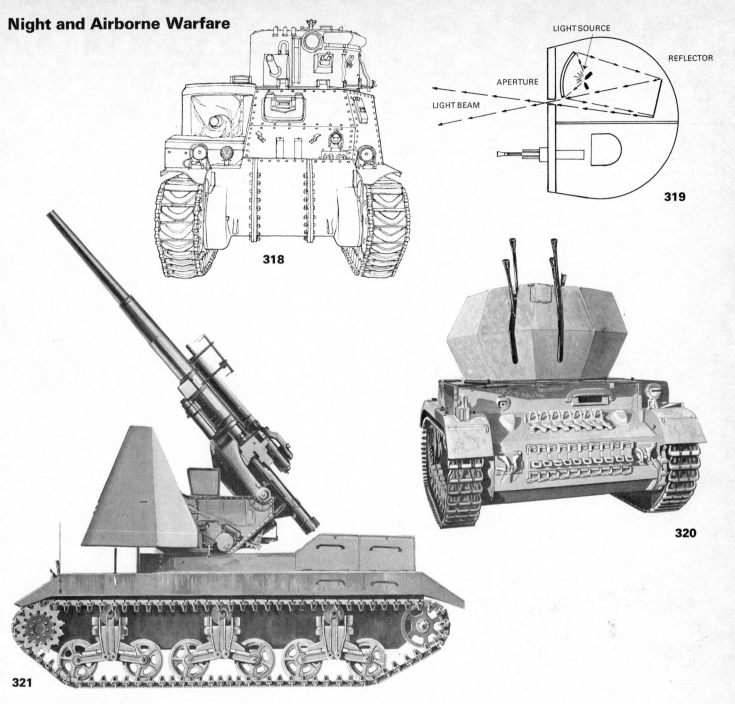

318

LIGHT SOURCE
REFLECTOR
APERTURE
LIGHT BEAM

319

320

321

As the threat to armour by day grew, only slow progress was made in helping tanks to fight at night. The earlier reluctance to do so was understandable, for a tank crew can be blind enough by day when its vision is limited to what can be seen through periscopes and the gunner's telescope: by night that vision is reduced still further because the telescope can no longer accept sufficient light to allow the gunner to aim his weapons. Hence tank leaders tended to use the night to cloak surprise movements from one part of the front to another, but to decline combat in darkness except in dire emergency or when the enemy appeared to be hopelessly disorganized.

Night fighting by the light of searchlights was examined in the 1930s but, for lack of encouragement, did not get far. However, a French invention to mount a very powerful carbon-arc light behind armour received British encouragement before the war and was one of the few specialized tank projects to get their whole-hearted backing even in the difficult days of 1940. From this came the Canal Defence Light tank (CDL) (318) which the British mounted successively on Matildas, Grants, and Centurions – though only the Grant model aspired to operational status. The 13,000,000 candlepower arc light (319) had the advantage that it could be focused through a slit in the armour and therefore was not as vulnerable as an unprotected searchlight. As an aid to shooting by night in conjunction

with ordinary gun tanks it was unrivalled, but the concept suffered from over-secrecy because of a subsidiary claim that a flicker device would so blind the enemy that the CDL tanks could not be shot at. In fact this claim was exaggerated, while the extreme secrecy accorded to CDL made it difficult for front-line soldiers to learn how to use it, with the result that, in the end, it was put aside for want of sufficient interest after millions of pounds had been spent on its development, its construction, and the training of crews.

Towards the very end of the war, when Allied air power had driven the German air force from the sky, German armour found it difficult to move even at a distance from the front by daylight for fear of air attack. In the event this forced them into becoming fantastically good at concealment, but it also made them give special attention to tanks mounting a battery of anti-aircraft guns to move alongside their armoured formations. Here is one such version – Wirbelwind (320) with its four 20-mm guns. The Allies also built anti-aircraft tanks, using the hulls of obsolete tanks in the same manner as the Germans. We show here a rare version – the 3.7-in anti-aircraft gun on a Canadian Ram chassis (321) that never got beyond the experimental stage but might also have had an anti-tank role in emergencies.

Contenders for an unimaginable battle

At the end of the Second World War vast fleets of armoured vehicles were left standing idle, large-scale production had to be run down, and a great scrapping programme set in motion to turn swords into ploughshares. There were enough old fighting vehicles left over to satisfy the reduced need of many armies for a decade or more to come – and some do service to this day – while the ones that had not come off the drawing-boards or passed beyond the experimental stage tended to mark time for shortage of financial backing. In America, above all, the feeling that armour might have passed its days of greatness, took quite a firm hold. In Russia, however, the opposite idea held sway and soon, in concert with a belief that armoured mobility might be the only antidote to nuclear hazards and the deepening freeze of cold war politics and pressures, this faith and the continuing rise of Soviet armour came to the attention of the Western powers. Experience in Korea in 1950 showed that, while armour could be contained by strong defences, it was as deadly as ever once on the rampage.

So the disarmament and stagnation of post-First World War days only sounded a faint echo after the Second, and the development of fighting vehicles began again – and apace. Moreover, it was soon discovered that what had been a slim commercial export market in the 1920s, boomed in the 1950s and the selling of tanks along with other weapons occupied an important place in national economic policies. In this atmosphere the construction of tanks that might have to fight in a sophisticated

tactical nuclear war, and which were good value for money to suit tighter peacetime budgets, could only come from nations with large-scale production facilities – and this put the Russians and the Americans, followed by the British and French, in the forefront – each practising cold-war politics to steal an advantage from the other, sometimes under-cutting in foreign markets, one suspects, regardless of loyalties or alliances.

The most important Russian development to follow T-34/85 (after the latter had found its way into the Chinese Communist Army and thence to the North Korean Army and the armies of Eastern Europe) was T-54 (322). T-54 came into being through an intermediary model, T-44, which demonstrated once again the care that Russian designers were taking in the angling of armour. But while T-44 only mounted an 85-mm gun, T-54, when it appeared in 1954, had the 100-mm gun such as, up to then, had only appeared on self-propelled guns. Here was a new sophistication in Russian tank construction, for though T-54 had the same ruggedness of its predecessors, it also mounted much better electrical traversing gear and was soon to exhibit all sorts of modern gunnery devices and night fighting aids, such as a searchlight with an infra-red capability which would enable it to shoot in the dark.

Apart from the British Centurion III (see page 146) the West had nothing which was immediately ready to match T-54. The American pause in tank development reflected their army's uncertainty of the future and their reluctance to regard the tank as an anti-tank as well as a support weapon. To them the heavily armed and armoured tank was of doubtful value, but caught in the sudden blast of the cold war with T-34/85s cutting loose in

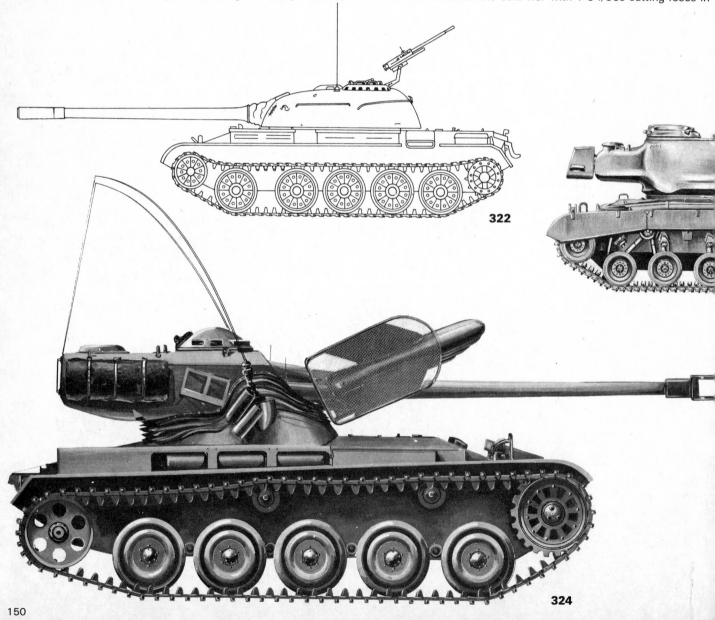

322

324

Korea, they had to improvise on the Pershing design with which they had finished the war, producing successively the M-46 (a reworked M-26), M-47, and M-48 – each an improvement on its predecessor but a bit below the standard of its foreign competitors. Here we show M-47 (323) (called Patton after the American tank leader) incorporating a newly-designed turret on the old M-46 hull. A year later would come M-48 with M-47's turret and a new hull – the whole process indicative of the dilemma of improvisation in which the Americans found themselves.

At the same time the French, with understandable nationalistic instinct, revived their own tank industry, trying to take up where they had left off in 1940 but making use of what they could learn from modern foreign equipments left on their hands. Their efforts to produce a medium or heavy tank were a long time coming to fruition, but in 1949 they announced a new light tank that had been specified in 1946 – AMX-13 (324). This tank was designed to be airportable and tried to make up for its lack of protection by speed and the excellence of its long 75-mm gun (a replica of the same 75 as on the German Panther) fed by an automatic loader. Although sold to many nations, AMX-13 has not been a great success in action, its light armour not being compensated for by its hitting power and speed. The version shown here carries the SS-11 wire-guided missile with a range of 3,000 yards – a line-of-sight missile whose long time of flight only partially enhances hitting power, for the time of flight may impose even greater uncertainties on AMX-13's chance of survival by forcing it to loiter for a fatal length of time in an exposed fire position. Nevertheless, this early, service example of the futuristic anti-tank guided missile incorporated in a tank was

technologically and tactically very significant.

Also in the airborne category was the US Ontos (325) light tank with its six 106-mm recoilless guns. This was another attempt to mount a weapon with a heavy punch on a light carriage that would otherwise not be capable of absorbing the forces imposed by firing an equivalent high-velocity gun. It has not yet been used in a serious anti-armour engagement where the problems of reloading might be awkward and where its light armour would probably cause it to suffer the same fate as AMX-13.

Also just airportable, but primarily designed as a swimming tank to spearhead river crossings, the Russian light PT-76 (326) has many interesting features though it should not be assumed that she in any way cancels Russian dedication to the omnipotence of medium and heavy tanks. PT-76 was specially designed with a boat-shaped hull to raise its speed in water and this, with propulsion by hydrojets, probably makes it the fastest swimming tank in the world with a speed of 6 knots in water. But clearly with such a light gun and only thin armour, it could not survive long in a tank mêlée.

	T-54 (322)	M-47 (323)	AMX-13 (324)	Ontos (325)	PT-76 (326)
Weight:	36 tons	44 tons	14.5 tons	7 tons	14 tons
Power Plant:	580 hp	810 hp	270 hp	—	240 hp
Crew:	4	5	3	3	3
Armour:	105 mm	115 mm	40 mm	—	40 mm
Speed:	34 mph	35 mph	35 mph	40 mph	27 mph
Armament:	1 100-mm	1 90-mm	1 75-mm	6 106-mm	1 76-mm
	2 mg	2 mg	4 SS11	1 mg	1 mg
			1 mg		

323

325

326

The advent of nuclear weapons to the battlefield brought it home to soldiers that tactics of the future would be conditioned even more by evasion – but now of a different kind since the threat from radio-active fall-out made survival dependent either upon digging a very deep hole or living in vehicles whose outer skin gave a measure of protection against radiation, as well as shot, and whose mobility gave the means of escape from a contaminated area. For some time after the Second World War, only tanks gave a modicum of protection against radiation. But even they fell short of a reason-able level since air-conditioning was practically ignored and so radioactive particles would quickly be sucked into the fighting com-partments among the crew rather as gas was sucked in during the First World War.

This threat was far worse for unarmoured artillery and infantry. Hence the desire to put all guns on a self-propelled basis behind armour in an air-conditioned compartment gained momentum, even though the ultimate aim has yet to be fulfilled in most first-class armies to this day. The time had passed when an im-provisation on an old tank chassis would satisfy either the gunners or the infantry. All fighting soldiers now demanded specially-designed carriers, though not always did they get their way. The American T-99 E1 (327) with its 155-mm howitzer, like so many other US SP artillery pieces after the war, was built upon the old M-26 tank chassis, but the fully-enclosed armoured crew com-partment was an important departure from early American practice – over twenty years after the British Birch gun.

The Russians, who have been among the slowest to mount field artillery on armoured chassis, had been among the first in war to put anti-tank weapons behind armour – and this policy continues to the present day. Here we have the ASU-85 (328) based on the PT-76 chassis. Yet it is interesting to see more specialization creeping into their designs, for this machine seems to be com-mitted to airborne forces and has done away with the amphibious propulsion that belongs to PT-76.

The British and Germans have taken a different line when adapting vehicles to self-propelled artillery. With their Jagdpanzer the latter have merely taken a version of the armoured personnel carrier HS-30 (see page 154), and fixed a limited traverse 90-mm gun in front (329) just as they did with cast-off tanks in the Second World War. But the British have done more than take the chassis of their existing armoured personnel carrier – FV-432 – to carry their 105-mm artillery piece; from the start they worked to a special design in order to come up with a fighting compartment that gives complete protection to the crew. This is Abbott (330): it will be noticed that only a limited supply of ammunition can be carried in this vehicle, so like all artillery pieces that fire great quantities of shells, it is dependent on extensive resupply from supply vehicles that might need to be no more invulnerable than itself. Unlike the other vehicles on this page, however, it can be made to swim by raising side-screens and driving itself through the water with its tracks.

That a need exists for continued orthodox artillery support on the battlefield – with or without nuclear weapons being tossed around – there can be little doubt, even though the number of targets with vulnerability to high explosive shells get less as even more men are carried under armour instead of being left unprotected. But there will still be the need for the destruction of strong enemy emplace-ments (which suggests that only heavy guns of greater than 105 mm may be appropriate), the need to lay smoke-screens of pro-tracted duration, and the desirability of firing great quantities of parachute flares to illuminate the night battlefield. And since battle tanks cannot carry sufficient ammunition to engage in large-scale programmes, it will be left to artillery to fill the gap.

328

330

	T-99 E1 (327)	ASU-85 (328)	Jagdpanzer (329)	Abbott (330)
Weight:	26 tons	14 tons	16 tons	18 tons
Power Plant:	500 hp	240 hp	235 hp	240 hp
Crew:	5	3	3	4
Speed:	30 mph	27 mph	35 mph	30 mph
Armament:	1 155-mm	1 85-mm	1 90-mm	1 105-mm
	1 mg	1 mg	1 mg	1 mg

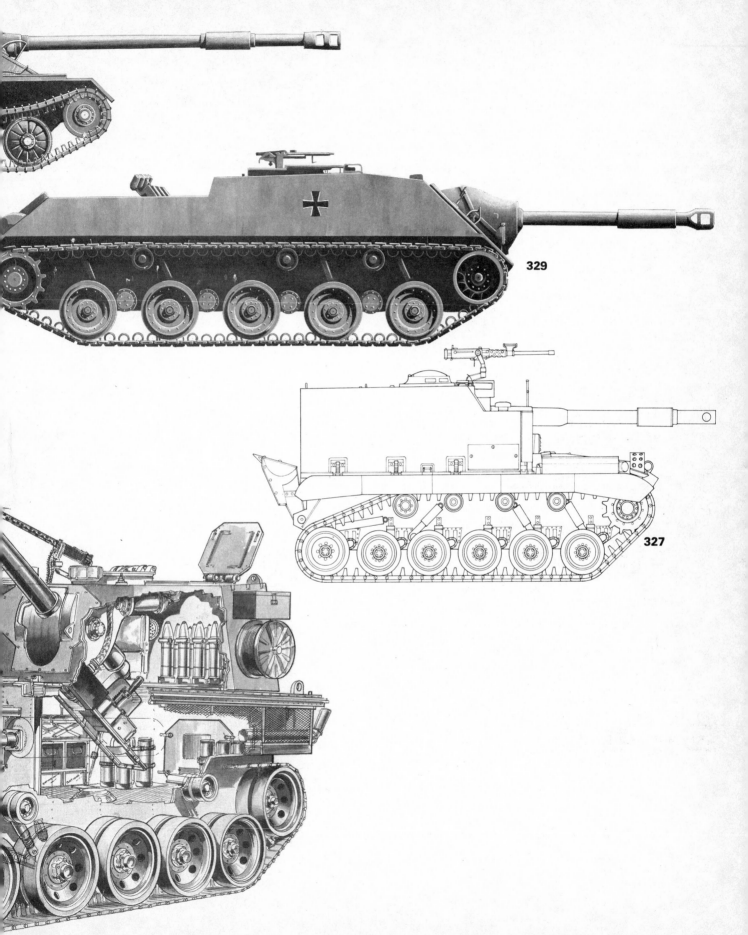

329

327

Although the gunners could be satisfied with adapting existing tracked vehicles to carry their guns, the infantry were forced to insist upon special configurations for their armoured carrier, since it is usually impossible to adapt a tank hull to enable infantrymen to get in and out without climbing over the top and thereby exposing themselves unnecessarily to fire. It has been generally accepted by most armies that a specially-designed infantry carrier should allow its men to enter and exit through doors at the rear. But at that point agreement just about stops since certain fundamental tactical differences are then introduced into the discussion. Along with others the British army, until recently, adopted the policy that infantry carriers ought to be armoured taxis which transported their passengers to the front, dropped them at the mercy of the enemy and smartly withdrew. Hence, for some time, the British army was content with a wheeled APC — the Saracen (331) — that went well on the roads, bogged all too easily cross-country, required great skill to drive and maintain, and which could not swim.

The Germans always believed that infantry must travel in their carriers close to the forefront of battle and the Americans tended to agree when they produced their M-59 (332). This heavy vehicle's layout did not permit the whole crew to engage the enemy when mounted; but it could swim and it foretold the shape of many APCs to come. Indeed, the American M-113, which superseded M-59, managed an enormous reduction in size and weight, partly by making use of aluminium armour, and this vehicle (which has been in great demand in Vietnam) has been produced in thousands in a period when the tactical idea of the fighting APC (as opposed to the taxi) has gained almost universal acceptance.

Strangely enough, the Germans, who most loudly espoused the cause of the fighting carrier, accepted the Hispano-Suiza 30 (333) with exiting through the top. Yet in so doing they solved one of the more difficult dilemmas facing the designer when he tries to let all the infantrymen use their personal weapons from the vehicle. The Germans had only to open up and lean over the side of HS-30 — the Americans could not do that with the box-like M-59.

In their latest APC the Russians, with their so-called BMP-76PB (Amphibious Armoured Infantry Combat Vehicle) (334) have tried to solve all problems at once in a small vehicle which contains a 76-mm gun, a small Sagger anti-tank guided missile, a crew of three and eight sardine-packed infantrymen in the back. How they crouch down to fire through the loop-holes is difficult to imagine — but this derivation of the PT-76 series is certainly an improvement on earlier Russian APCs which often had no overhead cover at all.

Clearly this Russian vehicle has little room for ammunition stowage, so very few of the Sagger missiles will be carried. Moreover the Sagger, which is a line-of-sight missile related to the SS-11 family, has only a small HEAT warhead and is therefore unlikely to have a very high chance of effecting a kill when hitting its target.

The British Swingfire line-of-sight anti-tank missile mounted on an FV-432 — which is the British equivalent of the US 113 APC — and called FV-438 (335), is a very different proposition to Sagger. FV-438 can carry a good load of this hard-hitting missile under armour and can fire it either under the commander's control through the elevating periscope, or by parking the vehicle out of view and allowing the commander to engage the enemy from a remote position using a special sight. This means that FV-438, or any guided missile vehicle which can open fire by remote control, has a considerable tactical advantage over a tank with a gun which has to expose itself to the enemy in order to engage.

But clearly, for the reasons given on page 151, the guided missile, though a most useful complement giving better destructive power at long range, is not yet ready to take over from the gun. It is upon gunned, main battle tanks that every army still relies and it is with a look at these that we conclude.

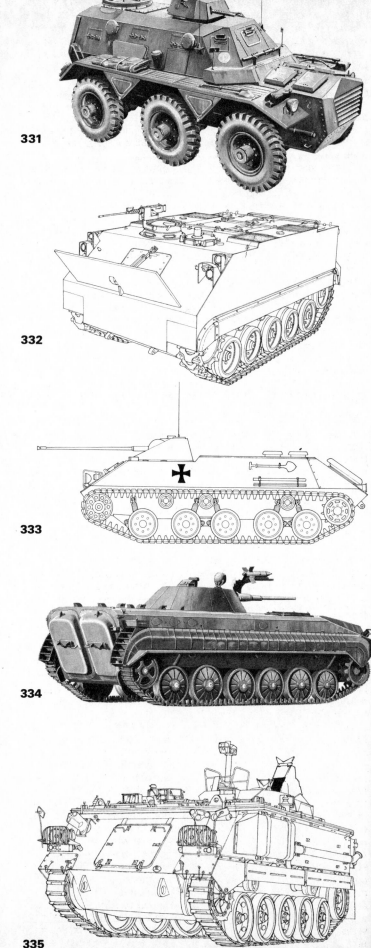

331

332

333

334

335

	Saracen (331)	M-59 (332)	HS-30 (333)	BMP-76PB (334)	FV-438 (335)
Weight:	10 tons	19 tons	15 tons	13 tons	17 tons
Power Plant:	170 hp	290 hp	235 hp	280 hp	240 hp
Crew:	12	12	8	11	3
Armour:	12 mm	10 mm	30 mm	10 mm	15 mm
Speed:	43 mph	32 mph	40 mph	36 mph	32 mph
Armament:	1 mg	1 mg	1 20-mm	1 76-mm Sagger	Swingfire 1mg

Just as there has been a tactics debate surrounding the prospective employment of APCs, so there has been deep discussion concerning the future role and employment of tanks, and in truth the debate has not changed much in substance since T-34 first gave the Germans a fright. Still the argument revolves around whether the tank is a primary or a secondary weapon – whether it should act independently, as part of a team, or as a sort of mobile anti-tank gun. Interwoven in the debate – but of crucial importance to a designer trying to adjust his compromises to the soldier's dilemmas – is the eternal search for a tolerable balance between armour, gun-power, and mobility. And the solutions are still determined by the nature of the battle to be fought, terrain and climate, the calibre of man to crew the tanks, the money and production facilities available, and so on – the reader knows it already.

But if there is general agreement on what size armament, what speed, and what level of protection is required – and at the moment most armies demand a specified and reasonable level of protection (with or without air filtration) and insist on nothing less than a speed of 25 mph and a 105-mm gun – then the tanks which emerge are likely to be very similar to look at and not so very different in internal detail. The British Centurion (see page 146) when given a 105-mm gun, as in the later Marks, looks and performs like many another tank of the above specification that came into service after 1960. Little is told of armour thicknesses because, although most nations publish details of their fighting vehicles always in hope of making a sale, they have to be reticent on the subject of armour protection since it is not just knowledge of the maximum thickness at the most vulnerable point that is of interest to hostile nations, but the relative thicknesses of armour protecting less vital parts which, taken together, expose the roots of a nation's armoured philosophy and policy.

The Russians persevered with T-54 and its 100-mm gunned successors for nearly a decade and then came out with T-62 (336) which looks quite like T-54 except that it has a new 115-mm gun with a fume-extractor midway down the gun barrel. (The fume-extractor is to be found on most modern tanks after it was discovered that, by drilling the barrel and surrounding it with a hollow chamber, the fumes could be drawn off after firing instead of being allowed to waft back and foul the fighting compartment.) Along with nearly every other modern tank, T-62 can wade at depth by the use of a schnorkel tube and has an infra-red, night fighting searchlight mounted above the mantlet.

A joker in the pack came from Vickers with their Main Battle Tank (337) armed with a British 105-mm gun and powered by the same engine used by the British Chieftain (see page 156). Fast, lightly armoured and comparatively cheap, it has been built in India under the name of Vijayanta. By raising a collapsible screen it has been given a swimming capability, attaining a water speed of 4 mph. As a private venture it is, thus, in the truly competitive tradition of the first Vicker's tank of the 1920s.

The Japanese Type 61 (338) looks so similar to the American M-47 series that one wonders why they bothered to make it at all. Yet this vehicle is interesting since it incorporates almost the same controlled differential steering as featured in the pre-war Japanese tanks and has been improved in internal layout because the Japanese have been able to take advantage of their population's small physical stature to reduce the space normally allotted to a Western crew – a factor that can be critical.

Germany's Leopard (339) and France's AMX-30 (340) both shared the same incentive to keep close to 30 tons in weight and both have appeared near the 40-ton mark. Although both mount a 105-mm gun, only the Germans have bought British since the French have adopted a lower velocity gun of their own to fire HEAT ammunition: but this sort of warhead does best when it is not spinning, so the charge is made to rest on internal roller bearings in the round to counteract the spin of the warhead induced by the rifling of the gun. No doubt a good chance of a kill is obtained, but a low-velocity gun will still present the gunner with the usual range assessment problems. In power to weight both these tanks are very strong and this gives the Leopard, in particular, a fast cross-country performance. Unhappily this is not as simple a proposition as it sounds, since a crew that is cut and bruised by being flung about because the suspension is not equal to speeds above 30 mph (and no modern suspension is) is not fit to fight. It is a fact that while modern, compact engines and gunpower have risen sharply, suspensions have not kept pace.

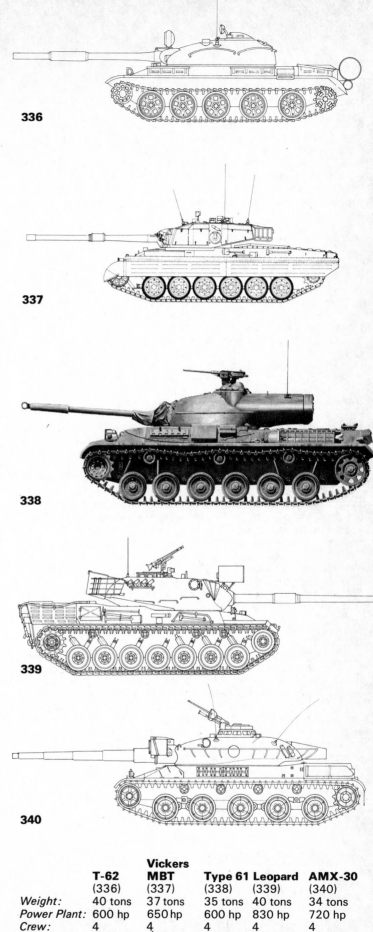

336

337

338

339

340

	T-62 (336)	Vickers MBT (337)	Type 61 (338)	Leopard (339)	AMX-30 (340)
Weight:	40 tons	37 tons	35 tons	40 tons	34 tons
Power Plant:	600 hp	650 hp	600 hp	830 hp	720 hp
Crew:	4	4	4	4	4
Speed:	30 mph	35 mph	35 mph	40 mph	40 mph
Armament:	115-mm 1 mg	1 105-mm 1 mg	1 90 mm 2 mg	1 105-mm 1 mg	1 105-mm 1 mg

The Future

341

It remains to be seen if the guided missile or some quite revolutionary 'flying tank' (as has sometimes been postulated by inspired visionaries) eventually sweeps conventional fighting machines off the battlefield. But it must be recorded that, so far, every new anti-tank weapon that has been hailed as marking the end of the tank, from the early anti-tank rifle to the bazooka, has only made tank designers and commanders more crafty and successful in their art. There are still a few red faces among successive generations who foretold the end of the tank – though they rarely suggested a more feasible way of crossing a shell- and bullet-infested field – but it *could* be that nations who continue to invest millions of pounds in future generations of tanks might also have red faces within the next decade.

For better or worse, tank development evolves. First of a new generation off the production line was the British 'Chieftain' (341) – and it does not mean that, just because it is of relatively orthodox shape, it is not a better fighting vehicle than more sophisticated looking designs. For Chieftain, unlike all its competitors, puts armour protection and simplicity on the highest priority and matches them with a gun of unparalleled power and accuracy. In a way Chieftain is a gamble against the emergent power of guided weapons armed with HEAT warheads, and because those weapons do not yet seem to have justified their promise, the gamble looks like paying off. Chieftain is heavy and bulky, yet in a fire position shows less of itself than the other two battle tanks illustrated on this page. By means of a 'ranging' machine-gun matched to the 120-mm gun Chieftain establishes the range to the target by short bursts of fire; its ammunition is stowed with least chance of fire risk (ammunition is quite the most frequent cause of battlefield fires) and a good crew can shoot a great many 120-mm rounds one after the other.

The Swedish Bofors S – so-called Tank (342) (for nobody can really classify this rather super self-propelled gun with the turreted tank) – only mounts a 105-mm gun and two machine-guns. It is an engineer's dream (or nightmare) powered by the same engine as

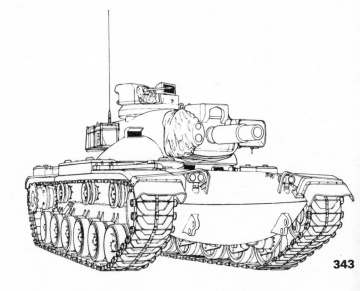

343

in the British FV 432 with a Boeing gas-turbine as auxiliary, and fitted with an ingenious hydraulic system that enables the suspension to raise and lower the hull. For this suspension does much more than help give the crew a smooth ride: along with the normal neutral turning capability of regenerative steering it enables the commander/gunner or driver to aim the whole tank and, therefore, the gun at the target. Thus all the essential automotive, transmission, steering and suspension functions are merged to get the gun on target – resulting in a complex but compact machine with superb protection from well-sloped armour, high rate of main

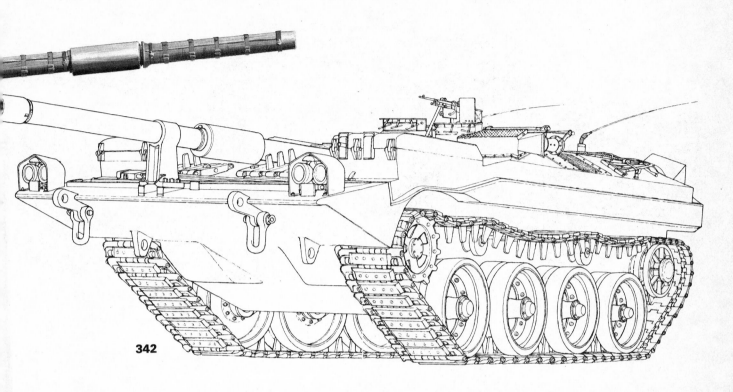

342

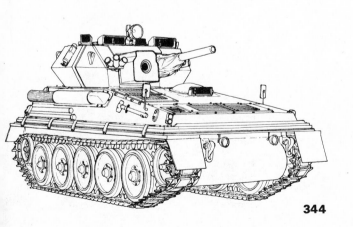

344

Germany, failed because the Germans rejected the proposed Shillelagh weapon system and the US Congress vetoed the project on grounds of excessive cost. Even in its early days MBT-70 (later known as XM-803) cost £215,000 against £105,000 for a Chieftain. So the Americans have been forced into modification of M-60, first bringing into service M-60 A2 (343) with the Shillelagh.

Shillelagh is, in many ways, superior to SS-11 and Swingfire. As a gun it can fire conventional high explosive rounds while its anti-tank guided missile is guided by an electronic link — the gunner simply laying his cross-wires on the target and the missile following the line of sight.

Finally the British have produced the Scorpion light tank (344) which is air portable and can be equipped with a 76-mm (as shown), or a 30-mm gun, or guided missiles. It is the first all aluminium armoured tank and is intended for reconnaissance rather than combat. In consequence it has been given sophisticated night viewing and radar devices.

The debate continues with politicians and economists calling the tune to the soldiers. Each purchaser must decide on a best buy when replacing equipments that are now in service and wearing out. Combat Vehicles are options for the future in a world that tries to maintain peace through a balance of military power and are important check weights in that balance. They have been as often misunderstood as correctly evaluated in the past. Either way their influence has been enormous and sometimes decisive. It could be the same again in the future.

armament fire assisted by an automatic loader — and a dreadful potential for being put out of action if even one of a vast number of components is broken. For once this machine is broken down it is all but useless, whereas a broken-down turreted tank might still traverse its gun and fight on.

The USA, too, has had its tank design problems. M-48 was improved upon in power plant, armour and given a British 105-mm gun because research into high velocity guns in the USA had been neglected. The improvement was called M-60 A1. Then a fundamentally new tank, called MBT-70, a joint venture with West

	Chieftain (341)	S Tank (342)	M-60 A2 (343)	Scorpion (344)
Weight:	50 tons	37 tons	45 tons	7.2 tons
Power Plant:	650 hp	730 hp	750 hp	195 hp
Crew:	4	3	4	3
Speed:	26 mph	30 mph	32 mph	50 mph
Armament:	1 120-mm	1 105-mm	1 152-mm	1 76-mm
	2 mg	2 mg	2 mg	1 mg

Index

AIR PORTABLE COMBAT VEHICLES
British
Tetrarch; 122, 146.
USA
Christie Airborne Combat Car 1932; 69, 70.
Locust; 146.
Ontos; 151.
ANCILLARY EQUIPMENT AND COMPONENTS
Armour
In general; 119
Aluminium; 119, 154, 157
Bolted; 100, 105.
Cast; 100, 119.
Face-hardened; 119.
Frame; 100.
Homogeneous; 100, 119.
Riveted; 100, 105, 119.
Spaced; 119, 120.
Welded; 100, 105, 119.
Brakes
Independent's; 52.
Engines and Power Plants
AEC; 74, 105.
Armstrong-Siddeley 90 hp; 54.
Bedford twin six; 102, 111.
Boeing gas turbine; 156.
Chrysler 5 bank; 129.
Daimler 1899; 9.
　　　105 hp; 24, 25, 31, 111.
Ford Model T; 39.
Ford V-8; 92, 107.
General Motors; 105, 129.
Hispano Suiza 750 hp; 69.
Liberty; 69, 104.
Maybach V-12; 118.
Ricardo 150 hp; 36, 110.
　　　180 hp; 74.
Steam; 43.
Submarine diesel 800 hp; 21.
Rolls-Royce Meteorite; 108.
Russian V-12; 110, 113.
Wright Whirlwind; 111, 129.
Gearboxes and Transmissions
Braked differential; 122.
Cletrac; 62, 122.
Controlled differential; 122.
Merritt-Brown; 102, 123.
Regenerative; 74, 122.
Wilson; 74.
Stabilisers for guns
129, 146.
Suspensions
Christie; 71.
Hydraulic; 156.
Peerless armoured car; 45.
Renault NC; 71.
Scissors; 71.
Unit sprung; 71.
Vickers trailing; 71.
Tracks
Bowed; 16, 17, 50, 122.
Cable; 50.
Holt; 21, 26, 36.
Manganese steel; 57.
Snake; 50, 51.
Tritton; 23.
Wide Mk. IV; 47.
ANTI-AIRCRAFT COMBAT VEHICLES
In general; 149.
Canadian
Ram with 3.7-inch; 149.
German
Wirbelwind; 149.
ARMOURED CARS
Austrian
Daimler; 10.
Australian
Rhino; 91.

British
AEC III; 136.
Austin; 33, 45.
Beaverette; 136.
Crossley; 84.
Daimler II; 136.
Guy wheeled tank; 85, 136.
Humber IV; 136.
Lanchester; 84.
Peerless; 45.
Rolls-Royce 1914; 17, 18.
Seabrook; 17, 18.
Sizaire-Berwick; 17, 18.
Canadian
Otter; 91.
Dutch
Daf 1938; 91, 119.
French
Charron; 9, 10.
de Dion Bouton; 9.
Panhard 178; 90.
German
Daimler; 9, 10, 17, 19.
Ehrhardt 1906; 10.
　　　1915; 17, 19.
SdKfz-232; 90.
　　　234/2; 136.
　　　254; 77.
Puma; 136.
Italian
Bianchi; 10.
Fiat 40; 90.
Lancia 1915; 17, 19.
Japanese
Sumida M-2593; 90.
New Zealand
Schofield; 77.
Russian
Bronniford BA-10; 91.
South African
Marmon-Herrington II; 90.
　　　VI; 136.
Swedish
Volvo M-40; 91.
USA
Cadillac 1915; 17, 19.
Greyhound; 136.
Staghound; 136.
ARMOURED TRAINS
British; 114.
German; 114.
Russian; 114.
USA; 114.
BATTLES AND CAMPAIGNS
Afghan War; 45.
American Civil War; 7, 12, 114.
Amiens; 33, 37, 45.
Arab/Israeli 1967; 129, 145.
Boer War; 114.
Cambrai; 28, 32, 33, 40, 142.
Chemin des Dames; 26.
Dieppe; 102.
Dunkirk; 102, 105.
East Africa 1941; 90.
El Alamein; 102.
First World War; 13 sqq.
France 1940; 73, 92, 93, 96, 104.
Gaza; 33.
Greece 1941; 93.
India, North West Frontier; 45.
Korea; 150.
Kursk; 128.
Kutna Hora; 6.
Normandy; 130, 132, 138, 142.
North Africa (Western Desert);
　　　93, 105, 109, 112, 136, 140.
Pacific; 139.
Passchendaele; 33.
Poland 1939; 73, 87.
Port Arthur; 12.
Russian 1941–45; 98, 105, 112–15, 118, 140.

Russo-Japanese; 12.
Somme; 26.
Spanish Civil War; 73.
Vietnam; 154.
Villers-Bretonneux; 33.
CHARIOTS AND ANCIENT COMBAT VEHICLES
American two gun; 7, 8.
Assyrian chariots; 4, 5.
Cowan's machine; 7, 8.
da Vinci's machine; 7, 8.
Hussite battle wagons; 7.
Hurrian chariots; 5.
Kaiser's land battleships; 7, 8, 36.
Siege devices; 5.
Ur war carts; 1, 2, 5.
Valturio's machine; 7.
Vigevano's machine; 7.
COMMUNICATIONS EQUIPMENT
Pigeons; 40, 41.
Radios; 78.
British Mk IV wireless tank; 40.
British radio 1918; 40.
French Renault TSF; 40.
Semaphore; 40, 41.
CREW POSITIONS AND EQUIPMENT
In general; 121.
Driving position in British Mk V; 36.
Face masks; 44.
Leather helmets; 44.
Locations and tasks; 121.
Respirators; 44.
EXPERIMENTAL DEVICES AND VEHICLES
Miscellaneous vehicles
Ansaldo wheel-cum-track; 68, 69.
Bullock tractor; 21.
Christie 1928; 68, 69.
de Mole 'tank'; 16.
Flying Elephant; 27, 33.
Holt tractor 1906; 14, 15.
Killen-Strait tractor; 21.
Landswerk wheel-cum-track; 76, 77.
Little Willie; 24, 27.
Pedrail machine; 21.
Praying Mantis; 143.
Roberts 1907; 15.
Sims quadricycle; 9.
Sueter articulated; 22.
Tritton No. 1; 23, 26.
Vickers wheel-cum-track; 68.
Vickers Medium wheel-cum-track; 68, 69.
Suspensions and Tracks
Batter 1888; 14.
Diplock 1910; 14.
Dunlop, A; 14.
Edgeworth, R; 14.
Edwards; 14.
Elephants' Feet; 22.
Fender; 14, 15.
Hetherington Big Wheel; 20, 21.
FIELD ARTILLERY AND ANTI-TANK GUNS
British
18-pounder; 11.
25-pounder; 89.
57-mm; 116.
Petard; 142.
French
75-mm gun; 11.
47-mm anti-tank; 88.
German
14-mm; 33.
37-mm anti-tank; 88.
77-mm field; 11, 33.
88-mm dual purpose; 89.
88-mm anti-tank; 116.
150-mm howitzer; 11.
420-mm howitzer; 11.
Italian
47-mm anti-tank; 88.

Russian
45-mm anti-tank; 116.
Swiss
20-mm Oerlikon anti-tank; 88.
USA
75-mm anti-tank; 116.
FLAME-THROWING COMBAT VEHICLES
British
Crocodile; 144.
Valentine; 107, 108.
USA
Adder; 143.
Steam tank; 42, 43.
GAP-CROSSING COMBAT VEHICLES
Churchill ARK; 143.
       AVRE; 142.
        Fascine; 142.
         SBG Bridge; 142.
Mark IV Fascine; 32.
Mark IV Ramp; 45.
Mark V** Bridge; 42, 43.
Valentine Jumper; 108.
       Scissors Bridge; 106.
GUIDED-WEAPON LAUNCHER AND REMOTELY CONTROLLED DEVICES
British
FV-438/Swingfire; 154.
French
AMX-13/SS 11; 151.
Russian
AAICV/Sagger; 154.
USA
MBT-70/Shillelagh; 157.
INFANTRY PORTABLE ANTI-TANK WEAPONS
British
PIAT; 148.
German
Panzerschreck; 148.
USA
Bazooka; 148.
LIGHT TANKS AND CARRIERS
British
Bren-gun carrier Mk I; 67, 122, 144.
Carden Loyd Mk III; 64, 65.
        Mk V; 64, 65.
        Mk VIa; 64, 65.
Crossley Martel; 64, 65.
Medium A (Whippet); 33, 37, 45, 50, 122.
Morris Martel; 64, 65.
Tritton Chaser; 27, 37.
Vickers machine-gun carrier; 54, 55.
       Mark I light; 84, 85.
       Mark VI C light; 84, 85.
       6-ton twin turret; 56, 57.
       Scorpion; 157
Czechoslovakian
MU-4; 67.
35t; 85, 104.
38t; 104.
French
AMX-13; 151.
BS; 38, 39.
H-35; 62, 63, 71.
M-17(FT); 33, 37–40, 59, 60, 62, 64.
NC; 71.
R-35; 62, 63, 71.
UE; 66, 67.
German
Leichter Traktor; 58, 73.
LK II; 37, 58.
PzKpfw-I; 73, 78.
    -IIA; 82.
Italian
3000A; 59.
CV-33/5; 66, 67.
Japanese
Renault NC-31; 59.
Type 95; 84, 104.
Polish
TK-3; 67.

7 TP; 58.
Russian
Lenin; 39.
T-18; 59.
T-26A; 57.
T-26B; 57.
T-27; 66, 67.
T-60; 130.
Swedish
Landswerk 60; 104.
M-21; 37.
USA
Christie 1919; 39.
Christie T-3; 69–72.
Ford 3-ton; 39.
Locust; 146.
M-1; 97, 109.
M-2A1; 97, 111.
M-1917; 38, 39.
Stuart Mk I; 109, 130.
T1 E1; 57.
T1 E4; 57.
MAIN BATTLE TANKS
Australian
Sentinel; 130
British
A-7; 74, 75.
A-9; 92, 93, 100, 105.
A-10; 92, 93, 100, 105.
A-13; 104.
Cavalier; 120.
Centurion I; 146.
       III; 146, 150.
       others; 155.
Challenger; 130, 131.
Chieftain; 156, 157.
Churchill I; 102, 111, 123.
       III; 102, 111.
       VII; 111, 144.
Comet; 133.
Covenanter; 112.
Cromwell; 120, 130, 133, 146.
Crusader I; 109, 119, 120.
       III; 120.
Mark I (Mother); 24, 25, 27, 54, 71, 122.
Mark IV; 28, 30–2.
Mark V; 36, 110, 122.
Mark V**; 42, 43.
Mark VIII (Liberty); 42, 43.
Matilda I; 92, 93.
       II; 71, 87, 98, 100.
Medium B; 50, 51.
       C; 50, 51.
       D; 48, 50, 51, 57.
Sherman Firefly; 132, 133.
TOG I; 99.
      II; 133.
Valentine I; 105.
      III; 105.
      VIII; 105.
Valiant; 108.
Vickers No. 1; 51, 54.
Vickers Independent; 52, 53, 98.
Vickers A 6 E1-3 (16 Tonner); 74, 75, 98, 102, 110, 122.
Vickers Medium C; 56, 71.
      I & II; 54, 55, 58, 71.
Vickers MBT; 155
Canadian
Ram I; 112.
     II; 130.
Valentine VI & VII; 105.
French
AMX 30; 155.
2C; 52, 53.
Char B; 60, 61, 87, 99.
D-1; 61–3, 82.
D-2; 61–3, 82.
St. Chamond; 26, 36.
Schneider; 26, 36.
SOMUA 35; 82.

German
A7U; 73.
A7V; 33, 36, 43, 73.
Grosstraktor; 72-4
K; 42, 43.
Leopard; 155.
Maus; 132.
MBT-70; 157.
Panther; 128, 129, 130, 132, 151.
PzKpfw-IIIA; 82.
    -IIIJ; 112, 126.
    -IVA; 82.
    -IVJ; 113, 119.
    -V; 74, 75.
Tiger I; 118, 129, 130.
    II (Royal); 132.
Italian
Fiat 2000; 43.
M11/39; 104, 109.
M13/40; 109.
P-40; 130.
Japanese
Chi-Nu; 130.
Type 89A; 56.
     92; 56.
     97; 104.
     1961; 155.
Russian
BT-5; 72, 73.
BT-7; 73.
JS-2; 130.
JS-3; 133.
KV-1; 99, 110, 130.
KV-85; 130.
SMK; 98.
T-34/76; 110, 113, 118, 119, 128.
T-34/85; 128, 129, 130, 150.
T-35; 98.
T-44; 150.
T-54; 150, 155.
T-62; 155.
USA
Liberty (Mk VIII); 42, 43.
MBT-70; 157.
Medium M1; 57.
M3 A1 (General Lee); 111, 112.
M3 A5 (General Grant); 112, 121, 122, 124.
M4 A4 (General Sherman); 111, 122, 128, 129, 132, 133.
M6 A2; 124.
M-26 (General Pershing); 133, 150.
M-46; 151.
M-47 (General Patton); 151, 155.
M-48; 151, 157
M-60; 157.
T-1 E1; 57.
T-2; 76.
T-4 E1; 97.
T-14; 124.
T-20; 133.
MACHINE-GUNS
British
Puckle; 11.
German
Maxim; 9, 11.
MINE-SWEEPING COMBAT VEHICLES
British
Baron; 140.
Crab; 140.
Plough; 140.
Roller; 42, 140.
Scorpion; 107, 140.
NIGHT COMBAT VEHICLES
In general; 149.
CDL; 149.
ORGANIZATIONS
British
Armoured Divisions; 78.
79th Armoured Division; 142.
Mobile Division; 78–80.
Tank Brigades; 78–80.

May 19

Happy Birthday Don.

Mom & Dad

AFRIKAKORPS

SELF PORTRAIT

DAL McGUIRK

AFRIKAKORPS

SELF PORTRAIT

Motorbooks International
Publishers & Wholesalers ®

DEDICATION

This book is dedicated to the memory of Friedrich Kägebein,
a twenty-year-old grenadier in the 7th Company Panzergrenadier Regiment
104, killed at El Alamein in October 1942, as representing all the men and
women on both sides who died in North Africa during World War II.

This USA edition published in 1992 by Motorbooks International,
Publishers & Wholesalers, PO Box 2, 729 Prospect Avenue,
Osceola, WI 54020, USA.

© Dal McGuirk, 1992

Published by Airlife Publishing Ltd., Shrewsbury, England, 1992

Printed in England by Livesey Ltd, Shrewsbury.

The information in this book is true and complete to the best of
our knowledge. All recommendations are made without any
guarantee on the part of the author or publisher, who also disclaim
any liability incurred in connection with the use of this data or
specific details.

We recognize that some words, model names and designations,
for example, mentioned herein are the property of the trademark
holder. We use them for identification purposes only. This is not
an official publication.

Library of Congress Cataloging-in-Publication Data Available
ISBN 0-87938-719-X

Motorbooks International books are also available at discounts in
bulk quantity for industrial or sales-promotional use. For details
write to Special Sales Manager at the Publisher's address.

CONTENTS

Acknowledgements
Introduction
CHAPTER 1   Fatherland
CHAPTER 2   The Army in Europe, at Home and at War
CHAPTER 3   Transit: Goodbye Germany, Hello Africa
CHAPTER 4   Before and After
CHAPTER 5   Typically African
CHAPTER 6   Rommel
CHAPTER 7   Camp Scenes
CHAPTER 8   Faces
CHAPTER 9   Food and Drink
CHAPTER 10   In General
CHAPTER 11   Camouflage
CHAPTER 12   Rest and Relaxation
CHAPTER 13   In Battle — Under Fire
CHAPTER 14   Artillery
CHAPTER 15   Infantry, African Grenadiers
CHAPTER 16   Medical
CHAPTER 17   Motorcycle Battalion
CHAPTER 18   PAK and Flak
CHAPTER 19   Panzers
CHAPTER 20   Pioneers
CHAPTER 21   Reconnaissance
CHAPTER 22   Signals
CHAPTER 23   Transport and Supply
CHAPTER 24   Graves
CHAPTER 25   The Enemy
CHAPTER 26   The Italians
CHAPTER 27   The End, Tunisia 1943
CHAPTER 28   For the Record
CHAPTER 29   Ernst Zwilling

The Principle Moral Elements

They are: *the skill of the commander, the experience and courage of the troops, and their patriotic spirit*. The relative value of each cannot be universally established; it is hard enough to discuss their potential, and even more difficult to weigh them against each other. The wisest course is not to underate any of them — a temptation to which human judgment, being fickle, often succumbs. It is preferable to muster historical evidence of the unmistakable evidence of all three.

Efficiency, skill, and the tempered courage that welds the body of troops into a single mould will have their greatest scope in operations in open country.

Carl von Clausewitz, *On War*

Quotation from *On War* by Carl von Clausewitz, edited and translated by Michael Howard and Peter Paret 1976, reproduced by permission of Princeton University Press, Princeton, New Jersey.

ACKNOWLEDGEMENTS

The photos reproduced in this book came from a variety of sources, from former soldiers on both sides of the fighting in North Africa, from friends and relatives, from militaria dealers and from fellow collectors. To everyone who helped in my search for original wartime photos I owe more than I can measure. Without their interest and assistance such a book of photos as this would obviously not have been possible.

For photos obtained from old soldiers, in New Zealand I had the assistance of the members of the 21 NZ Infantry Battalion Association, especially the ever-gracious Tony Ivicevich; and in Germany I was again fortunate to have the wonderful help of Karl-Heinz Böttger, Oberst a.D., and my good friends from the Association of Former Members of the 2nd Company, Sonderverband 288 — Dr (med) Manfred Auberlen; Werner Kost, Major a.D.; Hans Müller; Willi Prell; Andreas Rein; the late Franz Seidl; Alois Stockmayer; Joachim Thümser; Fritz Wenger.

I am indebted to Dieter Hellriegel for photos connected with Rommel's *Begleitkommando* (Escort Squad) in 1941 and from Rommel's *Kampfstaffel* (Battle Squadron) in 1942 and 1943.

For all the former members of the *Afrikakorps* who have shared their memories of Africa with me, I owe a debt of gratitude I can never repay. It was you who made the photos come alive for me; you shared those glimpses I would otherwise not have seen.

I thank Helmut Weitze for leading me to the personal photo albums of the late Georg Briel, with his photos relating to (Army) Fla. Battalion 606 and PzGrenRgt 200, the units which he commanded in Africa.

Two families in particular took special interest in my work on this book, and encouraged me in my working on it with their love and friendship: Jos and Hans Schilling, and Patsy and Dick LaFayette. These two families, who share the roles of godparents to my two children, Emma and Karl, incidentally also gave me photos which are reproduced in this book.

I owe a special debt of gratitude to my good friend Charlie Hinz for his generous offer to provide photos for this book taken by the *Afrikakorps* chief official photographer, Ernst Zwilling, photos that came from Ernst Zwilling's own private collection of photos he had taken in Africa.

I had the willing help of my wife Christine, my daughter Emma, and our friend Kate Lange in the long job of matching a thousand photos with the right captions. Thanks.

And for everyone else, in alphabetical order, with warm thanks: Birgit Andreas; Russel Andrews; the late Major (ret'd) Ted Andrews; Gary Armitage; Siegfried Augustin; the late Robert Borchardt; Herbert Brandhoff; Gregory N. Carter; Alan Coates; Peter Cue; Alan Culhane; Horst Dahlke; John Damon; Jörn Dressel;

ACKNOWLEDGEMENTS CONT.

Dr Hans H. Duesel; Sepp and Joan Egger; the late Jürgen Eichler; Malcolm Fisher; Kerry Foster, Walter Fromm, Major a.D.; Robert Gilmore; Konrad Günzel; Dieter and Otti Hellriegel; Peter Hill; David Hunter; John Keener; Antoine Lebel; Bob Lyons; Paul Kenwary; Wayne McDonald; Kerry Thomas McGee; Ron Manion; Alois Marcata; John Nicholson; Detlev Niemann; Hans Neumann; David Oldham; Geoffrey P. Oldham; George A. Petersen; Heinz and Lydia Puschmann; Rüdiger Rinklef; Manfred Rommel; Adolf Rössler; Marlis Schroten; Rudolf Schulz; the late Carl Theodor Toepfer, Oberfeldvet, d.R.; Dieter Sandbeck; Paul Erich and Ingrid Schläfer; Robert Sevier; Keith Skilton; Peter Steger; Rex Trye; the late Wally von Schramm; Paul Wansbrough; Kurt Watermann; Alan Webb; Phil Wernham, Jan Wessels.

For printing the black and white photos that were copied in Auckland, a big 'thank you' goes to Ruth Rowland and Marcel de Ruiter of PCLab in Parnell, Sue Campbell of 'Black and Bright' in Ponsonby, and Barbara Ross and Harley Wilson from GM Studios in Onehunga.

Unless otherwise credited, the photos reproduced in this book are from the author's collection.

Dal McGuirk, Auckland, May 1991.

Manfred Rommel, Lord Mayor of Stuttgart and son of the Field Marshal, with the author.

INTRODUCTION

There are two very different types of photos available for anyone interested in researching the pictorial record of the German side of the war in North Africa from 1941 to 1943. First there are the collections of photos kept by many state and military libraries in the former belligerent countries, containing for the most part photos shot in Africa by German army and propaganda news photographers.

These photos were mainly, though not solely, taken to record an official view of the war in Africa, and to show it to the wartime German population through newspapers and magazines. This official pictorial view closely corresponded with the militaristic ideology promoted by the propaganda organs in wartime Germany. The army photographers were experienced professionals who had good cameras and their work showed careful framing and composition. They worked near the front in order to get the best possible action shot and many of these men were killed while using their cameras. These photographers were assigned by the *Wehrmacht* to every front in World War II where German soldiers fought, to record scenes of their day-to-day existence and the battles they fought and died in.

Looking through the negative film strips snapped by these *Wehrmacht* photographers, one sees the care they took to get the 'right' shot in just the way they wanted it from the number of slightly different views of one subject, taken from a variety of angles to get the one really effective photo. They made certain that their photos showed to the best advantage clear details of the soldiers' faces, their uniforms with medals and equipment, and their weapons. All of these things were accorded proper attention in line with the recognition given at the time to the heroic military face of the German nation at war.

In Africa, and in other theatres too, the 'battle' scenes however were not always shot during actual fighting. Some photos purporting to show 'battle' scenes were taken during what were obviously training sessions, staged somewhere away from the front but giving a realistic impression of battlefield combat. (The evidence that this is so can be seen on the strips of negative film that show posed 'battle' scenes interspersed with other views of the 'battle' being set up in front of the cameras.) In North Africa it was extremely difficult to get good clear photos while the fighting was going on. The main actors were usually on the move and could not be stage-managed to best close range effect. The open desert was too vast, the soldiers too dispersed, for the familiar scale of warfare and backdrops that had been captured on film in Europe. In any case, most desert fighting did not take place at close range. In reality the enemy were usually no more than dots on the horizon among the clouds of dust thrown up by exploding artillery shells, or totally obscured by the haze caused by the extreme daytime heat. The truest photos were those taken during lulls in the fighting, showing the faces of the soldiers themselves rather than scenes of actual desert combat.

When looking at the large numbers of press release photos and official military photos taken by these German armed forces photographers, housed today in various institutional archives, one gets a feeling of having seen the same photos, somewhere else and at a different time. Seen together these German photos bear a close resemblance to the photos taken by the wartime photographers on the Allied side. Instead of the lines of German and Italian prisoners one is used to seeing, here are crowds of captured British or American soldiers. Rather than seeing photos of German dead, here the bodies are Allied dead. In place of the burning Panzers, there are burning Shermans, Grants and Crusaders. Whether viewed from the German or Allied side, the face of war recorded by the teams of official photographers in North Africa looked much the same from the middle distance. Only at close range could one see the different uniforms and badges that distinguished the two sides.

The propaganda element so effective in portraying a biased view of events during the war still confuses the reliability of some wartime photos as an accurate record of what happened. German military photographers, like their Allied counterparts, sometimes snapped an artificially contrived scene to play up some aspect of official propaganda. When published, the 'truth' of such photos was much harder to challenge than the stories where dishonest words could be sniffed out. After all, the photo was like a mirror held up to the time and place, was it not? Even today it is not easy to decide which wartime photos were arranged by photographers to suit their military and political masters. One famous example of this practice, from the Allied side in North Africa, was where an APFU photographer in Tunisia grabbed 'the most evil looking Arab' he could find and snapped him wearing German helmet (with French tricolour!) and German army sweater as an example of the 'Master Race'.

Certain photographs, however, snapped by the teams of military photographers were not meant for propaganda use. They were intended as the German *Wehrmacht*'s own picture record of the campaign. To prevent these photos from being mixed up with press release photos, the army's own photos all had the distinctive stamp on the back. *Nur für den Dienstgebrauch*, 'For Service Use Only'. With the exception of exercises being photographed for use as training aids, showing the correct and approved way of doing something, these photos were very much a straight record of what happened. The captions were generally more factual and informative too. One section of these photos is included here to show just what went into the German army's own wartime photo albums as the official 'self portrait' of the *Afrikakorps*.

The second main category of photos that cover the campaign in North Africa are those taken by the ordinary German soldiers themselves, and these make up the majority of photos in this book. Unfortunately for the student of the North African war, collections of these private photos are not housed in large and centrally located storage points, all conveniently filed and catalogued. These unofficial photos are now well scattered, some still in the possession of their original owners, or with their families, while others are in the hands of their old enemies.

When I started to gather the material for this book, I had intended using a mixture of official and private photos, with rather more of the former because of the much higher 'professional' quality. The market appeal of such a book containing many striking and previously unpublished photos was obvious, especially if using only the cream of those photos obtained from state and military archives. However, I realised that the overall view given by such an assortment, using mainly archive photos, was not the same view that I was familiar with from using my own collection of photos as an area of reference, that is, some thousands of photos snapped by the average German *Landser*. It followed, then, that a book of photos relying heavily on the most dramatic and detailed official photos was not an honest representation of the time, the place or the people who took part in these events, nor, more importantly, how they saw themselves.

In this book are many photos that were taken by the rank and file German soldiers. Some of these photos I obtained directly from former members of the *Afrikakorps* living in Germany, while other photos came from the New Zealand and Australian returned servicemen who originally picked them up as souvenirs on the North African battlefields — including those photos that had been brought to Africa from home in Germany, as well as ones snapped in Africa. These personal photos, once owned by German soldiers, joined all the other war mementoes collected by Allied troops. The photos were removed from rucksacks and from pockets on the clothing of prisoners (and in some instances from corpses), taken from captured tanks, trucks and cars, from abandoned weapon sites, trenches and foxholes, all the way from El Alamein to Enfidaville.

These personal photos give a much truer overall view of their owners' army life, at the private and individual level of experience and of the war in North Africa, as seen by the average German soldier. The photos record how these men saw each other, and what they felt was important enough in the world around them to put on film. Those snapshots taken earlier in Germany and carried across the Mediterranean reveal common backgrounds of home life, and the face of German society in the Third Reich. Many of these photos show their former owners as members of such organisations as the Hitler Youth, the Stormtroopers, or the State Labour Service, and taking part in the parades and rallies that were a normal part of life in Hitler's Germany.

The information contained in the photos often illustrates small things that may not seem important in themselves but do say something about the personalities and attitudes of the soldiers involved: for instance, many men preferred wearing their tropical pith helmets back to front, a sensible modification as the wider rear rim gave better shade to the face. In the many photos taken in and around camps it is extremely rare to see any personal weapons, the small arms all soldiers were issued with, as one would have expected if the photos had been taken in Europe. Obviously, it was not expected that a raiding party of the enemy would suddenly appear from out of the desert. In Africa there were no partisans (if one excepts the occasional Arab sniper or the LRDG who ranged far in the rear) and the fighting usually took place along organised if moving lines of combat, involving mostly motorised artillery and tanks rather than large number of infantry, as was still the case in Europe at the time. What was seen around the tents and vehicles in camp scenes were trenches and rock-walled sangars built for protection against air attack. (In the event of a ground attack it would be more likely that the first reaction would be to jump into the nearest vehicle to get away as quickly as possible, not to jump into a trench to defend what was only, after all, a map reference.)

For those photos that can be placed at a certain location at a specific time there is information one can deduce, knowing the context of time and place. We see, for example, that even during the heaviest of battles, such as at El Alamein in October and November 1942, soldiers out of the front line stood around talking during mealtime, and that the usual routines of army life went on largely unaffected by the battle raging nearby. The battle itself did not reach out to disrupt the lives of those who were not actually engaged in the front line fighting, and for those men stationed behind the line their daily duties went on much as normal if at a faster tempo.

Cameras could not close the distance across which most of the fighting in North Africa took place. Wide angle and telephoto lenses (for detailed close-up and distant views) were not fitted to personal cameras. Only after the tide of battle had passed could close-up photos be taken of disabled or knocked-out tanks and other vehicles, groups of prisoners, enemy dead, and the debris of modern war that always littered the battlefields later.

Photos taken in Africa by German soldiers are not, of course, a totally accurate reflection of their day-to-day lives. Film was not always readily available and this meant that it was more likely to be used taking photos of the unusual and extraordinary, rather than the more mundane scenery and events — though this side of daily existence received its share of photos, too, for want of anything else to shoot with a camera.

In the same way that the official army photographers arranged shots to show 'battle' scenes, some German soldiers did the same thing to simulate in a photo the appearance and feel of battle. These photos were snapped after first arranging specially posed scenes with weapons for a suitable 'combat' backdrop. Of all the things that one would wish to record on film, it was that one most dangerous and memorable act — actual fighting — that was most difficult to photograph. Therefore, instead of real life battle scenes, the posed shots had to make do instead. Such photos, taken by ordinary soldiers, show to what extent the official view sanctioned by state propaganda and commonly seen in magazines and newspapers — essentially a romantic view of war as a heroic game — was accepted without irony by some soldiers as a real and serious record of themselves at war (and what would presumably be shown as part of one's personal war history later at home to family and friends).

The range of subjects covered in captured film and photos picked up on the battlefields was restricted by the type of military unit their previous owners had belonged to. Advancing troops were unlikely to overrun the rear base units of a motorised opposing army as these troops were invariably long gone by the time their former living and work areas were occupied. Thus, the majority of German soldiers who had their film and photos captured by the advancing enemy usually belonged to those who served in or near the front line — infantry, engineers, artillery, Flak and Pak gunners, and tank or reconnaissance units. Soldiers in these formation were, naturally enough, the ones most likely to lose their personal possessions, and their lives, in the fighting. Therefore, the majority of the photos reproduced in these pages are those that belonged to combat soldiers of the *Afrikakorps*, and not the men who served in any of the multitude of units stationed behind the lines. In this collection of photos I have not bothered to separate the Luftwaffe from the Army; both served, after all, as frontline soldiers in the one army in Africa.

To find photos showing the work and living areas of the rear support units, one has to go either to the official collections housing photos taken by wartime army photographers, or track down the surviving members of these rear units, or their children, living in Germany. In the German army in North Africa in World War II, there were roughly two soldiers serving in the frontline combat units for every one soldier behind the lines in some sort of rear support role. (For the Allied armies in North Africa, the ratio of frontline troops to rear support units ran the opposite way, with slightly more numerical strength in the rear area than in the combined frontline combat units.)

The scenes from this other war zone, often far behind the front lines, have received little attention in books covering the war. In addition to the view of the frontline area with which we are already familiar, with its combat vehicles and trenches, makeshift tents and foxholes, artillery and anti-tank guns with their piles of ammunition ready for use, there was an even more extensive area stretching out far behind the lines where a large number of the *Afrikakorps* carried out their duties. There were firstly the thousands of motor vehicles and their drivers who daily criss-crossed the desert roads and tracks, transporting everything from petrol and ammunition to cigarettes and vitamin pills up to the front; there were the large networks of supply dumps and their attendant staffs; extensive mechanical engineering workshops, complete with furnaces, welding gear and panel-beating equipment; the motor repair centres were numerous, with their well-equipped lorry-borne workshops and large compressors to provide the air pressure for blasting sand and dirt from engine parts, and gantries for lifting engine blocks in and out of vehicles; workshops permanently set up with heavy lathes and tools capable of rebuilding a wide range of mechanical equipment; paint shops where the innumerable roadside tactical signs were made up; there were carpenters' workshops, too, where thousands of tables, chairs and benches were made; Engineer companies busy rebuilding roads and erecting or repairing harbour facilities and setting up defensive fortifications; large bakeries cooking bread for thousands of men; there were Flak units guarding the ports; the Luftwaffe had meteorological units whose job it was daily to send high altitude balloons into the atmosphere to measure wind speeds and their moisture content and who travelled far and wide in the desert with their vehicles carrying tanks of compressed hydrogen; there was, in addition, the bureaucracy of the German army which followed it to North Africa, and these clerks in uniform worked busily from one end of Libya and Egypt to the other and finally across to Tunisia, creating on the way a small mountain of paper. There were other units as diverse as military police, meat butchery companies, units detailed for POW guard duties, military postal companies running mail sorting operations as large a one would find in a modern city; entertainers in the propaganda companies, tailors with their sewing machines mending uniforms, cobblers fixing boots, water purification units, hospitals and their staffs of nurses and doctors, dentists; ordnance companies whose job it was to service and repair weapons, journalists who produced the *Afrikakorps*' own newspaper, and so on. The photographic story of this other face of the *Afrikakorps* must wait for another book.

This book is, above all, a story in photographs of the men of the fighting units of the *Afrikakorps*, even though little of the fighting itself appears in the photos. Whether attempts to capture on film something of the true face of battle were made by amateur or professional photographers, the results were invariably the same — clouds on the horizon caused by the smoke rising from burning vehicles or from the columns of dust-filled air thrown up by exploding artillery shells. Whenever the battle moved much closer than the horizon, using their cameras was hardly the thought uppermost in the minds of the amateur photographer soldiers. The more common type of photo taken on the days when fighting had taken place showed groups of comrades snapped after the battle had passed, their faced showing the elation of survival and victory, or fatigue from what had been a period of great physical and emotional strain.

I have yet to see a photo taken by ordinary German soldiers of their own dead as they fell in battle, or any photo showing a comrade in death. (The official photographers did take shots of German dead.) For the average soldier it was common enough to snap the enemy dead, and funeral services and the graves of one's own comrades, but not the faces of the corpses of your own side. It was the same for Allied soldiers. It was as if the images of these deaths frozen in private memories were enough to last a lifetime.

As much as possible, the photos selected for reproduction here are ones that show the ordinary and common-place view of the world seen by the average soldier in the *Afrikakorps*. (To preserve the authenticity of these photos I have had to ask the people who produce this book not to clean up prints that at first seem dirty and 'spotty' — what look like grains of dirt printed from a filthy negative are most likely only flies.)

For the soldiers of the *Afrikakorps*, this was their world, its sights and faces. Much has been written about the war in North Africa since these photos were taken. As is the nature of history, our understanding of the events and of the period itself gradually changes as we look back from the ever-moving mood of the present. Time softens the lingering effects of the emotion-charged propaganda from the wartime years, and facts become easier to separate from what was invented, both at the time and later. Although stories of the war will alter with the passing of time, these photos will always remain unchanged, a timeless personal record.

Very little of the great volume of military stores transported across the Mediterranean by the German army from February 1941 to May 1943 now survives. Many of the photos taken during this period have also now disappeared. More than 20,000 German soldiers lie buried in North Africa, some of this number in unmarked and unknown graves. They deserve to be remembered, as do the dead of all armies.

Given the origin of many of these photos, picked up on the battlefield, many of their owners, the faces on these pages, will be among those who fell in Africa and whose bodies lie buried there today. It is my hope that readers will feel their imagination has been touched by something they see in one or more photos in these pages, and give it meaning.

CHAPTER 1 | # FATHERLAND

Most German troops took photos to Africa that belonged to that part of their lives outside military service and before the war, photos that said much about who they were and where they came from. These photos illustrated life in the Germany of the 1930s and early 1940s, its towns and villages and countryside, its political, social and historical cultural identity.

While much Allied reporting of the war referred to German troops as 'Nazis', it was not a fair and accurate description of the average German soldier. There was little among the range of souvenirs collected by Allied troops that would have led one to believe the *Afrikakorps* was made up of 'Nazis'. There were of course photos that showed their owners as once belonging to Nazi organisations like the Hitler Youth and the State Labour Service, but this was obligatory for all young men in Hitler's Germany, and did not mean everyone had therefore become a 'Nazi'. The swastika clasped inside the talons of the eagles worn on German army caps and tunics was at the time the German national emblem, and did not in itself make individual soldiers 'Nazis'. If one looked for evidence among souvenirs for some indication of personal beliefs, one would probably conclude much of the *Afrikakorps* was from a Christian society. The *Afrikakorps* included military chaplains amongst its personnel, and many German soldiers, especially the Catholics who came mainly from the southern states and the Rhineland, carried various religious items among their personal effects, including bibles and prayer books. The men of the *Afrikakorps* were soldiers, no different from the soldiers of other armies of the period, under the same sort of military discipline, and with the same intense patriotism.

Wartime Allied propaganda deliberately, and very effectively, confused the political and social morality (or immorality) of the Nazi state with the personal and cultural morality and values of the individual German. The two were, in fact, not the same, except in a relatively small number of cases. Although some German soldiers serving in Africa were ardent Nazis (more so the younger soldiers and a smaller number of officers, if their behaviour in POW camps is taken into account), they were a small minority within the *Afrikakorps*. The German army at this time was not a 'Nazi' organisation in the sense that the SS was a Nazi organisation, nor was it committed to the goals of the Nazi state as was the *Luftwaffe*. The much older tradition of the German army, an imperial tradition with its values still firmly set in the *Kaiserreich,* was at this time strong enough to resist many of the political values espoused by the Nazi state. Only in the last year of the war did the German army accept the primary place of the party in its ranks, in the wake of the bomb plot of 20 July 1944. The greatest motivation for ordinary soldiers fighting in Africa was a pure and simple nationalism, albeit a Prussian sort of nationalism, militaristic and jingoistic. Reading through files of unit records from the period, or the letters written by soldiers and their families, one is struck today by the ordinary things that were talked about, not the 'Nazism' of Allied wartime propaganda with which the whole German population was painted. Postcards and photos of Hitler were often collected by Allied soldiers looking for souvenirs, but in the absence of other specific or general 'Nazi' literature one must assume that the photos of the Fuehrer were carried more to mark the charismatic 'leader' figure rather than the political ideology of the Nazi party. There is no doubt Hitler was idolised by a very large majority of soldiers at this early stage of the war. However, apart from the Hitler postcard portraits there was very little, if anything, that one could point to as explicitly representing 'Nazi ideology' among the personal possessions taken from German POWs in Africa.

Wartime German propaganda was very forcefully and cleverly communicated, and it was no different for German troops in Africa. This propaganda was an effective blend of Nazi ideology and straight patriotism, all wrapped up inside the familiar military virtues of honour, obedience and sacrifice. This propaganda reached the ordinary soldier through daily army orders, letters from home (where news stories were repeated verbatim), through newspapers and magazines sent from home, in movies seen in Africa, in radio broadcasts from Germany, and in their own local army newspaper, 'The Oasis', reporting information received from official sources in Germany.

Some soldiers, especially officers, carried with them to Africa items from World War I that had once belonged to their fathers, and with some of the older officers, such things were the very same items they had used themselves in that war — binoculars, pistols, leather map cases etc. Even photos of scenes in World War I were found among the private papers carried to Africa by some soldiers. Presumably these military shots were personal and family ones, but they showed that the nature of war had changed little, only the scenery and weaponry were different.

From newspapers, and the postmarks on letters and postcards picked up along with the photos (which provided information on the origins of the photos), there was a strong local flavour in 1941 for the original two divisions of the *Afrikakorps*, Berlin, Potsdam, Görlitz, Wünsdorf, Western Silesia for 5th Light Div, and the Upper Rhineland and Swabia for 15th Panzer Div. By the end of 1941 the local geographical flavour associated with the first two divisions of the *Afrikakorps* was diluted. It began with the creation of the 90th Light Div. (which had in its ranks many former members of the French Foreign Legion who came from every corner of Germany) and the other divisions that arrived in 1942 and 1943 included many Saxons, Austrians, men from other parts of Prussia, and Bavarians, and so on. The practice of taking replacements from other parts of Germany for the original divisions drew in new areas as well. By the second half of 1942, most geographical areas of Germany were represented in the *Afrikakorps*.

If German soldiers had only their photos to remind them of their homeland, it must have been a very idealised view — family picnics in the countryside, weekend gatherings with family and friends, holiday snaps, homes, civilian jobs, sweethearts, children... When looking at such tranquil peacetime scenes as these photos today, there is a sense of unreality about their more recent origins in burnt-out tanks and vehicles, in foxholes and trenches, in the North African desert in the middle of a war.

A German soldier snapped during the First World War, a photo found among the personal belongings of German POWs in Bardia in January 1942.

Parade in the pre-war years of the uniformed German Labour front, the Nazified trade union movement.

One of the many postcards of Adolf Hitler carried to Africa by German soldiers in 1941 and 1942.

Parade of Stormtroopers, the brown-shirted para-military arm of the Nazi Party.

Family shot. The uniform worn second from left is RAD (Reichsarbeitsdienst) State Labour Service.

The Brown House, the Nazi Party HQ of the 1920s and 1930s in Munich.

In RAD uniform.

RAD camp, wooden huts in the pine forests.

RAD service.

Six female members of the RAD.

Not all time in the RAD was spent in hard work.

Night shot of young members from an unknown paramilitary organisation on a training camp before the war.

Gymnasts drawn from a Panzer Regiment practice their routines for a military display.

An army band prepares for a weekend concert.

THE ARMY IN EUROPE, AT HOME AND AT WAR

Photos dealing with German military service before Africa were of great interest to the Allied troops who acquired them. The photos seemed to answer questions about the origins or ancestry of the *Afrikakorps,* to make real the imaginings of Allied soldiers about just who it was over the other side of the hill. In fact, the *Afrikakorps* were only ordinary German troops, in spite of the different tropical uniforms, and their elementary training at least was little different from that which the Allied soldiers themselves had received.

Most groups of photos removed from POWs and other sources found on the battlefield included at least a few showing military service in Europe before being posted to Africa. Many of these photos were taken at army bases during basic training, the six months done by those who had joined after the outbreak of war. The DAK in 1941 however was a mixture of the professional soldiers from the pre-war army, and young conscripts or volunteers who had joined the army after the outbreak of war. The German divisions arriving in Africa after 1941, and the later reinforcement drafts, consisted increasingly of rank and file men who had joined up in wartime.

For the younger generation of soldiers in the *Afrikakorps* their military education had started while still adolescents with the Hitler Youth, and continued with the RAD (State Labour Service) and the other paramilitary organisations all young Germans were encouraged to join. Their time in the army was seen thus as the normal progression towards more specialised military training, something expected of all young German males.

en of Panzer Regiment 5 the Winter of 1939-40.

While the German army's basic training may have been similar in most respects to that which other armies gave their recruits, German military tactics were the most progressive, and the most modern, in the world at that time. For the individual soldier this emphasised one's overall military function inside a moving battle with its mechanised units and two-way radios joining up units with each other on the battlefield and with the *Luftwaffe* planes in close support. Most Allied armies still taught a more narrow and singular arm of service training (reminiscent of World War I) and hence fast co-operation between these arms of service was missing on the battlefield. The German 'all arms' training gave its commanders the confidence to undertake the penetration attacks with armour deep into enemy territory, ignoring old fixations with secure lines of supply and cover for the flanks at all costs. The training *Afrikakorps* soldiers were given led to their ability to fight easily and surely in close co-operation with all other arms of service, always aggressively counter-attacking immediately when put under attack. The 'Battle Groups' that were made up as mixtures of component parts of available units were to become just as familiar as the old established units. Above all, it was the abiding high morale of these soldiers, and the professionalism of officers young and old, ready converts to the new tactics of mechanised and armoured war, *Blitzkrieg,* that carried the new doctrine of modern warfare so forcefully to their enemy in Africa.

The campaigns in Poland and France were seen in these captured photos too, and even scenes of the Eastern Front on Soviet territory found their way to North Africa in 1942 and 1943.

A new barracks, one of so many such built for the *Wehrmacht* in the 1930s.

'The soldier', aiming a small pistol for a very posed photo.

Horse drawn transport through a Sudeten village in September 1938 as Hitler incorporates the German-speaking part of Czechoslovakia into the Reich.

Basic training, hauling the 15cm *schwere Feldhaubitze* 18, the heavy field howitzer of the German Army, Erfurt 1940.

Anonymous personal shot taken some time over 1939–1940 and found near Fort Capuzzo in late 1941.

By the River Rhine, late summer 1940.

Basic training Erfurt 1940, climbing down ropes suspended from the ceiling, wearing the stuffy gasmask.

Ramming the shell into the breech of the heavy 15cm howitzer in basic training for these artillery recruits, Erfurt 1940.

1939, war in Poland, German panzers of PzRgt5 in a Polish village.

A PzII of PzRgt5 in the Polish campaign.

Men of a Luftwaffe Flak unit being addressed on their barracks parade ground by the commanding officer on the eve of departure.

Home leave for a young soldier in early 1941, brother and sister.

Farewell to Germany – the mountains of Austria and Bavaria, snapped through train windows in 1941. For many German soldiers, this was to be their last view of Germany.

TRANSIT: GOODBYE GERMANY, HELLO AFRICA

Before departure for Africa there was normally a home leave, seven to ten days in 1941 but reduced to a shorter time by 1943 of three or four days only. Photos taken on these last home visits were carried on their person by many troops in Africa. For the first main units to leave Germany in 1941, the 5th Light Division, and *Luftwaffe* Flak *Abteilungen,* there were formal farewell parades on barrack squares surrounded by snow-covered buildings, a ceremonial send-off that was not repeated after 1941. A similar atmosphere of occasion and ceremony awaited them in Tripoli, endless columns of tanks rattling down main thoroughfares, straight lines of troops standing waiting for inspection by Rommel and the Italian General Garibaldi.

In direct violation of orders that all photographs were to be taken away from POWs (for their alleged intelligence value), it was common for some kindly Allied soldiers to leave snapshots of family groups with their German POW owners (and just as common for other Allied captors to regard these private snapshots as another interesting and rightful souvenir for themselves).

Members of the 5th Light Division and 15th Panzer Division travelling through Rome in 1941 remember the NSDAP (Nazi Party) booths set up on the railway station, dispensing food and drinks to trainloads of troops passing through. These refreshment stalls were operated by German women whose husbands had diplomatic, military or commercial postings in Rome.

The very first troops from 5th Light Div. to arrive in Libya during February 1941 still wore their woollen continental uniforms. They were the first and the last troops to do so. From March 1941 the German army issued its soldiers travelling to Africa with tropical uniform in Germany itself.

Those troops who travelled on to Africa by ship from Naples in 1941 had to wait for convoys to be arranged. This gave them time to do the usual tourist trips around Naples, and many photos were taken of the preserved Roman city of Pompeii and the lava flows below the slopes of Mt. Vesuvius.

Regardless of when and how he arrived in Africa, the German soldier carried his weapon with him and a canvas rucksack containing spare uniform and clothing items, along with his basic field equipment. The German army had to transport everything it needed to fight in Africa as there was nothing to be had locally to supplement its own resources. Absolutely everything had to be transported across the Mediterranean — food, vitamin pills, heavy and light weapons, ammunition, all vehicles and spare parts, fuel, typewriters, paper, soap, spare buttons, medical supplies, toilet paper, complete engineering workshops, thousands of kilometres of telephone cable, spare stocks of everything, literally everything... (hence the magnitude of the problems caused by high losses of supplies sunk crossing the Mediterranean).

After the summer of 1941, the most common route for troops travelling to Africa was by rail through the Balkans, then by aircraft from Greece or Crete to airfields in Libya. Photos taken in transit by *Afrikakorps* soldiers in 1941 and 1942 show a variety of backyard views of cities and towns stretching from Berlin to Naples and Taranto, from Vienna to Belgrade and Athens, snapped through train windows.

From the second half of 1941 many German soldiers spent long periods in Greece, waiting for transport across the Mediterranean to North Africa. By late 1941 tent cities had sprung up around Athens and the harbour at Piraeus. Photos dating from this time showed soldiers in tropical uniform, either singly or in groups, standing in front of a stone block wall and date palm trees. One candid street photographer in Athens did good business at this particular spot judging by the large number of photos taken against this one recognisably Mediterranean backdrop.

The new tropical uniform. Hans Schilling (on right) and friend stand in newly issued *Afrikakorps* uniform at Baumholder, June 1941.

Passing time in the warm sunshine in Naples in April 1941.

TRANSIT: GOODBYE GERMANY, HELLO AFRICA

Unlike the reception given to troops arriving in Tripoli in 1941 who had crossed by sea, and were then handled by the well-established German military presence in this large city, things were very different in 1942. Nearly all reinforcements sent to Rommel in 1942 were flown in by the Luftwaffe to remote Libyan or Egyptian airfields from where they often had to make their own way to whatever unit they were assigned to. Transport was scarce, and fuel was even scarcer, and so it was that new arrivals had to move on with a minimum of help from the rear area units. It was usually up to the combat units to arrange vehicles to go back to the airfields to collect their own reinforcement drafts. Such organisational niceties that allowed reception facilities to be set up in Tripoli in 1941 were an extravagance in the desert war of 1942. There were no parades before the propaganda cameras for the steady trickle of troops arriving in the Ju52s at airfields such as Fuka, Derna, Gambut, El Adem and El Daba.

Reception in Tunisia for arriving troops was more in line with conditions then operating in Italy or Greece where there was a considerable German military presence, including all the usual rear support services. In Tunisia the German army was able to take over French army facilities, barracks and depots. In November 1942 Parachute Rgt5 paraded through the streets of Tunis, as a successful propaganda display, in a manner reminiscent of PzRgt5 in Tripoli in March 1941.

For some troops there was only a short stay in Africa, as dysentery struck down many who then had to be repatriated to hospitals in Europe. For those who fell in Africa — the 18,594 officially listed as killed, and 3,400 missing, it was a one-way journey.

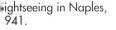

ightseeing in Naples, 941.

The harbour dockside at Naples in 1941.

Cargo ship crane hoisting up a Volkswagen.

Passenger ships at Taranto in the summer of 1941.

Tanks of Panzer Regiment 5 on parade through Tripoli, and taking the road to the front in March 1941.

Mediterranean crossing.

A 10.5cm howitzer of Pz Art.Rgt 33 comes over the side and on to African soil.

Lined up for torpedo drill with kapok filled vests strapped on.

A Ford 3-ton truck of Pz Artl.Rgt 33 being unloaded in Tripoli.

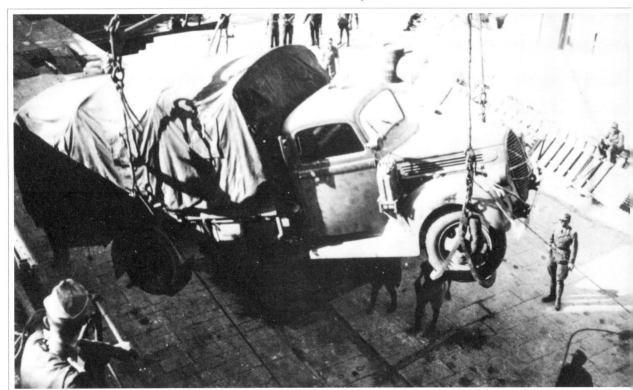

One of the many photos snapped by a Greek candid photographer who did good business in front of this wall and gate with the large palm trees behind.

Tripoli waterfront cafe, 1941.

In late 1941 and for most of 1942 the only safe way to reach Africa was by Junkers 52, as it was here for *Sonderverband* 288 in December 1941.

35

Sidewalk cafe, Crete or Greece, 1941.

A group of men who had been lucky enough to get home leave in 1942 (or who had been sent back because of wounds) wait on an airfield in Crete for a flight to take them back to Egypt.

BEFORE AND AFTER

A common assortment of photos taken from POWs consisted of groups of photos showing their previous owners at various stages in their civilian and military careers. These photos taken from leather wallets and cardboard packets usually showed the man firstly as a civilian, later as a recruit in basic training and finally as a soldier of the *Afrikakorps*, marking out the milestones in the lives of these young German soldiers. The photos were very often large size studio portraits, wedding photos or pictures taken at the time of a home leave to show off a smart-looking new military uniform.

Studio shot, Germany 1940.

Snapshot, Africa 1941.

Two photos of a member of 15th Pz Div, on his wedding day (with Hitler Youth badge on his left top pocket), and in the field, Africa 1941.

Two shots of a man who trained in 1942 and was sent to Tunisia with the 5th Panzer Army; in civilian dress (with Nazi Party badge in buttonhole) and in Tunis wearing tropical uniform with pistol on his belt.

Dieter Hellreigel in peace and war, as a Hitler Youth, and as a seasoned *Afrikaner*. (Dieter Hellriegel)

The 'Arco dei Feleni', or Marble Arch, on the Via Balbia marking the boundary between Tripolitania and Cyrenaica, one of the most photographed features in Libya.

The border wire strung along the Libyan border with Egypt, intended to keep the troublesome Arab tribes from crossing from country to country.

A timeless scene, petrol being slowly siphoned from the van's tank into a tin containing sand, which will be flamed to burn under something heated up for lunch.

TYPICALLY AFRICAN

The scenery that met the soldiers of the *Afrikakorps* in Libya in 1941 was not what they had expected — the desert was often rocky instead of being smooth and sandy, and the German army had not prepared them for the day-to-day problems connected with desert-living health and hygiene. The oases so familiar from Hollywood movies were generally nowhere to be seen, and the swarms of flies came as an unpleasant surprise, as did the host of other insect pests. The German army had in fact done very little to prepare its soldiers for life in North Africa. Troops who arrived in 1942 and 1943 were somewhat better prepared for what awaited them, though this had more to do with a higher level of general awareness by everyone in the human supply pipeline rather than from any specially prepared instruction. It was the same for the whole units and the smaller reinforcement drafts sent over after 1941 — they continued to receive only the usual basic training meted out to all German recruits, regardless of where they were to serve. The official military attitude in 1942 and 1943 to North African service seemed to be that if the units sent over in 1941 had coped without any major preparation then so could the following reinforcements who would be instructed by the units already there.

Photos recording the popular romantic images of Africa were not as common in 1941 and 1942 from Libya and Egypt as they were later in Tunisia — of the Arabs themselves, date palms with camels and donkeys, Arab villages and mosques. Photos taken of Arabs in Tunisia were easier to get, because their villages were more numerous and closer to the main roads, and because the Tunisian Arabs were friendlier than those in Libya and Egypt. However, some of the few German soldiers who managed to get a closer view of Arab living conditions in Libya in 1941 and 1942 also recorded the poverty of the Arab villages, showing that not all Germans wished to photograph only the romantic movie images of Arab desert life.

The Mediterranean beaches were popular photo subjects, and not only as a backdrop for swimming parties. The Libyan (and Egyptian) beaches were more attractive looking to *Afrikakorps* soldiers than German Baltic and North Sea beaches and were so seen as worthwhile photo scenes in themselves.

Photography undertaken in the open desert was not easy, unless someone had a good camera and used it with the knowledge of how to compensate for the bright glare (to shoot away from it and so make use of it). Many shots taken in the desert were not successful, the brighter light meant the photos were often over-exposed and, in any case, it was difficult to capture any sense of scale and proportion for larger scenes when the horizon was just a hazy junction between shimmering desert and bright atmospheric light.

The absence in the desert of any of the features that distinguished the European landscape made any sort of landmark an important point from which one could get

CHAPTER 5

some bearings, a wrecked vehicle or tank for instance. Sometimes there were photos of insignificant pieces of wreckage that seem to have been photographed for no other reason than that they were some variation on the endless vista of desert from horizon to horizon, and something on a more familiar human scale. Photos showing the Via Balbia and vehicles were very common — this long asphalt ribbon with its heavy traffic was a sight known to every German soldier who served in North Africa in 1941 and 1942. Photos taken at or near areas that had been the scene of a battle invariably show the amazing amount of debris left by the fighting, literally everything in part or whole that had been carried there by soldiers, from bits of clothing to small personal items, from mess tins to petrol canisters and tyres, wrecked vehicles and weapons.

Some photos were taken of the arable areas in Libya, around Tripoli and in the hinterland to Benghazi where there was natural vegetation and some agriculture. That not more photos exist of these areas is explained by the short time German soldiers spent there — they were usually glimpsed only in transit with most time spent camped out in the open desert.

The old Roman ruins were always well photographed, and were popular places to visit, especially those at Leptis Magna, Apollonia, and Cyrene, which were the most accessible. For the professional as well as amateur photographers, the distinctive stone forts built mainly during the period Libya was occupied by Turkey, made another popular subject. These desert forts with their distinctive battlements, along with palm trees, camels and mosques, seemed to fit the popular image 1940s Europe had of the North African desert.

Another puncture, another rip
Bardia. (Note that the tyre ha‹

Typical of many 1941 photos,
an expanse of desert, rocks an
Plateau.

Tapping artesian water with help from Arab villagers.

a cross-country vehicle of 15 PzDiv, summer 1941, near
...nged as well as a wheel and tube.)

...tanding before
...the Libyan

Dieter Hellriegel's photo of the most important African possessions — two
jerricans, paybook, his cloth field cap and two photos of his girlfriend, at El
Alamein September 1942. (Dieter Hellriegel)

The Mediterranean as bathing beaches.

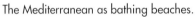

The view from the bluff above the harbour at Bardia, 1941.

Der Spatengang (the walk with spade), heading off to a quiet spot with the necessary spade and a folded sheet of newspaper.

Arab villagers snapped in the hinterland of Benghazi in the summer of 1941.

Camels, face to face, 1941.

A sandstorm *(Ghibli)* rolls in from the desert towards a village on the Libyan coastal strip.

Flies, flies, flies, flies... here sucking up the perspiration left on a steering wheel.

The arable belt of Libyan coastal land and Italian colonial farmhouses near Tigrinna.

Water collection point from a well using an Italian lorry.

Washing in an irrigation race by a LW Flak unit.

Arab villager and *Luftwaffe* gunner, 1941.

Arab villager with an egg to trade, Bardia, 1941.

The main Bardia township above the harbour.

Waiting, 1941
Pz.Abw.Abt.39.

Morning wash, using the rationed little portion of water poured into the small rubberised canvas folding 'bowl' all German soldiers in Africa were issued with for this purpose.

Another function for the gasmask tin, as a seat.

Oft-photographed desert wreckage, such as this Italian Fiat CR42 biplane.

Desert navigation, using a compass.

Bomb crater next to an Italian
vehicle workshop near
Bardia in summer 1941.

Protection for tyres from the
hot sun.

The rear HQ bus of 15th Pz.Div. nearly afloat, caught in a wadi in flood after heavy rain near Tmimi on 17 February 1942. On top of the bus are Major (GS) von Loeffelholz, his aide *Oberleutnant* Karl-Heinz Böttger, and the *Gefreiter* who was its driver.

After driving through a sandstorm, *Oberleutnant* Karl-Heinz Böttger and the rear HQ bus of 15th Pz.Div. Both show signs of being coated with sand in April 1942.

Reporting for orders, south of Tobruk in 1941.

A rare sight, a pet dog, Egypt 1942 (very likely brought across in an aircraft from Greece or Crete).

One of the soldiers' bars set up in the rear settlements along the Libyan coastal strip in 1941.

55

Rommel standing with Walter Fromm on the dockside in Tripoli, watching the first men and equipment of Pz.Abw.Abt.39 unloading on 14 February 1941. (Walter Fromm)

Rommel's *Luftwaffe* pilot holds the door back as a smiling Rommel prepares to get out.

Rommel on one of his many visits to frontline areas in 1941, here at Sollum with a party of German and Italian officers (the officer to the left with binoculars around his neck is Heinz Werner Schmidt, Rommel's ADC in 1941). (Charles Hinz)

ROMMEL

U ndoubtedly, Rommel was the most photographed person in North Africa between 1941 and 1943. The official German photographers followed him around and snapped him in many thousands of photos. The personal cameras of the ordinary soldier took many more thousands of photos.

Rommel was not averse to having his photo taken, and was known to have walked towards a person with a camera in their hands. He made an effort to be known by his soldiers, to be recognised by them on and off the battlefield, and to this end he always tried to show himself to his men.

It was not difficult to recognise Rommel, even though he invariably had a train of officers following behind him. For most of the time he wore the woollen continental Generals' service cap with its high crown and silvered insignia, and there were always the distinctive lightweight British anti-gas goggles worn around the cap. His other uniform was no less distinctive, a long olive-tan leather greatcoat, or the tailor-made cotton tropical uniform quite different in cut to the normal army issue tunic, and he usually wore high black leather boots. Rommel had a characteristic stance when talking to someone, to plant his legs slightly apart and his head cocked to one side, a posture that was soon well known.

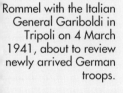

Rommel with the Italian General Gariboldi in Tripoli on 4 March 1941, about to review newly arrived German troops.

Rommel showed real concern for the welfare of his soldiers, and they knew it. He did not lose the common touch and always felt at ease talking with rank and file troops. The soldiers realised that the very strict rules affecting their daily existence ordered by Rommel were in their best interest. Very simply, they believed in him.

Many German soldiers saw him fleetingly during the fighting as he arrived standing in his staff car to check dispositions rapidly and urge on his junior commanders before driving off at speed to some other part of the battlefield. He had a terse style of giving commands and expected his officers to jump to their tasks as soon as he had finished giving instructions.

Rommel's shoulder straps for a General were silver/gold-coloured twisted braid with silver pips over a red felt underlay. After the fall of Tobruk, he wore the crossed batons of a Field Marshal on his shoulder straps.

Rommel also took his share of photos while in Africa and he was often to be seen with his Leica case unbuttoned and camera ready for an interesting shot. Sadly, many of these photos taken by Rommel did not survive the war.

Rommel receives a high Italian decoration during a visit to an Italian HQ in the late summer of 1941.

An Italian submarine that had run supplies into Bardia while it was cut off by the British advance in June 1941 received a visit by Rommel, who was given a glass of wine by the captain.

With Hauptmann the Reverend Wilhelm Bach (at left) and members of 1st Battalion Inf.Rgt.104 (mot) at Halfaya in July 1941.

Obviously pleased with his visit, Rommel smiles as he prepares to leave, and one Italian officer makes a formal bow.

The *Chef* arrives in his personal Fieseler *Storch* (Stork).

A postcard that was available in the second half of 1942, taken in very early 1942, with Italian decorations prominently showing. (This photo was taken six months or so before he had been promoted to Field Marshal, in spite of the card's caption.)

Rommel on the cliff above Bardia Harbour with the Italian submarine he had just visited visible in the bay below.

A typical impromptu conference around Rommel's *Horch* in September 1942, with officers from Pz.Gren.Rgt 200 at El Alamein. The officer sitting in the back with Rommel is Colonel Baylerlein.

61

A permanent lavatory was used outside this camp near Bardia in the summer of 1941 – a 44-gallon drum half buried in the ground with a board placed on top of the open upper end.

The common way of lowering the daytime heat inside a tent was to rig a second canvas skin above the actual tent to make an insulated layer of cooler air between the two canvas surfaces.

CAMP SCENES

T he usual accommodation for German troops living in the open desert consisted of various sized canvas tents. Often these tents were pitched two at a time, a larger tent over a smaller one with the space between them giving some insulation from the searing heat of the sun. Whenever the ground was not too hard, the tent tops could be erected above pits dug into the sand. This gave effective cover against enemy bombs and artillery fire (unless there was a direct hit). If the ground was too hard to dig into, tents could be slung alongside vehicles which provided some protection and shade, or surrounded by low mounds of rocks (sangars). The tents were always well dispersed, with tents and vehicles spread out across the desert to minimise the risk of heavy damage from air attack by presenting a large number of separated small targets instead of larger clusters of targets. It was usual for foxholes, or slit trenches, to be dug close to tents if time allowed. Few German soldiers were ever fortunate enough to pitch their tents for any length of time inside an oasis, with its shady date palms and abundant fresh water.

A special treat on Adolf Hitler's birthday for these members of 15th Panzer Division recently arrived in Libya, a three course meal served up after making camp on the evening of 20 April 1941.

CHAPTER 7

The usual objects scattered around all campsites were jerricans (especially the ones with the white cross on the sides used for water only), wooden and metal ammunition boxes which served as outdoor seating, and the simple wooden tables and chairs made in the army's own carpentry shops in the rear. Nearby there were usually trenches or rocky sangars for use in the event of an air attack. The chimneys of the German army kitchen on wheels, the 'Goulash Cannon', were likely to be sited near the larger and more permanent camps. In smaller and frontline living areas meals were transported in insulated containers from a central kitchen, or were cooked and warmed up over small fires by men remote from permanent kitchens. Petrol poured over sand in a tin and then lit was a popular method of making a fire to warm one's meal.

Only a few photos recorded the mundane and routine scenes that were repeated many, many times, a soldier sewing on a button or sleeve insignia for example, or the means by which uniforms were cleaned — woollen overcoats were brushed to remove sand and dirt, while the cotton uniforms items of cap, tunic, shirt and trousers were washed in petrol or seawater and then rubbed with clean dry sand (unless soap was available to rub into the dirtiest patches).

Personal weapons were only rarely seen in photos of campsites, and even the heavier weapons like artillery or tanks were normally sited some distance away from the tents. Larger and more permanent campsites with caravans or buses like battalion or regimental HQs were normally well camouflaged, using the abundant camelthorn bushes to break up the familiar outline of vehicles.

Wadis were popular places for campsites too, but there was always the risk that a flash storm out in the desert would sent a torrent of water down the wadi. Hence most camps put up in a wadi were more likely to be for a short time only.

Camps were often dotted with signposts, both the official army tactical identification signs and the unofficial ones that counted the distance in kilometres to Berlin, or advertised such and such a site as the 'beautiful tropical holiday resort of the 104th Infantry Regiment' etc.

Campsites always meant time for a haircut.

Regular chore, washing underclothes and socks.

Paul Erich Schläfer sews a button on his woollen greatcoat, November 1941.

Four camouflage shelter quarters have here been joined on the back of a Hanomen truck in a camp near Bardia in the summer of 1941.

This collection of signs at the entrance to a camp includes one warning that mines are ahead, another advertising tourist trips to 'beautiful Germany' (*Besucht das schöne Deutschland*) and the bottom sign advises that here is a 'track' for cyclists only.

These three men have unloaded their cargo of water jerricans to arrange protective walls to sleep inside for the night.

A tent home in the desert for members of 15th PzDiv south of Bardia in the summer of 1941.

Pfingsten (Whitsun) 1941
AFRIKA — place and unit
unknown.

The personal staff of the
Surgeon-General of the
Afrikakorps at their campsite
under the palms near
Misurata in March 1942.

CHAPTER 7

Beside a trench dug to give protection against air attack, 2nd Company *Sonderverband* 288 in the summer of 1942.

The company tailor with his table-top treadle-operated Singer sewing machine. The *Afrikakorps* tailors were busy prolonging the life of uniforms when supplies were not reaching North Africa.

Mass being celebrated for members of the Pioneer Battalion in 15thPzDiv in the summer of 1941.

Photograph showing shelters dug into the ground and covered with canvas and sand used by members of a Flak unit south of Tobruk in 1941.

[Pi]n-up that accompanied
[m]embers of Rommel's
[B]egleitkommando in late
[1]941.
[(D]ieter Hellriegel)

Photo taken to record visit
from Arab villagers who
arrived with eggs and dates
to sell.

Franz Seidl, 2nd Company
Sonderverband 288, June 1942.

Unteroffizier, from Rommel's *Begleitkommando,*
Wadi Matratin November 1941.
(Dieter Hellriegel)

FACES

T he faces of the German soldiers in the photos on these pages are from individual snapshots taken in Africa, studio portraits taken in Europe, family snapshots, and the official ID photos removed from the soldier's army service passbook *(Wehrpass)*. Except in those instances where the photos were obtained from original owners still living today, no names are known. These other photos are identified only by their origin, taken by Allied soldiers from German POWs and abandoned positions in North Africa in World War II.

They need no captions. In reply to the question, "Who were the *Afrikakorps*?" there is one simple answer. They are the faces in these photos.

ibya, summer of 1941, bareheaded member of 15Pz Divisional staff.

CHAPTER 8

Leutnant Wolfgang Doering, Rommel's *Begleitkommando* (Escort unit) in November 1941. (Dieter Hellriegel)

Oberzahlmeister Schmidt, Staff Company, Rommel's *Kampfstaffel,* El Alamein, 1942. (Dieter Hellriegel)

Panzer crewman, showing the special black woollen uniform worn by tankers in Europe, photo found in a knocked out tank near Tobruk in December 1941.

Prewar studio shot of a member of 21PzDiv as civilian.

In Basic Training, Erfurt 1941.

Oberschirrmeister Förderreuter, Staff Company, Rommel's *Kampfstaffel*, El Alamein, 1942. (Dieter Hellriegel)

73

Officer (by silver cording on cap), rank unknown.

Grenadier (infantry private rank).

Unflinching, as flies crawl over mouth and nostrils, this grenadier stands stiffly to attention as Major Briel awards an Iron Cross 1st Class in September 1942.

...e faces of Georg Briel in August 1942.

...ftwaffe, Flak gunner, *Kanonier* (Private rank).

Photo taken from wallet found at Belhammed, November 1941.

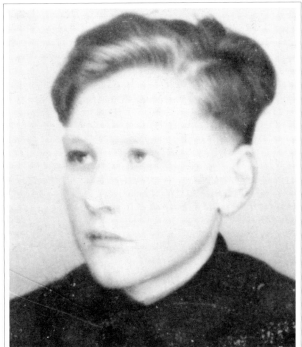

Typical assortment of rations for three days in the early months of 1942 for a *Zug* (platoon) of 2nd Company *Sonderverband* 288 — loaves of bread from the regimental bakery, tins of Italian sausage meat and Norwegian sardines in olive oil, oranges, tubes of cheese (in the cloth sacks) and a few tins of ersatz coffee and sugar.

Rations being handed out on the Egyptian border on 3rd May 1941, a dollop of fruit conserve into the lid of the mess tin and two oranges.

FOOD AND DRINK

N o German soldier who served in North Africa could ever forget the standard diet as provided by the army — processed cheese in tube containers, tinned sardines in olive oil, Italian military issue tinned sausage meat (the infamous 'AM'), German Dauerbrot (a wholesome and popular moist long lasting bread, made from 'black' rye or wheat, and wrapped in foil), the occasional fresh wholemeal bread, onions and dehydrated vegetables (legumes), an oatmeal gruel, the hard and dry Italian army biscuits, and whatever captured food was available (always seen as the ultimate luxury by German troops bored with their own rations).

The staple drink was usually purified water — heavy with chemical agents — and drunk as reconstituted lemon 'juice' or as *ersatz* coffee (a synthetic substitute for coffee), which still tasted of the chemicals added to make the water suitable for human consumption. What water was not used for drinking or cooking had to stretch to cover shaving and washing, cleaning teeth, and for rinsing out socks, singlets and underpants.

It was normal practice for the *Wehrmacht* to issue vitamin tablets to its soldiers as a dietary supplement, a policy actively encouraged by Hitler who believed in the power of vitamins to improve one's health and well-being. British Intelligence officers in the 8th Army, whose job it was to analyse all captured German material, including food stores, showed amazement when cartons of vitamin pills were discovered among German stores in Libya in November and December 1941. Stories of these then relatively uncommon pills used by the *Afrikakorps* gave rise to stories in wartime Allied press that the German soldiers in Africa were some sort of new twentieth century Aryan supermen, using drugs *(sic)* to increase their physical strength.

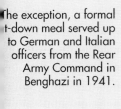

The exception, a formal sit-down meal served up to German and Italian officers from the Rear Army Command in Benghazi in 1941.

However, the average German soldier envied the diet of their enemy. By common agreement in the *Afrikakorps* the most delicious food in the desert was captured from the enemy — tinned corned beef and fresh white bread, followed closely by tinned fruits, especially peaches, apricots and pineapple. The issue of German gastronomic delights from the homeland such as ham, beer and sausage, fresh potatoes, and sweets such as chocolate, were rare events. American army food captured in Tunisia caused acute envy among German troops also.

The only regular supplementary food available to the *Afrikakorps* (apart from captured stores) either came from home, the occasional fruitcake sent by families through the post, or what was obtained from local Arabs. Whenever it was possible to trade with Arab villagers food was always at the top of the list — eggs, chickens, fruit, tomatoes and fresh dates.

Efforts by so-called 'experts' in nutrition in Berlin who sent a stream of advice to units in Africa aimed at improving the standard diet were usually wildly out of touch with reality. One such official pronouncement circulated through the 5th Light Division in May 1941 contained a recipe for a 'nutritious liquid snack suitable for times when on the move', consisting of a mixture of the following ingredients: '$\frac{1}{2}$ liter water; $\frac{1}{2}$ tube cordial; 30gr marmalade; 30-35gr sugar; 30gr groats or rice.

Like any army, Germany soldiers in Africa were pre-occupied with their stomachs and what went into them. Food was a popular subject of conversation (especially for the black humour of soldiers), even if the fare itself was not popular. Many of the photos taken by *Afrikakorps* men were to do with eating, and with the preparation of food.

The standard German diet was a constant source of concern, for the soldiers forced to eat it, and the supply units who were unable to substitute it with anything more wholesome or tasty.

A common scene at the time of the midday meal, gathered around the cookhouse truck with the usual collection of water jerricans. Sign on the back door reads 'Entry Forbidden' *(Eintritt verboten!)*

Three shots taken by a cook of a special meal, which included fresh meat, being prepared in the summer of 1941.

The end result: serving up portions in the proferred mess tins of the company.

One of the cooks slicing pork.

A bowl of noodles being tossed inside the cookhouse vehicle.

Evening meal for a platoon of 2nd Company *Sonderverband* 288 in early 1942, a stew with the usual ingredients of tinned Italian meat, tomatoes and reconstituted dried legumes in boiling water.

Fresh bread baked by a regimental bakery company is loaded on to a truck for distribution to companies and platoons.

FOOD AND DRINK

Peeling onions, Inf.Rgt.115 (mot) in the summer of 1941.

Kitchen area of a battery of 33rd Artillery Rgt in 15th.Pz.Div in the autumn of 1941.

The tip of a bayonet opens the Italian tin of sausage meat, the notorious 'Old Man' *(Alte Mann)* with the stamp 'AM' on the end.

Evening meal. A member of Infantry Regiment 361 in the 90th Light Division in November 1941 has constructed a stove dug into the sand with a chimney fashioned from an artillery shell that has had the detonator end cap knocked out.

A meal in the shady garden of the
O/R soldier club in Apollonia.

Water collection from a
well via hoses to fill
200-litre drums.

A Military Police
(Feldgendarmerie) detail from
5th Light Division near Sirte
in early 1941 with their Auto
Union Horch cross country
car (Kfz70).

German soldier shaving, using
the small mirror inside his
compass.

IN GENERAL

T he following photos are ones that could not be easily classified under other sections. The photos are worth reproducing, however, both for their own interest and because they are so typical. Of all the thousands of photos that passed into the hands of Allied servicemen as souvenirs, picked up at random off the battlefields, many are like these photos, with no definite background or history.

Postausgabe, Postal Delivery, somewhere in ypt behind the Alamein ne in 1942. The volume of mail handled by the *Afrikakorps* was vast.

Soldier's humour, a cactus plant with wide grin and cigarette joins the *Afrikakorps* and is given a field cap.

A not uncommon sight, letters being written before battle.

| # CAMOUFLAGE

A lthough the German High Command took little official notice of the need for the individual German soldier to camouflage himself in the desert, the men of the *Afrikakorps* did manage to blend in with their surroundings, using canvas sheets, rock mounds (sangars), piled up camelthorn, dugouts covered with equipment and battlefield debris (a most effective way of creating camouflage on the battlefield was by hiding under or among the plentiful junk left by the fighting), by painting vehicles and personal equipment with the light coloured beige or orange-tan paint supplied for vehicle camouflage and by using sand sprinkled over wet paint to completely cover reflective surfaces on metal equipment.

The faded uniforms which were so fashionable were a practical response to desert conditions, their bleached-out look made a perfect sand-coloured camouflage, making a less conspicuous contrast than the newer and darker uniforms against the light-coloured desert.

Company Commander's tent at Alamein in 1942 bedecked with the usual tufts of camelthorn.

This member of *Sonderverband* 288 wears his helmet with beige coloured paint (issued for vehicles) and a coating of sand that has been sprinkled over the still wet paint.

The vista of rocks and brush give a mottled pattern to the landscape that effectively absorbs tents covered with sprigs of camelthorn. Note the high wooden pole in the middle background, an anchor point for radio antenna. This photo was taken from high up a similar pole.

| # REST AND RELAXATION

T he only organised effort by the German army to entertain its troops serving out in the desert involved the *Propaganda Kompanie Afrika*, attached to *Afrikakorps* HQ, a band of wandering minstrels who sang songs, performed excerpts from popular light opera, played magical tricks on their audiences, made up bands to play modern and traditional music and showed a selection of popular movies.

Soldiers serving in the propaganda company wore grey piping on their shoulder straps and field caps, and had as their own tactical symbol a winged camel in profile, rather like a humped quadruped angel, above the letters 'PK'.

For the rest, the German soldiers in Africa made their own rest and relaxation, as the following photos show. Football games were popular, as were tug-of-war contests set up between neighbouring units. Reading and writing letters took up a lot of spare time, as did the German card game *Skat*. Food and stories involving the opposite sex helped to while away idle hours and according to Allied wartime intelligence reports, some soldiers enjoyed gambling with the little money they had. The Army's field newspaper, *Die Oase*, was well-liked and was always read from cover to cover. Radio reception was good in the desert and a fair number of European stations could be picked up on short wave radio bands from late afternoon through the early night.

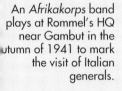

An *Afrikakorps* band plays at Rommel's HQ near Gambut in the autumn of 1941 to mark the visit of Italian generals.

Any soldiers stationed in Tripoli, or passing through, were able to use the brothel operated for the German Armed Forces in the large building at 4 Via Tassoni. This brothel was serviced by Italian women.

There were facilities such as bars and canteens in Tripoli and Benghazi, and rear locations such as Derma, Tobruk, Sollum and Mersa Matruh also had places for off-duty soldiers to get a drink. These were mainly used by the transport and supply troops or quartermaster units stationed there.

A quiet and absorbing time was always in store when newspapers and journals, such as this issue of the *Berliner Illustrierter*, arrived.

Not an uncommon experience, but an attempt to ride a donkey always brought a crowd of onlookers with cameras out.

The old Roman ruins at Leptis Magna.

A visiting Italian bookshop and newsagent on wheels with German novels and writing materials.

On the beach north of Bardia, 1941. (This photo belonged to a member of M/Cycle Btln 15.)

Listening to the popular radio programmes broadcast from Germany provided occasions to gather and socialise. (15PzDiv, summer 1941.)

Italian women working in the *Wehrmacht* brothel in Tripoli.

ets were popular, such as
is large chameleon. (Photo
opied from a wartime book
n the *Afrikakorps.*)

Euphonium, and players, in
the *Afrikakorps* band at El
Alamein.

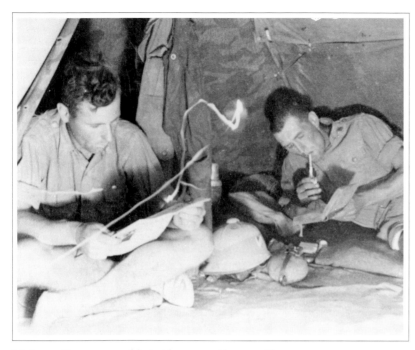

Night reading was possible inside a tent with a good lantern.

A body wash standing in metal lined ammunition cases for *Unteroffizier* Vogt of Rommel's *Kampfstaffel* at Alamein in September 1942. (Dieter Hellriegel)

During the early part of 1942 a conjuror/magician attached to the *Propaganda Kompanie Afrika* toured units before Rommel's offensive against the Gazala line. Here a card miraculously appears from under a volunteer's collar.

ven the top brass relaxed, as with this birthday party for General
rüwell at *Afrikakorps* HQ on 20 March, 1942.

Reading the popular DAK newspaper, *Die Oase*, which was
distributed weekly through the field post system.

A game of football between teams drawn from companies
stationed on the Egyptian frontier in 1941.

IN BATTLE – UNDER FIRE

POSITE:
erleutnant Dröber (at
ht) of 33rd Pz.Artl.Rgt,
•ks towards the panzers
mmel had ordered up
save his battery from
pture near the Egyptian
rder in June 1941.

N otwithstanding the difficulty of taking photos during the fighting, some troops did manage to use their cameras and the following pages show a few of their efforts (other photos snapped in battle are scattered among different parts of the book).

The phrase 'fog of war' best describes the general state of battle, where one's personal view of what was happening was clouded by an ignorance of the larger picture of things. Once battle was joined between two opposing sides a large element of the unknown was introduced. At the individual level there was a loosening of the actual control and sense of order that originated from contact with one's higher field commanders. Circumstances changed so quickly once fighting started that it was beyond communication technology alone to hold things together. Even with modern two-way radio sets in vehicles battlefield information relayed up the chain of command was often inaccurate, out of date and disjointed. Those men reporting on the battle were still limited by what they themselves saw, or perceived to be happening. The average soldier knew nothing more of the battle than what he saw by looking at the men nearest him. Friend and foe became mixed across the desert, and only the discipline and training imposed by one's own army, the morale of the soldiers themselves and their own will to win, carried the battle on.

It is therefore surprising that given the general state of battlefield chaos, with the failure of commanders to monitor effectively what was actually happening at the lowest level of organisation, most soldiers nevertheless believed *at the moment* there was still purpose and meaning and order in what was going on around them. They attributed even the smallest specific actions to intervention by some higher level of command, or as the result of some sort of prior plan. An example of this sort of belief was where an isolated random act of fire was followed by an equally indiscriminate and unconnected burst of enemy fire and in the minds of the local participants the two events were linked as to cause and effect, a sure sign that the other side was watching closely and reacting at a relatively high level of command to everything you individually, or your own side, was doing at that time. In reality the opposite was nearly always true — small units and individual soldiers were not the focus of attention by enemy commanders. It only seemed that way to the many individual soldiers scattered across the desert, immersed in the absolute importance and significance of what they themselves were doing. It was any large number of tanks together, or any columns of vehicles and guns, that seized the attention of enemy commanders. That was where threats were seen and had to be countered.

When fighting in the open and flat desert it was nearly impossible to believe you personally were not being observed by the enemy. The feeling that you were always exposed, and that the enemy knew your position, helped to give a personal meaning to the many things happening around you — an enemy plane flying overhead must be reporting on *your* position, dust thrown up in the distance by an enemy column would probably be their preliminary manoeuvres before an attack in *your* direction, artillery shells landing nearby would be aimed at *you,* and so on, regardless of whether this was true or not.

Given the lack of natural cover in the desert it was essential that commanders reacted quickly to enemy dispositions. In such conditions it becomes easier to understand how Rommel's style of command from the front was more effective, was faster to react to desert battlefield developments, than the British system of command from headquarters sited several hours away from the front lines. Rommel was able to cut through some of the 'fog of war' — until El Alamein at least — by mixing himself in the moving battle and by impressing a resolute will to win on those around him, regardless of what apparent confusion may have prevailed on the battlefield. A weaker system of command usually yielded in the belief that it must be losing if the other side held firm or attacked when it should have been retreating. Hitler firmly held this belief also, that willpower, if strong enough, could by itself turn the tide of battle in one's favour by undermining the nerve of the enemy.

Times of battle which could last over several days were invariably followed firstly by a feeling of well-being and of relief, then by a profound exhaustion that could only be overcome by sleep. This is why shots taken after the fighting had passed by often showed soldiers asleep, even in the most uncomfortable positions.

After the fierce fighting around Bir Hacheim in June 1942 a member of 2nd Company of *Sonderverband* 288 sleeps exhausted in a trench.

Battle was not continuous, it ebbed and flowed like the tides, and there were times of apparent calm when meals could be eaten, weapons and equipment checked, bowels emptied, and petrol, ammunition, water, food and other supplies brought up by the transport columns. Photos show it was common at such times for soldiers to get out bundles of letters from their packs and read them.

What one did in battle was largely determined by one's training, by a conditioned response to obey orders, and by the cohesiveness of the basic fighting unit. There was little imaginative or creative thinking involved in handling weapons. The first time under enemy fire was terrifying and unnerving, and it was always like this. With time each soldier found his own way of accepting the strain of battle, and of living with its brutality. The comradeship of the close-knit combat units made it somewhat easier to face up to what became an intimate shared experience. For those who faced enemy fire alone, especially those cut off from their comrades and under fire, it was far, far worse. For these soldiers, all alone, the psychological strains were enormous, and unrelenting, with thoughts of death or maiming injury never far away.

During the fighting south of Gazala in May 1942 two infantry seek some rest and shade under canvas shelter quarters buttoned together and slung from wooden stakes. Behind them is their foxhole with rifles propped up on the edge.

A blurry shot of a 10.5-cm howitzer with muzzle depressed firing at an approaching enemy column, November 1941.

An artillery crew snapped during a meal pause in the desert south of Mersa Matruh in late June 1942 as the DAK surrounded British forces there blocking the way along the coastal road.

eneral Grant tanks knocked out after they had come against a line of 3-mm guns in the early stages of the Gazala battle in May/June 1942.

t by Allied bombers. (NZ soldier's photo)

General von Bismarck, commander of the 21st Panzer Division (in glasses and peaked cap) snapped during the fighting before the capture of Tobruk in 1942.

The aftermath of battle, bodies and personal possessions lying scattered on the desert where artillery or mortar fire had caught them without protection. (British dead at El Alamein.)

Two photos taken by Paul-Erich Schäfler in June 1941 from the position his battery of 15.5-cm guns held on the Egyptian border.

Training, March 1942, an officer running forward with his men has his drawn pistol in his hand. (In reality, these light and short range hand weapons were almost never used.)

After the capture of Bir Hacheim, these members of 2nd Company *Sonderverband* 288 sit together with food and drink.

Mortar firing during the bitter fighting for Bir Hacheim in June 1942; here the real thing, from 2nd Company *Sonderverband* 288.

Tank crewman's view, dust from an enemy artillery shell hangs in the air as a following tank skirts the point of impact.

The popular image: in foxhole with gun at ready.

111

Watching fall of shot through scissor periscope binoculars while two men in the rear hold telephones to their ears waiting to relay information back to the gun batteries.

A 17-cm Kanone 18 of *Sonderverband* 288 moving up into battle in June 1942 (note the white air recognition band across the bonnet of the prime mover).

| # ARTILLERY

R ed was the distinguishing colour worn on caps and shoulder straps by artillery regiments (the same colour edging to the shoulder straps as shown by general rank officers). The artillery regiments serving in the Panzer Divisions in Africa had an establishment strength of approximately 2,000 (the artillery regiments in Infantry and Light Divisions were slightly smaller in size), though these full establishment figures were hardly ever reached in reality.

The artillery batteries, the basic tactical units, were closely integrated into the combat chain of command, responding even to requests for supporting fire from unit commanders as low as platoon leaders who could ask for fire against specified targets in their immediate area. Artillery fire was responsible for the greatest number of casualties on both sides in the North African campaigns. The stony ground absorbed very little of the force of exploding shells, with most of the lethal shrapnel therefore flying outwards to strike down anyone in range. Shrapnel from airburst fire was also a major cause of battlefield casualties.

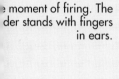

e moment of firing. The
der stands with fingers
in ears.

Whenever the *Luftwaffe* lost air supremacy, artillery sites were particularly vulnerable to enemy strafing by the hated and feared Fighter-bombers, the *Jabos*. The artillery guns were also likely to receive counter-battery fire from the enemy's artillery. Artillery displacements therefore were given some protection by putting up rings of rocks and sandbags whenever there was time to build these protective walls. These defensive walls did not completely enclose the gun sites; there always had to be at least one open side for the tractors to pull the guns away quickly. an important factor in such a mobile war. The tents used by the soldiers were always pitched some way away from where the guns were dug in.

However, all too often in battle the artillery batteries did not have time to protect themselves with stoneworks and by digging in, and they suffered from being exposed to enemy counter fire. Because of the clouds of dust thrown up by artillery guns when they fired, it was impossible to conceal their location once firing had started.

As with all other weapons, the fine desert dust was a constant problem for artillery gunners. Shells had to be carefully brushed to remove grains of sand, even when the shells were taken from stores and still packed in their wicker baskets. It was heavy work manhandling shells; their great weight meant crews had to work very hard while their guns were in action. Manhandling the guns themselves also called for great physical effort on the part of their crews.

Artillery units suffered heavy losses, especially when overrun after standing to fight off an enemy advancing with tanks. The heavier guns of the artillery batteries meant these units were nowhere near as mobile as the lighter anti-tank guns. The exception to this was of course when the artillery guns were mounted on a tank chassis as an 'Assault Gun', though such weapons were only seen in any number in Tunisia. Unlike their *Luftwaffe* counterparts manning anti-aircraft guns, army artillery crews initially were not issued with steel helmets in North Africa.

10.5 cm *leichte Feldhaubitze 18* (light field howitzer) with its Krauss-Maffei half-tracked prime mover in 1942, around the time of the capture of Tobruk.

Captured French heavy artillery piece, the 15.5-cm *Canon de 155 GPF-T (Grand Puissance Filloux-Touzard)* in Western Cyrenaica in early 1942.

General view of war from the artillery gunner's position, moving up to and away from the gun as it is loaded and fired again and again . . .

Each artillery unit had its own signals platoon, and guns were always linked by telephone cables to OP sites, with their distinctive 'scissor' binocular periscopes set up behind rocky parapets. From these OP sites it was possible to register the actual fall of shot and to communicate this information directly to the battery of guns. It was standard practice for artillery batteries to have three observation posts, one sited near the guns, another as close as possible to the front, and the third being integrated into the main line of resistance (i.e. behind the actual front line in the fallback position).

Ammunition supplies were a continuing problem because of the critical overall supply situation, and because of the large number of various 'booty' guns used by the *Afrikakorps* (British, French, Russian etc.) requiring their own special supply of ammunition.

Heinz Köllenberger of 33rd Artl. Rgt in 15 Panzer Division with a captured British 87.6-cm 25-pounder on the Egyptian border, July 1941.

Moving a captured British 5.5-in howitzer used by 164th Light Div. at El Alamein into position in soft sand took an enormous physical effort, even with such large wheels.

ARTILLERY

A series of shots taken of a battery of the standard German army field howitzer of World War II, the 15-cm *schwere Feldhaubitze* 18, here in position north-west of Sidi Omar in late 1941.

Shells in wicker baskets stacked in readiness behind, and empty propellant cases lined up ready for use in charging the shells once they had been rammed into the breach.

Priming the detonator in the nose cone of the shell.

Side view of the battery showing all four guns.

After the action, the barrel is depressed to lower the silhouette and a light camouflage net has been thrown across the whole gun.

'Braut des Infanteristen' (Bride of the Infantry), the bolt action Mauser rifle model Kar98k used by the majority of soldiers in the *Afrikakorps*. This expression, used quite affectionately by German soldiers in World War II, had its origins in the First World War, where it had been also widely used with the Mod98 Mauser rifle.

Infantry commander, Hans-Günter Baade (centre), in early 1942 the commander of the 115th Rifle (Motorised Infantry) Regiment in 15th Panzer Division.

INFANTRY, AFRICAN GRENADIERS

T he motorised infantry units in the *Afrikakorps* in 1941, and for most of 1942, were known as Rifle Regiments *(Schützenregimenter)*, but from the second half of 1942 were renamed Panzer Grenadier Regiments *(Panzergrenadier-regimenter)*. There were no infantry units at all in the first division despatched to Africa, the 5th Light Div., and its two MG battalions and engineer troops had to take on the role of infantry. The divisions that followed later had their full share of motorised infantry regiments. Few infantry soldiers in Africa wore steel helmets until the fighting in Tunisia when they were in general issue.

The various motorised infantry units wore green piping on caps and shoulder straps, this colour being the most commonly seen among the combat units, reflecting their large numerical strength in the divisions during 1941 and 1942. In Tunisia there was one division with a regiment of unmotorised infantry, the 334th Division, and these 'foot' soldiers wore white piping on their shoulder straps (the other 'infantry' regiment in this division contained alpine troops and they wore a medium green colour).

When a line had to be held, it was not done with minefields and artillery alone or the anti-tank guns. Along the miles of 'front' were the infantry and their weapons which they had to carry themselves — mortars, machine guns, machine pistols, rifles and grenades. Theirs was the job of actually occupying the edge of whatever piece of territory happened to be in dispute.

Soon after firing a rifle
ɪd to be cleaned. It was
court martial offence to
have a dirty weapon.

Although the *Afrikakorps* was a fully motorised force, the need to fight from static positions meant that the motorised infantry very quickly became ordinary infantry 'foot' soldiers fighting from trenches and foxholes. After twelve days of heavy fighting at El Alamein in October and November 1942, the *Afrikakorps* had lost a high proportion of its Panzer Grenadier strength, and these losses (along with the all important Panzers) made it impossible for Rommel to hold on any longer. Although in numbers alone Rommel still commanded a large force, with the front line infantry units down to very low numbers, the British offensive could not be held and their relentless advance quickened, causing Rommel to order the retreat, even before Berlin and Hitler had been informed.

Along with mental pictures of the dusty Panzers and their crews, it is the image of an infantry soldier in bleached cloth field cap with rifle in hand in a foxhole that fills the popular image of the *Afrikakorps*. And rightly so.

The deadly MG42, the machine gun that had a phenomenal 1400 rpm max. rate of fire, first used in Africa by the German army in May 1942, had a sound like no other gun used by either side.

The typical face of the German infantry soldier in Africa, in faded field cap, overcoat in the early morning and late afternoon, with Kar98k slung over one shoulder, and dotted with flies.

At least one unit did not throw away their gas masks in the desert. These soldiers have just had an exercise using their gas masks, late 1941. (The gas masks here are worn around the neck on canvas straps.)

During a lull in the fighting near the Gazala cauldron in June 1942, men from MG Battalion 8 with their 'booty' British lorry.

Training in the early part of 1942, members of 2nd Company of *Sonderverband* 288 firing an MG34 from a trench protected by a line of sandbags.

CHAPTER 15

El Alamein: two soldiers loaded with the paraphernalia of infantry — machine pistol, steel helmet, water bottles, ammunition, bread bag, mess tins. The man on the right carries the heavy weight of a base plate for a mortar on his back.

Wheels of war, members of 2nd Company *Sonderverband* 288 with their personal equipment piled up on their 2.8-cm anti-tank weapon, a *Panzerbüsche* 41 with tapering bore-barrel which fired a tungsten-tipped projectile. The soldier to the left holds a British souvenir cap.

The highly successful close range infantry weapon, the automatic MP40 Machine Pistol.

A captured British 40-mm Bofors AA gun taken over by members of the 2nd Company in *Sonderverband* 288. Captured weapons and transport were often of crucial importance to the outcome of a battle.

(Above and left): By the end of 1942 Rommel was pulling the survivors of his *Afrikakorps* back across the Gulf of Sirte into Tripolitania. Here a mortar crew train their weapon (an 8-cm *Granatenwerfer* 34) towards the east, towards the British lines. Open boxes of mortar bombs are arranged near the entrance to their covered-over earth bunker.(Charles Hinz)

A wounded Grenadier from 90th Light Division picked up on the battlefield on 2 November, 1942. His right hand shows signs of advanced gangrene resulting from a tightly applied ligature.

Lining up for a cholera booster at a medical dressing station in 1941.

MEDICAL

Medical units were organised firstly inside each division, at company level for field hospitals, dressing stations, ambulance sections, and stores and supplies. The second level of medical support services, in the larger hospitals sited in the rear (in Tripoli and Benghazi for 1941), usually came under direct corps or army administration. These large base hospitals were fully equipped with surgical theatres, X-Ray plant, plaster cast and resuscitation sections as well as the critical care wards. These hospitals, especially the ones at Tripoli and Derna, were most used in 1941 and early 1942, Later in 1942, when the *Afrikakorps* found itself deep inside Egyptian territory, it was easier to transport wounded by air from airfields in Egypt to the large Wehrmacht hospitals in Athens. Such a trip was in fact shorter than going back to Tripoli and hospitals in Greece or Italy did not have to be supplied with materials and staff carried across the Mediterranean.

Personnel serving in medical units wore a dark blue piping on their field caps and shoulder straps. Medical units were made up of very high numbers of volunteers, including those who had offered themselves for this non-combatant role, such as those for whom religious beliefs precluded actual fighting. Female nurses also served in the field hospitals in Africa, with exceptional bravery and devotion to their patients. In all, about two hundred female nurses went to Africa with the *Afrikakorps* and served alongside their male colleagues.

The German army's attitude to treating their wounded was really quite simple: they aimed to identify as quickly as possible those who could be returned to their units after treatment, and to ensure that those with serious injuries received appropriate medical care with maximum speed.

In the open desert the forward hospitals or dressing stations were no more than a collection of large tents, one of which served as a mortuary. In times of fighting the mortuary would always contain bodies awaiting burial, many only half-dressed and still showing the evidence of recent surgery as well as their wounds. In order to get a seriously wounded man to the operating table as quickly as possible, only the clothing in the immediate vicinity of the wound(s) would be removed, cut away with long handled shears. If these men died during surgery, they were carried to the mortuary tent and left as they had come off the operating table. In the middle of battle there was no time to lay out the bodies as one would in a funeral parlour.

Anyone who spent time serving in one of these forward field hospitals, and the smaller dressing or medical aid stations, never forgot the odour that was associated with those places — a mixture of blood, perspiration, ether and antiseptic solution. These forward dressing stations received their patients on stretchers delivered by ambulances or by truck. They dressed all wounds, and could handle blood transfusions, the administration of drugs, splinting of fractures, and most types of emergency surgery including amputations. As much as possible the forward dressing stations attempted to save lives by stabilising the condition of the more seriously wounded who would get specialised treatment later at the larger hospitals to the rear. This was the case for serious chest and abdominal wounds, and skull damage. Those seriously wounded were evacuated quickly by air from the combat zone if it was possible, firstly by small Feiseler Storks to one of the larger base hospitals, and then back to Europe. In 1941 and 1942 this meant travelling by hospital ship to Naples, or by air to Athens. Evacuation of wounded from Tunisia was efficiently organised using fleets of Ju52s flying from the many former French airfields, right up to the last hours of the campaign. For most of those sick or wounded who were evacuated to Europe a long period of recovery was ahead of them, for some stretching into many months.

The greatest single cause of wounds, and death, for soldiers in Africa was from artillery fire. Other main causes of battlefield casualties were aerial strafing and bombing, from mines, and MG fire (usually fired over some distance). Apart from critical damage to one of the vital organs which resulted in almost instant death, most battlefield deaths came from loss of blood, shock, and dehydration. It says a lot for the standard of care in the forward dressing stations that there were not many deaths attributable to infected wounds.

At El Alamein the living conditions were so unhygienic that in August and September 1942 more men were being withdrawn from their units and repatriated to Europe because of sickness than from battle-related wounds. Indeed, for a period in August and September 1942 the number of sick being repatriated exceeded the number of new replacements reaching the front line units. Serious bowel disorders were particularly common, usually necessitating hospitalisation in Europe. Skin ulcers that constantly discharged were a problem too, though not in the same category as the bowel diseases. Jaundice was another common condition that ultimately required treatment in Europe if the patient was to recover. Even so, in these difficult conditions the average German managed to keep himself relatively clean, German military discipline saw to this. Axis medical records showed that for every one German infested by lice there were on average ten Italians who urgently needed delousing.

A Ju52 painted with a red cross unloads its cargo of wounded *Afrikakorps* soldiers at a Greek airfield outside Athens.

An Italian hospital ship anchored in Bardia Harbour in September 1941. Such ships were the main means of evacuating wounded troops back to Europe in 1941 and for the first half of 1942.

A wounded member of 2nd Company *Sonderverband* 288 stands supported by two comrades in front of an Italian ambulance in June 1942.

Booster shots against Paratyphoid or Cholera in the early part of 1942. The injections were given into the chest muscle rather than into the arm which may have rendered the arm useless for a time with any severe reaction against the immunising dose (left side of chest for those right handed, right side chest for left handed).

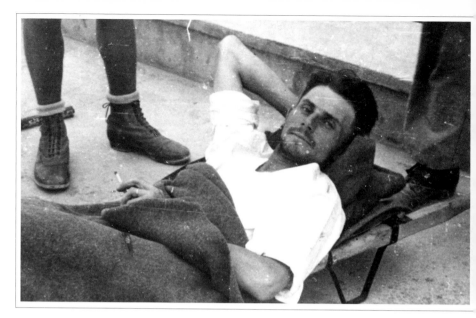

CHAPTER 16

A cigarette while lying waiting on a stretcher for the next stage of the evacuation back to the base hospital at Derna in May 1942.

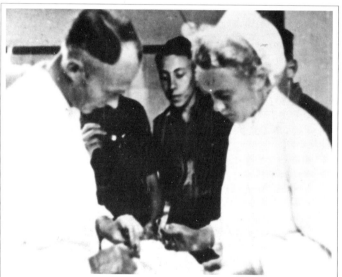

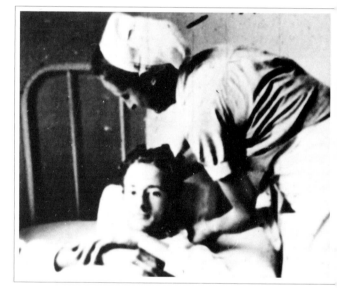

Two shots taken in the summer of 1941 in Tripoli of nurses and patients in the hospital operated by Field Hospital 200 which was attached to the 5th Light Division (later 21st Panzer Division).

The Forward Dressing Station of 21st Panzer Division situated west of Bardia in November 1941.

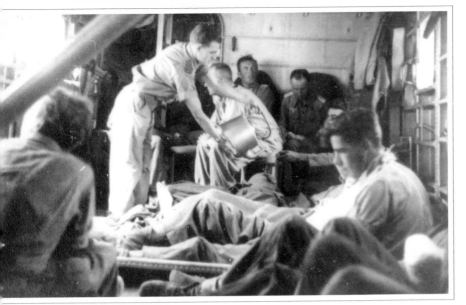

Interior of a bus that had
been converted into an
ambulance.

A German medic (centre
cap) sits surrounded by
some of the many patients
and Allied medical staff
at this dressing station at
the end of the day (the
station and most of its
patients and staff had
been captured by a rapid
German advance that
same morning).

During the fighting around
the Tobruk perimeter in
November 1941, this tank
was used to bring up urgently
needed medical supplies.

Cross-country acclimatisation trips, navigating by sun and compass.

April 1941. Fresh arrivals in Libya, with motorcycles and uniforms not yet showing signs of desert wear.

MOTORCYCLE BATTALION

T he one Motorcycle Battalion in *Afrikakorps,* the famous 15th Battalion under *Oberstleutnant* Knabe (its first commander) came to Libya with the 15th Panzer Division. The battalion took part in nearly all of the major battles in the North African campaign. Its primary function was one of fast battlefield reconnaissance, though it was also used as motorised infantry by Rommel in the first half of 1941. The battalion lost its separate identity after the end of 1941 when it was absorbed as a third battalion by Rifle Rgt 115 in 15 PzDiv. In spite of the battalion officially changing its name, such was the force and strength of its identity as '15th Motorcycle Battalion' that it continued to be known by its old title for a long time, even when its activities were being officially recorded in the war diary of the *Panzergruppe Afrika* in 1942.

While the primary function of the battalion may have been to carry out quick battlefield reconnaissance and to filter through any gaps in the enemy's line, not all vehicles used by the battalion were motorcycles. In its make-up the battalion also had its allocation of half tracks, anti-tank guns, signals vehicles and its own transport lorries.

In soft sand the heavy BMW R75 (750cc) could bog down.

CHAPTER 17

The 15th Motorcycle Battalion, as the major component in Battlegroup Geissler, suffered terrible losses in an engagement with the 28th (Maori) NZ Battalion supported by the NZ Divisional Cavalry Regiment on 3 December 1941. The casualties were so severe that the battalion was nearly wiped out. Travelling down the Via Balbia towards Bardia it was ambushed by the New Zealanders who had spotted its advance and were lying in wait. The only support for the motorcycles pinned down under withering fire by the New Zealanders came from a solitary long range artillery piece firing indiscriminately from inside Bardia. The 15th Motorcycle Battalion bravely counter-attacked but could not make any advance against the stronger NZ positions. By the end of the day only forty-eight Germans, officers, NCOs and ORs got away out of a strength of around 450 that morning. Among the prisoners taken that day was the battalion commander, Major von Debschitz. After this disastrous engagement Rommel had to order that the survivors of the battalion were not to be used in front line combat until further notice. The battalion was rebuilt in early 1942 and fought again and again with distinction in the campaigns throughout 1942, and into 1943.

In 1941 troops serving in the Motorcycle Battalion wore a special soft shade of green piping on their shoulder straps and caps but this was replaced by copper brown in late 1941 (the same colour being used by reconnaissance units).

Changing a sidecar wheel.

Maintenance, with a supporting jerrican beneath the sump.

MOTORCYCLE BATTALION

About to slip another tube over a wheel rim.

Holes in the mudguard show where the edge of a burst of enemy MG fire has arced past.

November 1941. Nights were getting cold and the long coat was good protection against the cold air until the sun was up.

The owner of the camera that took most of the photos in this section, in the late part of 1941.

A lorry belonging to Anti-tank Unit 39, the very first part of the Afrikakorps to arrive in Libya, with three men of this unit, soon after reaching the front in late February 1941.

Driver of the lorry in the photo above after the vehicle had been given its desert camouflage in a light sandy-yellow paint very early in the campaign, around mid-March 1941.

PAK AND FLAK

T ogether with the tank crews, the PAK (anti-tank) units were the hard hitting edge of the *Afrikakorps*, both shield to the spear of the Panzer regiments, and anvil to their hammer.

It was fitting that the PAK crews wore the same pink piping on their caps and shoulder straps as the tank regiments. The anti-tank guns, and their gunners, were just as much a part of the tank battles as were the crews of the tanks. The long-barrelled anti-tank guns themselves were found not just in the specialist PAK units. They were used by reconnaissance, engineer, armoured infantry, and even HQ staff sections as main line protection against enemy tanks.

The anti-tank gunners wore steel helmets, unlike the gunners manning the heavier artillery, who were usually further behind the front line (as long as the fighting was not moving from place to place around the desert).

Half tracked prime movers with the distinctive long-barrelled PAK guns towed behind were never far from the Panzers in battle, and in retreat it was always the PAK guns that were among the last to pull back as the enemy advanced.

In fast moving battles of 1941 and the first half of 1942, anti-tank gunners fought in the open with no cover other than the small shields mounted on the guns, or what was given by the half track vehicles they travelled in. The PAK units usually moved right up with the tanks, and when the tanks stopped then so must their anti-tank escort, wherever it might be and usually without the time to dig in before fighting resumed.

In a typical configuration, the 5cm PAK 38 with its light half-tracked prime mover (Sd.Kfz.10) carrying crew and ammunition.

Changing position without the horsepower of the prime mover takes the united effort of the seven-man crew of this 5 cm PAK 38 (*Sonderverband* 288, May 1942).

The rare 4.2 cm lePAK 41, a tapered bore weapon firing special tungsten core ammunition, here as used by *Sonderverband* 288 in early 1942.

After the Alamein retreat *Sonderverband* 288 formed the rearguard for Rommel's retreat back the Gulf of Sirte. Here two crew of a 5-cm PAK wait in their prepared position near Mersa Matruh, November 1942. (Out of sight their tractor stands ready to move the gun and its crew at short notice.)

The original German anti-tank gun with a tapered barrel to fire special tungsten core ammunition, the 2.8 cm sPZB41, which narrowed to 2 cm at the barrel exit point. This example from 2nd Company of *Sonderverband* 288 in early 1942.

Crew positions for the 4.2 cm lePAK 41 (light anti-tank gun model 41).

CHAPTER 18

British Matilda 'I' tank, stopped by German PAK fire near Halfaya in July 1941.

Left in the retreat from El Alamein, when it could not longer fight on, this 88 crew 'spiked' their gun by blocking the barrel and firing a round. This gun must have been firing during the retreat; it is not dug in and has only a few sandbags and rocks as protection, sure signs the crew had not been in that position for very long (Australian solider's photo).

Mainstay of the DAK anti-tank units in 1941, the 5 cm PAK 38, here in an ordnance repair base.

Flak units were drawn from both the army and the *Luftwaffe*. (Army anti-aircraft units were designated 'Fla.' to distinguish them from the *Luftwaffe* units who took the more commonly used 'Flak'.) For both services, it was ground action rather than anti-aircraft fire that provided the bulk of their action in the desert. The single most powerful weapon used on the North African battlefield was an anti-aircraft gun that was the supreme battlefield anti-tank weapon, the high-velocity 88-mm capable of firing against tanks with the accuracy of a sniper's rifle. There was no Allied tank in North Africa able to withstand the 88-mm guns. Nearly all of the 88-mm gunners were *Luftwaffe* personnel, but they fulfilled the role of anti-tank gunners like their army counterparts. The *Luftwaffe* saw to it that their Flak soldiers all had steel helmets.

The smaller automatic cannons originally designed for low altitude anti-aircraft fire were also employed in front line fighting against ground targets by their army and *Luftwaffe* crews. Against lightly armed vehicles and 'soft-skinned' transport lorries such weapons were highly destructive.

Army anti-aircraft units wore white piping on their caps and shoulder straps, and the *Luftwaffe* Flak units wore red.

Four views of Army Flak Battalion 606 loading vehicles and guns at Naples on 23 March 1941.

Motorcycles were an important part of the panzer regiments. This one from 15 PzDiv (1st Company PzRgt 8) is loading in Naples, April 1941.

PANZERS

T hough in popular imagination they epitomise the *Afrikakorps,* in numbers the panzer crews were only a fraction of the total strength in the German divisions of the *Afrikakorps.* In the Panzer divisions themselves, the number of officers and soldiers in a Panzer regiment did not number more than 1,800 (including Rgt HQ staff, signals platoon, workshop company and supply column) out of a total theoretical divisional strength of 12,500. Pink piping on caps and shoulder straps, and the distinctive metal skull badges affixed to tunic lapels, marked their uniforms apart as belonging to a panzer crew. They used the small metal skulls removed from the lapel badges on their black woollen Continental uniforms, and attached the skulls to the lapels of their tropical tunics. This simple modification to their uniform insignia set the tank crews apart from any other arm of the service in the *Afrikakorps* (even within their own arm of service, the pink piping was worn by everyone in the regiment, even company paymasters and cooks wore it). The panzer crews were an élite, they knew it, and they showed it with their collar skull badges.

Just as important as the tank crews inside their 'steel coffins' were the recovery and maintenance crews who worked on and off the battlefield to restore damaged tanks back to fighting condition. Another essential service supporting the tanks was provided by the transport and supply units who had to bring the ammunition and petrol right up to the tanks on the battlefield. These support services were an integral part of the panzer regiments.

Death rates in the Panzer regiments were high, indicating not only the scale of action involving these men but the high risks they faced in their 'steel coffins'.

Panzer Regiment 8, on the Egyptian frontier in May 1941, make a halt for a meal with a small aff car from Recc. Unit 3 point 206 (inland from Bardia).

Hammock strung alongside a PzI of the regimental HQ company.

Basic maintenance was carried out by the tanks' own crews; weapons maintenance such as cleaning and greasing, replacing the road wheels, and adjusting the tension of the tracks, as this crew of a PzII from 15th PzDiv are doing in the autumn of 1941.

PzIII moving at speed through desert dust, the dust that clogged air filters and penetrated every moving part of the machine, accelerating wear and tear, especially on tracks and wheels.

PzIII in a repair workshop during the fighting of late 1941.

Tank crew photo after the award of the silver Tank Assault badge in July 1941. (Paul Kenway)

CHAPTER 19

The stencilled signs on the armour of this PzIII show the palm tree and swastika tactical symbol of the *Afrikakorps* and the two quadrants symbol of the 21st Pz Division. (Paul Warnsbrough)

Two of several photos taken in the workshops established to the west of Tobruk in 1941.
Above: Dropping the repaired engine back into a PzIII.
Right: A lathe worker in machine workshop.

El Alamein, and the face
of a seasoned desert
Panzer gunner.

snapped by a member of
PzReg 8 during the
fighting near Sidi Rezegh,
in late November 1941.

Front view of a PzIII in early
1942. The spare track
draped across the hull of the
tank acted as an extra layer
of protective armour.

A PzIII snapped during the fighting in late 1941.

PzIII, PzRgt8, front view, early summer 1941.

A PzIII that had the misfortune to drive over a mine during the Sollum Battle of June 1941.

Tripoli, March 1941, and Italian women lining the road throw flowers at Panzers of PzRgt5 driving off to the east.

Battle, PzIII and its victim, Libya, December 1941.

37 mm anti-tank gun of a *Pionier* HQ staff company.

On the Egyptian border in the summer of 1941, three of these sapper soldiers are wearing their gauze mesh mosquito/fly protective head nets. The half track vehicle is a Sd.Kfz 250/2 and the stone cairn at left conceals a periscope binocular.

PIONEERS

The Pioneers or *Pioniere* were the combat engineers, the sappers, the ones who went in first during an attack, the ones who lifted the enemy mines, cut a path through the barbed wire for others to follow, and who placed the explosive charges next to the enemy bunkers. They were the storm troops of the Panzer divisions in the *Afrikakorps*. These units, organised as an *Abteilung* or light battalion were assigned to each division. These élite assault troops wore black piping on their caps and shoulder straps.

It was they who had to accept hand-to-hand fighting, 'Close Combat', using grenades and machine pistols as well as bayonets and entrenching tools. This sort of fighting, so often described in war stories, rarely happened in fact. When it did, it was very likely the *Pioniere* who had to do it, the same pioneers who were usually the first to advance and the last to retreat, laying mines and booby traps as they went.

A medium signals car (*Horch*) Kfz15 of the Staff Company of a *Pionier Abteilung* at Fort Capuzzo in 1941. (The insignia faintly visible on the left front mudguard makes this identification possible, a rectangle with wheels on lower corners and a barbed arrow on the top.)

The now familiar dockside architecture of Naples harbour frames vehicles and equipment of Reconnaissance Unit 3 in February 1941.

An observation post manned by men from Recc. Unit 33 (15PzDiv) in 1941 on the edge of the escarpment above Halfaya displays a 'No Parking' sign and a machine gun mounted on an AA tripod.

A half track prime mover (Sd.Kfz.10) of Recc. Unit 3 with attached supplies trailer on a Mediterranean beach in early May 1941.

CHAPTER 21 | # RECONNAISSANCE

W hen the desert campaigns started, the reconnaissance units (*Aufklärungs Abteilungen*, abbreviated to AA) still wore the traditional cavalry colour of gold yellow as the piping on their shoulder straps and field caps. By the end of 1941 they had been given a new identifying colour, copper brown, to distinguish them from cavalry units. The importance of reconnaissance can be gauged by the strength of these *Abteilungen* in the Panzer divisions, over 800 men, consisting of an HQ staff with a signals platoon, two armoured car companies, a motorcycle company, a heavy weapons company (anti-tank and artillery) and their own supply column. In Africa it was common to see this considerable strength reinforced with even more PAK and Flak weapons, often mounted on flat top lorries or half track vehicles, to create a stronger hitting force better able to break quickly through enemy lines.

The main function of the reconnaissance units was to accelerate an advance against enemy territory. Quick and deep penetration was vital to the success of new tactics designed for modern, mobile armoured warfare. These units were used aggressively, not only to obtain up to the minute battlefield information but actually to take possession of the territory being reconnoitred. In every campaign fought in Africa, the reconnaissance units featured prominently.

A small BMW light staff car of Recc. Unit 3 in Libya in 1941, with a twin MG34 mounted at the rear.

Telephone switchboard inside a communications van attached to a regimental HQ is home to a chameleon.

Radio base, here set up next to an eight-wheel armoured car from a Signals *Abteilung* in the late summer of 1941.

Rigging telephone cables in 1941 outside Tobruk. The vehicle in the background is a Büssing NAG survey party truck, Kfz 415.

Typical signals point, radio car with aerials strung up on poles.

SIGNALS

T he identifying colour worn on the uniforms of these units was a pale lemon yellow. Radio and telephone lines were the main means of relaying information on and off the battlefield. The signals units were fully motorised and highly mobile, with their own special armoured vehicles packed with radio transmitters and receivers. Normally, the companies of the *Nachrichten Abteilung*, or signals detachment, were dispersed throughout the division according to the need parts of the division had to maintain contact with each other. The usual strength of a signals *Abteilung* was around 400.

When the fighting was localised and carried on from stationary positions greater use was made of telephones because they were a more secure medium for passing messages, even without codes. The first units to lay their own telephone cables after stopping anywhere were the various level HQ staffs, followed by artillery batteries and then those units closest to the enemy who needed to report their observations to higher levels of command. Some signals equipment, usually the telephone, was also operated by personnel not serving in signals units. Such telephone systems were operated by regular members of other units who had done special signals training rather than by members drawn from the signals units themselves.

A company commander rides in a special half-track vehicle fitted with a tubular frame radio aerial.

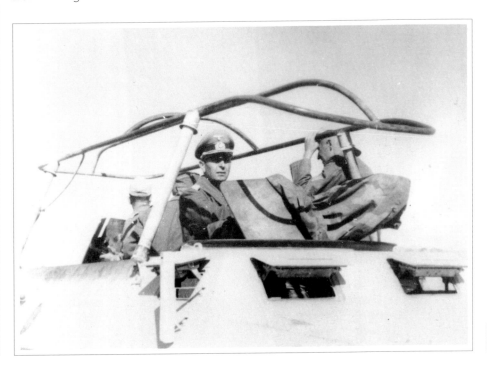

153

Spaced out to minimise the risk of being hit by enemy aircraft, the columns of supply vehicles follow the direction of the front line.

Men in a transport unit celebrating the award of decorations in early 1943. The awards are the Italo-German African Commerative Medal (pinned under pocket flap) and the War Service Cross with Swords (with ribbon attached to buttonhole).

TRANSPORT AND SUPPLY

T roops serving in these units wore sky blue piping on their field caps and shoulder straps. The soldiers whose job it was to drive supply trucks in Africa covered enormous distances, as was shown by a special award given to those drivers who had performed outstanding service, many of whom had driven over 100,000 km. Their primary task was to ensure the supply of ammunition, fuel and rations to the front line units, and the movement to the rear again of unused ammunition and whatever could be picked up from the battlefield and recycled.

Each division had its own transport and supply columns, responsible for ferrying material between the various storage points or depots and the front. The rear zone supply units who also ferried supplies and who looked after the rear material dumps came under overall command of the corps or army quartermasters.

Members of these units attached to major fighting formations should not be considered as rear support troops. Supplies carried from corps and divisional dumps (or 'parks' as the Germans called them) in the rear had to be taken right up to the front line by these drivers, and they regularly came under fire on the battlefield from enemy guns and tanks. They suffered particularly heavy losses from strafing and bombing attacks by the Allied air forces. In those periods when battle was joined by the two sides, the transport columns were often caught in the cross-fire.

It does not need to be pointed out that without supplies an army cannot survive, and in Africa absolutely everything had to be transported to the front, even drinking water and wood to fire the German army's mobile kitchen.

Drivers from the supply column and local Libyan Militia, in front of a Ford (German manufactured) 3-ton truck.

A small tracked vehicle used to pull away heavy material landed on the beach by flat-bottom vessels in Bardia during the late summer of 1942.

Wooden crates containing food were stacked in squares three crates high and then covered with camelthorn brush as camouflage.

Among the shallow draft vessels used to bring supplies into Bardia in 1942 were these two – a fishing scow and a barge that has had the words 'HAMBURG' and 'DAK' painted across the bow.

ows of jerricans cover the water's edge at Bardia in the late summer
1942. These jerricans full of gasoline, probably landed from a
bmarine, are swollen by the heat of the noon-day sun

Transport column with its NCO leader's
Volkswagen being pushed up a slope
slippery with loose rubble.

The heavy traffic along the
defined tracks through the
desert turned them into
highways of powdery dust up
to 60 cm deep.

157

A very typical burial performed at or near the site of death, a shallow grave covered in rocks with simple grave markers, here bearing the legend 'Two unknown German Soldiers, Fallen on 16 June 1941'. Two broken parts of German rifles and a pith helmet complete the visible marking of this grave site.

The German-Italian cemetery just outside Bardia in the summer of 1941. (The star represented the Italian Royal House of Savoy.)

The battlefield grave of *Gefreiter* Xaver Andrelang of 2nd Company *Sonderverband* 288, killed in May 1942.

GRAVES

G raves were one of the subjects most photographed by German soldiers in North Africa, taken both to make a personal record of where comrades were buried in an otherwise featureless desert, and to have prints to send back to families of dead comrades in Germany.

Unit after unit in 1941 took photos of three main Libyan burial grounds — at Km41 (to the west of Tobruk); just south of Bardia (both of these contained German and Italian dead); and the German cemetery in front of the damaged Fort Capuzzo. By 1942 the number of such official cemeteries had grown enormously. As well as the already established military cemeteries, it was quite common to find single graves, or two or three, near a burnt out tank or vehicle, marked by a simple wooden cross or stake. Quite often only some parts of a body could be found for burial, the missing pieces having been fragmented in an explosion, or burnt, and lost. In December 1942 a company commander in 15th Panzer Division, standing in conversation with other officers had his head blown away from his torso by a direct hit from a high velocity anti-tank shell, most likely solid shot which did not detonate on impact. His comrades searched the desert in vain . . .

All wartime grave sites were temporary, from the smallest to the largest. By the time of the final retreat from El Alamein in November 1942, there were already over four thousand German dead killed in Egypt, buried in the various cemeteries stretching from areas behind the Alamein position itself and from Sidi Abd el Rahman and El Daba back to Mersa Matruh. These cemeteries, and the large number of grave sites in Libya, survived into the immediate post-war years.

The isolated single graves on the battlefield, however, were shifted for reburial in the many larger cemeteries nearer the coast as soon as possible in the months after the fighting by the Allied Graves Registration Companies. Only after the war were all bodies disinterred from the larger wartime graveyards and collected during the 1950s for reburial in the three permanent German cemeteries in North Africa. El Alamein (Egypt), Tobruk (Libya), and Bordj Cedria (Tunisia). Today there are 4,549 buried in the El Alamein cemetery, 6,026 in the Tobruk cemetery and just over 8,000 in Bordj Cedria.

Wartime battlefield German graves often had a steel helmet or pith helmet left on top as markers, but such objects did not long survive to passing souvenir-hunting Allied armies. In rocky ground, graves had to be shallow for it was difficult to excavate a deep enough space in the hard ground. This gave graves the appearance of mounds, which is essentially what they were, built up above ground to enclose the corpse.

In many cases burial was an act performed by one's enemy. That it was usually done with some fair measure of decency and respect says a lot about the regard the ordinary soldiers of the opposing armies in the desert had for each other.

A German cemetery near Tunis in 1943. In the foreground, the gravestone reads 'Unknown German Soldier'.

An ornate grave for a soldier in 9th Company in Infantry Regiment 115, *Schützen* Emil Dessloch, killed on 19 September 1941. Dedication: *Du lebst in uns* (You live in us).

The often-photographed cemetery at Km 41 west of Tobruk on the Via Balbia, where many of the dead from the fighting around Tobruk in April and May 1941 were buried.

THE ENEMY

After every battle there were prisoners who had been captured or rounded up, having been left behind by their own side. These PoWs were usually held back out of sight of the front line. Somewhere out on the flat desert both sides collected their prisoners and put them under guard until they could be transported to an established PoW camp. Whenever a chance presented itself to get a closer look at the living enemy, it was usually taken by any soldiers in the vicinity of the collection points, and the cameras would come out to record the faces of the foe.

They were the English, Scots and Welsh (collectively known to the Germans as 'Tommies' or *Engländer,* 'the English'), and Indians, Irish, Australians, South Africans, New Zealanders, Rhodesians, Greeks, Free French, Poles, Nepalese Ghurkas, Palestinian Jews, Americans, Colonial (African) French, enemies all.

Australians of the 9th Division, taken in 1941.

CHAPTER 25

Indians captured in the advance to El Alamein, June 1942.

Prisoners taken south of Tobruk, early December 1941, waiting for a truck to take them and a guard detail away from the battlefield.

A PoW camp (Italian), somewhere well to the rear of the front in 1941.

An officer sits in the sand under an armed guard at El Alamein in July 1942, while another helmeted 'Tommy' stands looking on.

Interrogation was a reliable and tried source for information on the enemy, here being carried out by an English-speaking officer in June 1942, during fighting for the Gazala Line.

A close look at an enemy oven in a captured camp.

A Wellington bomber that came down behind German lines in the autumn of 1941.

The smiling faces of two Italians photographed by a member of 15th Panzer Division, near Sollum in the summer of 1941.

An interesting discussion on the wharfside in Tripoli in 1941 between a German soldier and two Italians. (The original German caption to this photograph describes it as 'a dud 33 cm naval shell'.)

A small Italian 'tankette', equipped with machine guns and flame throwers, but terribly inadequate for battle with modern anti-tank weapons.

THE ITALIANS

Though Germans and Italians were organised under the same Axis allied command, and fought under one battlefield leader (Rommel) against a common enemy, there was little actual physical contact between the two armies. This was so whether on the battlefield or off it, due mainly to their different training, and the logistical and equipment incompatibilities between the two armies. Language difficulties made most close battlefield cooperation a problem though staff officers were able to co-operate through interpreters. A large number of German speaking 'Italians' from the former Austrian province of the South Tirol served in the German army in Africa as interpreters.

There was some level of social contact in the rear army command areas between those Germans performing administrative duties and their Italian neighbours, both military and civilian. Only those German soldiers stationed in Tripoli for any time had opportunities for close contant with Italian women, and even then it was mainly with those working women who staffed the *Wehrmacht* brothel. (Very few German soldiers serving in combat units ever had such an opportunity.)

German soldiers sympathised with the ordinary Italian soldiers who had to endure an archaic social system entrenched inside the Italian army that allowed a majority of officers to take for themselves the best food and drink, thus enjoying a much higher level of overall creature comfort at the expense of the rank and file soldier.

The Italian army, maligned for so long during and after the war in reporting of the North African war written up in Allied countries, in fact fought bravely on the whole in North Africa. They did this in spite of their antiquated weapons and poor leadership. Indeed, given their poor weaponry and equipment, and deficiencies of leadership, many units of the Italian army showed as much if not more courage on the battlefield than their German allies or their British and Allied enemies.

A road making crew breaking stones to build a part of the 'Axis Road' that detoured around Tobruk in 1941, an achievement the Italian engineer battalions were rightly proud of.

A symbolic shot, two
Germans and an Italian on a
North African beach with
their backs to the sea.

A 1943 version of the
German *Afrikaner*, with a
new uniform made from a
generally inferior grade of
cloth, a tunic with no pleats
on the pockets, and field cap
without coloured braid
stitched over the cockade.
(Charles Hinz)

The giant six-engined air transport Messerschmitt Me323s (*Gigant*) carried their heavy loads
of petrol and ammunition across the Mediterranean until the Allied air forces began
operations around Sicily. Then German losses were crippling and the few Me323s not shot
down were withdrawn from service.

Luftwaffe Flak gunners with
an Italian comrade.

THE END, TUNISIA 1943

I n early November 1942 a large American and British army invaded north
west Africa, landing along the Atlantic coast of Morocco and on the central
Algerian coast in the western Mediterranean. The immediate German
response was to rush by air across the Mediterranean a scratch force just strong
enough to hold on to a bridgehead in Tunisia, until stronger reinforcements could
be moved over by sea. By the time the newly arrived German and Italian armies
had joined up with the remnants of Rommel's army inside Tunisia in late 1942, the
end phase of the North African campaign was in progress. In the six months of the
Tunisian campaign, 147,000 German soldiers (including those forces withdrawn by
Rommel from Egypt and Libya) were committed to battle in this Tunisian
bridgehead, as the much stronger American and British armies inexorably closed
in. The Axis armies were literally fighting with their backs to the sea.

Though the first photo in this section was probably taken at an earlier time, it
illustrates the ultimate fate of the Italian-German armies in North Africa, pushed
back almost to the sea until they could retreat no further.

The appearance of the German soldier in Tunisia was somewhat different to how
he had looked in Libya and Egypt. Apart from the one spectacular parade through
Tunis by the Paratroops of *Fallschirmregiment* 5 in mid-November 1942, there were
no parades of newly-arrived soldiers in their pith helmets marching down the
boulevards of Tunis. The soldiers recently arrived in Tunisia from Europe in their
new khaki uniforms went straight to the front. For Rommel's *Afrikakorps* in 1943,
after their long retreat from Egypt, uniforms were often patched and worn, and
extremely faded. The small amount of spare uniform items in stores carried across
with the 5th Panzer Army before the Allies closed the shipping lanes was soon
exhausted in early 1943. After satisfying the most urgent needs of the *Afrikakorps*,
who had lost their own stores in Egypt and Libya, there was little left over. After this
issue of available replacement uniforms, photos taken in 1943 showed
combinations of the new darker and older bleached colours, and there was a
mixture too of styles with a new model tropical tunic, first used in late 1942, without
pleats on the pockets. The German army in Tunisia did not wear the woollen
Continental uniform and all German troops sent into action in the Tunisian theatre
were issued with standard tropical uniforms.

In the last months of the campaign in Tunisia, nearly all supply space on aircraft and ships arriving across the Mediterranean was used to carry all-important
fuel and ammunition, as had been the case at Alamein. New uniforms had a low
priority when military tailors could mend old uniforms to prolong their useful life.
Bits and pieces of Allied uniforms were also used by German troops in Tunisia,
more so than at any other time in North Africa. In Tunisia items of US Army uniform
were mixed in with parts of British and Italian uniform, even in a few instances
including non-German tunics — something which had not been done before. Only

the distinctive German peaked cloth field caps and the German steel helmets remained as the essential parts of German army uniform in Tunisia.

Fewer personal photos survive from the period of the campaign in Tunisia. Not as many personal photos were taken in this period, and of those only a few made it back to Germany. For ordinary soldiers film was almost impossible to acquire in these last months, and in the confusion and destruction of material associated with surrender, many of these personal photos were lost, disappearing in the turmoil of capture.

As the end for the German army in North Africa neared in April and May 1943, morale stayed high right to the end. Even when defeat seemed inevitable, thoughts turned to evacuation to Sicily and to fighting another day in continental Europe, not to surrendering in Africa. This desire to get back to Europe before the approaching end arrived was not just faith in Germany's ability to somehow survive the war successfully; it also meant leave spent at home with family and friends. With the sea lanes closed by Allied air and naval superiority, and the Axis air corridor held open only at great cost to move a few essential supplies, there was no hope in 1943 of any large-scale German and Italian evacuation.

Photos taken in Tunisia do show that there was active support given to the Axis armies by the local Arab population, something that had not happened in Libya or Egypt. In photos of camp scenes taken in 1943 it was common to see Arabs living in close proximity to German troops, with some working as labourers, shifting and storing ammunition, and others carrying out various servant-type duties, behaving exactly like camp followers have done down the centuries in the train of a friendly foreign army. In this case it was more because the nationalistic Arabs in Tunisia saw the Germans as allies against their French colonial masters.

Many vehicles in the German divisions at this time looked as if they had reached the absolute end of their useful lives, after thousands of miles of hard driving across the desert. For the first time large numbers of US Army vehicles became a part of German army camp scenes.

The damage wreaked on a German supply train in central Tunisia in early 1943. The Allied air forces had control of the air by February 1943.

In Tunisia, the Arab population was not only friendly and supportive, but actually sought the company of German troops.

At the end, the two Axis armies became compressed in the north-eastern part of Tunisia. When over 120,000 German soldiers surrendered between 10 and 13 May 1943, more than half of these troops belonged not to combat units but were part of the various rear echelon support services. (This higher proportion of non-combatant troops in the total number surrendering showed to what extent the front line units had been losing their fighting strength.) For the rear area units, pushed back behind the shrinking front with no heavy weapons or ammunition, organised resistance was impossible, even had they been equipped to perform it. After the last surrenders on 13 May, all German troops were held at first in PoW 'cages', large tracts of flat ground laid out with German tents enclosed by perimeter fences of barbed wire and Allied guards. Later the German PoWs were transferred to proper PoW camps in Algeria or Egypt before being shipped off to other camps in the USA, Canada or the United Kingdom.

Inside the PoW cages the spirit of the *Afrikakorps* lived on, and the old familiar military discipline that had held them together in the field asserted itself in organising self-help in the camps. The welfare of all PoWs had to be entrusted to the tried and trusted systems of German military organisation. This was especially so in the case of personal hygiene and sanitary arrangements, food preparation and its distribution, and getting medical care to those who needed it.

After the surrender of the Axis military command in Tunisia in May 1943, the only German military presence in North Africa was the occasional flight by high altitude reconnaissance Messerschmitt Bf110s based at Foggia in southern Italy. These specially lightened aircraft with their high resolution cameras used forward airfields in Crete and Sicily or Sardinia for refuelling stops. They flew from the end of 1942 until the autumn of 1943, their flights covering the long coastline from the Nile delta to Algiers.

A very different terrain was encountered the further north one went in Tunisia. Shown here is a typical valley scene in central Tunisia, with an Arab village nestled against the side of a hill high above a wadi. (Dieter Hellriegel)

Dieter Hellriegel (right) and Unteroffizier Müller, in front of the Company HQ tent of the 2nd (Panzer) Company of Rommel's Kampfstaffel, near Sfax in March 1943. (Dieter Hellriegel)

Snap taken by an American GI of four German PoWs in captivity after the general surrender of 12/13 May 1943.

'FOR THE RECORD'

LIBYA, NOVEMBER-DECEMBER 1941

T he following photos were taken by members of the motorised company of military war correspondents (*Kriegsberichter*) attached to the *Afrikakorps* and commanded by Sonderführer Zwilling. They were taken between mid-November 1941 and late December 1941 and show scenes on and off battlefields that stretched from the Egyptian border at Sollum and Capuzzo to Tobruk and the many points in between, and back to the area near El Agheila on the Gulf of Sirte. This time marks the period of the North African campaign known to the Germans as the Winter Battle.

The few photos shown here represent a small part of the some 10,000 (270 x 36 frame 35mm spools) taken by this one company in a month and a half of extremely heavy fighting. They are representative of those specially noted as being intended for official military archive files, stamped on the back, *Nur für den Dienstgebrauch* (FOR SERVICE USE ONLY). Many of the remaining photos taken would have been sent back to Germany as illustrations for newspaper and magazine stories.

The following photos would have ended up in an official military archive, mounted on a cardboard-backed A4 size page under the headings *Heeresfilmstelle* and *Bildarchiv*. These standard *Wehrmacht* archive cards recorded a description of the scene depicted in the photo, along with information as to its time and place and identifying the unit concerned.

The special significance of these particular photos is that they show that face of the *Afrikakorps,* and its battlefields, that the Germany army considered making its own official record.

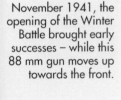

November 1941, the opening of the Winter Battle brought early successes – while this 88 mm gun moves up towards the front.

What next? Snapped on the afternoon of 23 November, the day of the famous 'Sunday Battle', a PzIII from 15 Pz.Div. and a staff car showing the commander's pennant of a motorised infantry battalion wait for orders.

PoWs from the 4th Indian Division, captured early in the fighting, Sikhs who have evidently lost their turbans.

Radio transciever of a regimental HQ on the *Sollumfront*, with signallers encoding a message (the man at rear holds a morse key device).

Italians with a Molotov Cocktail made from a champagne bottle with a flare pistol cartridge and fuse attached.

Batches of prisoners rounded up in the desert, here held under the gaze of two guards with MG34 machine gun. The 'Ib' daubed on the side of the vehicle is interesting, identifying it as belonging to a staff officer (logistics) attached to a divisional rear echelon column.

The scene on 24 November, south-west of Halfaya, the wreckage from the NZ 5th Brigade positions over-run by Pz.Rgt.5.

24 November 1941, near Sidi Omar, the body of a dead British soldier lying behind a small parapet of rocks, killed by airburst artillery shrapnel.

173

Photographed on 25 November, on the Sollumfront, two shots of a knocked out British Matilda Infantry Tank with the name 'Park Royal'. In the second shot, two Germans are pulling the limp body of a crewman through the hatch in the turret roof. The dead crewman's hair is matted with blood, indicating he may have received a fatal head wound. A British tank man (in beret) stands by watching.

1 December 1941, a PzIV moves past the photographer's camera lens near Bardia.

Another British tank crewman, probably from the same tank (this photo is four frames on from the previous shot on the very same spool) receives an abdominal injection of morphine from a helmeted German soldier. The British soldier, obviously in great pain, has worked up a mound of sand under his right boot as he convulsively bends and straightens his leg.

To increase the volume of supplies that could be flown in across the Mediterranean, the Ju 52s and bombers such as the He 111 and the Ju 88 were used to tow gliders which were loaded up with much-needed supplies. These four photos show one such glider, a Gotha 242, being unloaded at El Adem and then taking off again behind a Ju 52 heading for Crete to collect another cargo.

During the German withdrawal to the west on 5 December, this very typical view was taken of a small group of German infantry in a shallow wadi, doing the things all soldiers do during a pause in a battle – just sitting and looking around, cleaning weapons that have recently been fired, eating a quick snack, unloading and repacking the military and personal gear every soldier carried around with him, and all around are the bundles of field gear put down on the ground until the order to move again is given by the officers and NCOs.

Official shot of the official photographer, Sonderführer Zwilling, with his Leica and two Agfa cameras, snapped by one of his men south-west of Tobruk on 5 December 1941. On this day, Rommel ordered the DAK to pull back from around Tobruk. In the background, an 88mm gun and its crew packed up for travel drive past heading for new positions further to the west.

By 6th December, the Afrikakorps was digging in near Gazala in its withdrawl to the west, and this 5 cm PAK38 anti-tank gun and its crew make a familiar combination of shapes – a low parapet of rocks, gun and crew with their individual weapons and gear close at hand. It was common practice if the ground could be broken to dig a trench inside the rock wall. (In the Libyan desert today these low horseshoe shaped mounds of rocks still survive, showing where the anti-tank gunners once took up their positions.)

Sitzkrieg, the 'Sitdown War'. By late December 1941 the *Afrikakorps* were back in old positions of nine months ago in front of El Agheila, and the Winter Battle was over.

ERNST ZWILLING

O f the many thousands of photos taken by Germans during the North African campaign of World War II, one photographer took more than any other individual. This man was Ernst Zwilling, a *Luftwaffe Sonderführer,* who headed the company of official photographers sent to Libya in early March 1941 to record the German *Wehrmacht* in the North African desert. For the next two years he took tens of thousands of photos of the North African battlefields, seen from the German side. As the top ranking official photographer, he had constant and easy access to Rommel and his staff, and to the other main unit commanders too. Very many of the well-known shots of the German army and its commanders in North Africa are by Zwilling.

Ernst Zwilling's photos have been used as illustrations by nearly every author who has written on the subject of the *Afrikakorps* since World War II. His photos are to be found today in large numbers in military and state photo archives in the United States, England, Germany and France, where the largest number of his photos are held in Paris by EPCA, the French army's photo library. However, none of these photos acknowledge Ernst Zwilling by name as the photographer, and whenever they are reproduced the photos show the archive as the source, and the owner, of the photo.

Ernst Zwilling in Africa in 1941, on occasion of the award of the Iron Cross 2nd Class.

Rommel in late 1941, with his *Ia Oberstleutnant* Westphal at right in dark glasses, and chief of staff General Gause with back to camera.

This remarkable man was born on 25 September 1904 in the small Austrian town of Esseg. His family were well off and had provided generations of officers for the Austrian army. The young Ernst Zwilling developed a passion for hunting wild game, travelling frequently to the former German colony of the Cameroons to indulge himself in this rich man's sport. (After 1919 *Kamerun,* as it had been known, was ruled by France under a League of Nations mandate.) Ernst Zwilling was well known before 1939 as the white hunter who went further and for longer into the bush than other hunters. It was here he became as expert with a camera as he was with a rifle. He was educated as a geographer and while on his hunting safaris he also worked on mapping and recording the habitat of west African wildlife.

With this background it was not surprising that Ernst Zwilling was selected in early 1941 to head the small detachment of photographers being sent to Libya with General Rommel's *Afrikakorps.* Zwilling was given the rank of *Sonderführer,* a specialist with officer rank status. The unit he commanded was *Luftwaffe Kriegsberichter Kompanie 7 (mot)* or the 7th Company (motorised) of Air Force War Correspondents. While attached to the *Luftwaffe,* this unit was in fact deployed in North Africa to record all aspects of the German military presence there. Indeed, by far the greater part of Zwilling's own work was concerned with the German army and its commanders, and not the *Luftwaffe.* There were, of course, many other German military photographers in Africa, some in Zwilling's own unit, and there were more who came and went on special secondment. But it was Zwilling himself who took most of the now well-known shots of Rommel and other famous commanders who served with Rommel in Africa.

Zwilling was decorated for his bravery while he was in North Africa, in circumstances most war correspondents were not likely to find themselves in. While taking photos of an 88-mm gun crew of *I Abteilung Flak Regiment 33* in June 1941 on the Egyptian border, the gun received a near hit that killed and wounded most of the gun crew. The gun itself was not put out of action and Zwilling dropped his camera to take his place with the surviving crew as one of the loaders handling the 88-mm shells. For this action, which drove off a strong British tank force, inflicting heavy losses on the British, Zwilling was later awarded the Iron Cross 2nd Class.

After the surrender of the German and Italian armies in May 1943 in Africa, Zwilling continued his work as a photographer and war correspondent, serving in the Italian theatre and in the Balkans. He also spent some of this time on Crete and the Greek islands of the Aegean Sea. At the end of the war he was captured by the Red Army and spent two years in captivity as a PoW in the Soviet Union.

By 1950 Zwilling was able to return to Africa, both as a hunter and a photographer. He made many journeys to his old hunting grounds in French Equatorial Africa and organised three expeditions to Lake Chad. He also made journeys through the Sahara, and led expeditions into central Africa, up the Congo studying the pygmies and exploring the hinterland of Angola. In the 1970s the now Professor Zwilling was dividing his time between an academic life lecturing in Europe and running a safari business for 'white hunters' operating in Uganda and Kenya. By this time Ernst Zwilling had become a committed conservationist and he urged his clients to use a camera instead of a bullet to shoot their prey.

In November 1990 Ernst Zwilling died, in Vienna, in his eighty-seventh year. In his life he had been a hunter, an explorer, an author, and had mapped many unmapped parts of central and west Africa, photographed the highest and lowest ranking members of the German army at war for four years in Africa and southern Europe, spent two years in a Soviet PoW camp, had reclaimed his scholarly reputation as an African 'expert' after the war and was rewarded with academic honours, had built up a successful safari business for hunters of big game in east Africa, and ended his life as a prominent supporter of international conservation movements based in Africa.

The photos reproduced here were obtained from Ernst Zwilling by Charles Hinz, a long time acquaintance of Zwilling's and himself an authority on the German *Afrikakorps.* These few photographs are only a token representation of Ernst Zwilling's work with a camera, but at last his name can be shown here in print in company with his photos.

ommel, in a 1942 rofile shot, with *Oberst* lwin Wolz, commander f *Luftwaffe* Flak egiment 135.

Rommel in conference with Italian and German unit commanders.

Rommel in a typical pose, wearing his distinctive olive-coloured leather greatcoat, tartan scarf, and the British anti-gas goggles on his cap, that marks this photo as one taken in the winter of 1941/42.

A view of *Hauptmann* Walter Fromm, the Commander of I/Flak Rgt.33, Knight's Cross winner and veteran of the Spanish Civil War.

The *Luftwaffe Feldmarschall* Albert Kesselring, German commander of the Mediterranean theatre and Rommel's immediate superior, taken in the early summer of 1942.

Feldwebel Reinhard Melzer, another of the 88mm gunners of I/Flak Reg.33, who won his Knight's Cross in the fighting of June 1941, here examining the entry hole of an 88mm round in a British Matilda tank.

ERNST ZWILLING

Luftwaffe Medical Surgeon-General
Generaloberststabsarzt Dr Hippke
visited Africa in the late 1941.
(Walter Fromm at left of this photo.)

End of day, vehicles are formed into a
close ring for the night and the sentries
are posted. This practice was followed
for much of the fighting in November-
December 1941 over the open desert
of eastern Cyrenaica.

The moment of firing by a well dug-in
88mm. Notice the cloud of dust raised
from the muzzle blast.

Artillery gunner checks the optical sight on a 10.5 cm field howitzer.

Picking over a captured British food dump. (Note the smoke on the horizon, indicating burning vehicles.)

Regimental HQ signals vehicles.

88mm gun crew, during a lull in action during the Winter Battle of November-December 1941.

The Commander of the DAK in early 1942, General Ludwig Crüwell (centre). The German officer at left is Major Max Hecht, a regimental Flak commander and later Knight's Cross holder.

The inevitable sequel to battle, fatigue-induced sleep.

183

THE FORGOTTEN AFRICAN
(*DER VERGESSENE AFRIKANER*)

One of the most enduring and widely held images the soldiers of the *Afrikakorps* had of themselves was as a forsaken and largely forgotten part of the German *Wehrmacht*.

From very early on in the campaign it was evident to even the lowest ranking German soldier that the Axis position in North Africa was an uncertain one with tenuous supply lines running across the Mediterranean under attack by British naval and air forces. Many had personally experienced just such a terrifying attack during their own crossing to Africa.

Every German soldier knew of mail posted from home that had simply not arrived, a sure sign that ships and aircraft carrying mail were not reaching Africa. Everyone experienced the almost constant shortages of food, of uniforms and basic field equipment, of vehicles and spare parts, of weapons, and indeed of everything a modern army needed to fight with. It was common knowledge that Rommel gave priority to supplies of ammunition and petrol, yet even these two essential elements of modern warfare were often in short supply too. Their high morale, a boundless confidence in Rommel's leadership, trust in their weapons and training — all of these things in the end were not enough by themselves for the *Afrikakorps* to win every battle when the means of fighting had to be so carefully rationed.

The *Afrikakorps* soldiers handled this grim situation in the way soldiers react to such news, with the peculiar brand of black humour that stated the worst possible future scenario through ironic narrative story and graffiti. There were many variations to the theme that after the end of the war the survivors of the *Afrikakorps* would become a new 'African'* tribe, forlornly wandering the desert dressed in ragged remnants of military uniform and bits of Arab dress, waiting in vain for repatriation to Germany. In many of these stories 1945 was picked as the end of the war, an uncanny prediction.

The drawing shown [right] was photographed in late 1941 by a South African soldier on the walls of the Sollum barracks. This graphic sketch by an anonymous German expresses so well the feelings of many *Afrikakorps* soldiers, of being abandoned in desolate conditions, starved of supplies by their parent army organisation, and thus becoming 'forgotten Africans'.

* The *Afrikakorps* soldiers' slang term for themselves was 'Afrikaner', literally 'African' (i.e. 'a native inhabitant of the African continent'.)   *Jan Wessels*